SAVAGE SYMPHONY

SAVAGE
SYMPHONY

A PERSONAL RECORD
OF THE THIRD REICH

BY

EVA LIPS

Translated from the German by

CAROLINE NEWTON

With an Introduction by

DOROTHY THOMPSON

RANDOM HOUSE · NEW YORK

THIRD PRINTING

MANUFACTURED IN THE UNITED STATES OF AMERICA
BY THE STRATFORD PRESS, INC., NEW YORK

CONTENTS

INTRODUCTION

By Dorothy Thompson

A GREAT MANY BOOKS HAVE BEEN WRITTEN about Germany under Hitler, but I cannot think of any that gives so simple and clear a picture as this one does of what it meant to be a civilized human being during the Hitler revolution.

It has the advantage of being a subjective book, not an objective one. It is a simple factual account, written by a woman who has literary gifts and powers of observation, of what happened to her, to her husband, and to their friends when Hitler came into power.

Julius Lips and his wife, Eva, the author of this book, lived in a charming little villa in a beautiful garden in the Rhineland city of Cologne—a house and garden which they had earned out of the efforts of their own heads, both of them being scientists, and which they had spent eight years making into a lovely and civilized home. Professor Lips was the Director of the famous Museum of Ethnology, an anthropologist with international connections, a student of primitive people, engaged in 1933 in lecturing to students, and in writing a book in which he was attempting to penetrate the black man's mind, and disclose how he regarded the white man's civilization.

His wife was assisting him. They moved in conservative circles, among people like themselves, who were highly civilized, cultivated, and interested primarily in intellectual matters. They were not Jews; they were Protestants, and the Professor was one of the Presbyters of the Evangelical Community.

They were in no way active in politics. Their political tendencies were liberal, but not aggressive. They were, as scientists should be, devoted to the exploration of facts in an effort to find truth.

And so, in the course of the Hitler revolution, Professor Lips lost his job, his income, his friends, his students, his home, and his country. He lost them without committing any aggression whatever.

He lost them only because he remained loyal to the only ideal that had ever dominated his life: the ideal of truth based on facts.

He lost them because he refused to turn a scientific institution into a propaganda organization; because he refused to distort his anthropological knowledge to support anthropological nonsense.

He was not ousted from his office. On the contrary, the Nazi regime wished him to retain the directorship, but to retain it on terms which were incompatible with his intellectual integrity.

The tragic figures in this story are not Professor and Mrs. Lips. The tragic figures are the cowards among their friends who betrayed their own highest ideals for the sake of keeping their jobs and their necks. This book is not a very favorable commentary on the human race.

With the simplicity of a diary, Eva Lips describes day-to-day events. She takes in the whole circle of their friends, and tells of their intellectual and spiritual degradation.

From a suburban villa, and from the other-worldly circle of men and women devoted to science and art, she views and describes in a vivid and overwhelming way the rise to power of The Lie as the ruling force in national affairs.

And she shows that the rise of The Lie is the rise of barbarism.

She puts the emphasis, it seems to me, exactly where it ought to be put. The test of a regime is not whether more or less people are employed. It is not whether the nation is militarily stronger or weaker. It is whether the nation, under it, serves the spirit which has created culture and light, or the spirit that at recurrent periods in history has plunged the world into savagery and darkness.

Mrs. Lips does not editorialize much. She recounts events. The conclusion is inexorable.

New York
February 10, 1938

PART ONE

Prelude in Fortissimo

How pleasant a city was ancient Cologne,
Made lovely, says legend, by fairy and gnome.
August Kopisch

I

THE LITTLE HOUSE WAS BUILT OF YELLOW
sandstone. It stood in Klettenberg, one of the quiet suburbs
of Cologne, in the Siebengebirgsallee (Street of the Seven
Hills), so named after the seven pinnacles on the Rhine,
the scene of the story of "Snow White." On balmy mornings we were awakened by the twitter of blackbirds, and, as
the winter approached, by the brisk pecking of robins at
our window-panes, clamoring for crumbs. The house was
by no means pretentious, and its charm lay in simple
things: in the avenue of acacias leading up to it, in the wild
vine overhanging its door and in the good cheer in the
hearts of those who lived in it.

We had transformed the grounds from a bleak, stone-
cluttered vacant lot into a flourishing garden, digging up
the rocks one by one, turning up the soil, feeding it generously with humus and nitrates and coaxing it back to life.
We were rewarded with a smooth lawn, fruit-bearing trees
and masses of gay flowers. Our greatest success was the
round rose bed at the foot of the terrace steps. Along the
bare wall in the rear that separated us from the neighboring gardens, we had planted a stretch of rambler roses, and
fronting it, an arbor of goldenchain, Japanese quince, lilac,
laburnum and jasmine.

Being young and far from rich, the occupants furnished
the little house step by step, determined that everything
in it should be both practical and beautiful. We had spent
our year of honeymoon planning it, debating color schemes
and designs. Both of us had a loathing for the familiar
crocheted covers, the curlicues of carved walnut furniture,
the gold-framed photographs of respected relatives and sim-

[3]

ilar horrors decorating "comfortable furnished apartments."
We had a vision of our home long before we ever saw it,
and from the day we moved in we arranged it to the last
detail according to our long-cherished dreams.

. We bordered the front garden with a privet hedge and
started a clematis vine on its climb across the front of the
house, where its velvety flowers would glow purple against
the yellow stone. A little locked gate was set up to keep
trespassers out and enhance the pleasure of our own com-
ings and goings. Within doors, we softened the hall and
staircase with rugs and painted the walls in the bright hues
of the Mediterranean, of desert sunsets, of springtime and
of happiness.

Later a dog joined the household, a German Boxer with
a thick coat and a forbidding face—a bit of a scamp he was,
but also a comfort, a protector and a comrade. We called
him Tapir. His predecessor, Syphax, had been killed by a
passing motor car, so Tapir was to be kept off the street,
with the courtyard and the garden as his hunting ground.
He lived in a comfortable kennel, a straw-lined cement
enclosure under the terrace steps.

We had been occupying the house for eight years and
had finally brought it to the perfection of our plans. The
furniture had been made after designs drawn by its mistress; books crowded our shelves, edging farther and farther
along the walls, with the persistence of the waves of the sea
against a sandy shore, disputing for space with the many
trophies of our travels: spirit masks, skins and ivories transplanted from Africa to Cologne. The living room gleamed
with tables and chairs in poppy-red lacquer against walls of
jade, the brilliant colors heightened by contrast with the
ebony black of the grand piano. The desk faced the dining
room, from which an open terrace led down into the garden. Upstairs was the study, a harmony in orange and blue,
where the master of the house worked. In one corner hung
a bronze harem lamp, which at night cast crescent-shaped

shadows through its filigreed carving, throwing a pattern of crooked half moons on the ceiling. On the same floor were the bedrooms and bath, and on the next the guest room, store room and the cheery room overlooking the garden, in which Ziska lived—the young girl Franziska, who had come to us from an orphanage. She was devoted to our home and took scrupulous care of it when far journeys took its owners to other lands. "When a house is completed, death comes knocking at its door," say the Spaniards. But we were free from this or any other anxiety. Our home was dedicated to work and to happiness, to hospitality and to cheer, and, unlike Polycrates, none of us felt the need of tossing a precious ring to the gods of destiny.

It was quite far from the little house to the large house. One took the tram to the Barbarossaplatz, changed cars and rode past the Ulrepforte and the Severing Gate across the Clodwigplatz to the Ubierring. The large house, the Museum of Ethnology, the second largest of its kind in all Germany, was situated in a distinguished, quiet neighborhood of imposing homes, near the shore of the Rhine. Its lawns were planted with magnolia trees. The Museum, an immense structure in the classical style, housed one of the world's finest collections from the South Seas, and treasures gathered from Africa, Asia, Australia and from the remote provinces of India. The name of the institution was carved across the lintel: RAUTENSTRAUCH-JOEST MUSEUM, immortalizing the two citizens of Cologne who had endowed it, receiving in recognition of their generosity the patent of nobility from the Kaiser. Eugen von Rautenstrauch had married the daughter of Herr Joest, and thus the glory of the gift and the double name of the Museum had remained within the one family.

This building, which had been constructed in 1906 with all the lavishness of pre-war days, had been presided over by Professors Wilhelm Foy and Fritz Gräbner, both of whom had died suddenly and at an early age. There was a certain young instructor in ethnology at the University of Cologne whom Gräbner (known to the world as the originator of the *Kulturkreis* theory * in the science of ethnology) loved as a son, and in his will he had expressed a wish that his protégé be placed in charge of the Museum. This was done in 1927. In a short time the young instructor became a full professor; the acting head of the Museum became its Director, on a life appointment.

Then the modern spirit entered the large house, gave it a thorough airing and cleaning, removing from it the odium of lifelessness generally associated with a place of research and restoring it to the citizens of Cologne in full vitality. Since the young director's advancement to the head of the department of anthropology at the University, he had conducted the ethnology seminar at the Museum. There his students, between the magnificent library and the great collections, could, so to speak, wander freely in the gardens of the various civilizations of mankind. The administrative offices were cleaned and modernized, new projectors installed in the film division, the library enlarged and the collections rescued from their over-crowded, old-fashioned glass cases and brought to light in picturesque and arresting exhibits. At the same time the director inaugurated those Sunday lectures described in the newspapers of Paris and London as "models of Museum activity." One week he talked about the Plains Indians of North America, another he drew pictures of the high civilization of ancient China, or of the social life of the Tuareg tribe, the peoples of Peru, of Australia, of Ceylon or of the Cameroons. And every Sunday the lecture hall was so crowded that people sat on the steps of the platform to hear of his studies and adventures among the unfamiliar races of the world.

At that time the affairs of the city of Cologne were run

* The *Kulturkreis* (culture circle) means a geographical area in which all the diagnostic characters of a given culture-complex are to be found in their most approximately pure form.—Translator.

on a rigid budget, and the expense of all these innovations had to be met by the Museum itself. By an energetic campaign the membership list was increased ninefold. The programs distributed at the Sunday talks were so original and so informative that they came to rank as collectors' items. Since there was no money to engage an artist's services, the director's wife tried her hand at designing the programs, tinting them in faint pastels and illustrating them with scenes of tribal life, with drawings of Negroes and Japanese, of Indian squaws and grass-skirted Polynesian girls, of grotesque totems and weirdly carved human skulls. Enthusiastic volunteers lent their aid; students from the art academy near by contributed sketches; the leading shops donated fabrics and materials. Everyone talked primitive art. Popular songs took up the theme; posters advertised it; the most conservative of our artists and musicians began to introduce an exotic note into their work.

In one of the huge exposition buildings on the Rhine the Rautenstrauch-Joest Museum presented its treasures to the public in a strikingly new manner. A collection of primitive art was exhibited, but this was no "museum" display—rather, a glimpse into the mysterious fairyland of the unknown. The great bare hall was transformed into a jungle. Dried skulls lay spread before the rush mats of the spirit houses. Africa's wild animals, reproduced with startling realism, crouched among the trees of the untamed forest. The sun of Benin gleamed on the bronze images of her people and their gods.

Herr von Rautenstrauch began to pay frequent visits to the Museum, which he had avoided for years, eager now to win support for it among his business and social connections, proud of having founded an institution which brought his name before the world.

By far the most effective of the exhibitions was "The Masks of Man," held in honor of the twenty-fifth anniversary of the Museum's founding. It was designed to show mankind's attempts to give expression to the awe inspired by the miracles of nature and the mysteries of the human spirit. The collection had been gathered from all corners of the globe. It ranged from totems taken in the primeval forests of the North to relics found among the graves of Peru, from glaringly painted Australian skulls to the noble features of Beethoven's death mask. The programs for the occasion were issued in numbered copies, framed in the form of a Chinese calendar, featuring a portrait of Fukuroku, the god of longevity, of genius and of good fortune.

Dr. Adenauer, Cologne's distinguished and progressive Mayor, formally opened the exhibition. Herr von Rautenstrauch gave an enthusiastic address, lauding the director as the inventor of a great idea. Invited guests thronged the darkened room, now dim among the distorted shadows of the artificial forest, now clear in patches of imitated moonlight. Against the soft-toned walls, the rows of carved and painted masks stood out in bold relief; portraits of the spirits of the dead, to be invoked by sacred dances. An atmosphere of solemnity pervaded the hall. Suddenly a thin strain of folk music struck our ears. As the tones swelled, a line of swaying figures emerged from the dark, bizarrely costumed and masked in tribal dress—the lithe bodies clad in swinging capes of red-dyed hemp, the youthful heads adorned with pointed hats as black as towers, with bull's horns and with tossing plumes, the silvered, boyish faces disguised with beards of curling sponge, with huge ears and eyelids of gleaming shell. These were genuine masks, taken from the musty cabinets of the Museum and brought to life by the dancers as they advanced and turned to the beat of the thudding rhythmic music.

This was the Museum's hour of triumph, an hour of art and nature, of music and science, fused into harmony. The citizens and the newspapers clamored for more such presentations, for they heightened the fame of ancient Cologne and brought tremendous prestige to her great Museum.

The large house on the Ubierring and the little house in the Siebengebirgsallee were guided and inspired by one and the same master. In 1933 he was thirty-eight years old, had written seven books and had traveled in nineteen countries. He was tall and slender, with dark-brown wavy hair. He had a strong body and a spirit that never faltered. His name was Jules. He was my husband.

II

We divided our days between the large house and the little house. Ziska saw to it that our guests, our home and particularly our kitchen were well cared for. And there were many guests. The students knew that the house of their young professor was always open to them, that there they would find a warm response to their joys and to their sorrows. Of this group our most frequent visitor was Willy Fröhlich, who studied under Jules and acted as his assistant. The guest room was almost always occupied by some missionary, home on leave, or by some visiting colleague. There was a constant stream of callers from the city. All who were interested in science, music or art came and went.

Our Sundays were never free. During the week there were lectures, seminars and conferences. So it was only in the evening that we had time to enjoy the garden, the little house and the dog, Tapir.

Scattered about Jules' study lay the illustrations for his new book. He had been collecting them for five years on repeated trips through Europe and Africa. Correspondents throughout the world helped him. The subject was fascinating, and his treatment of it was to be unusual. Many books had been written about primitive races. The French, English, American and Dutch authorities had already established their views on primitive culture. But one book was still lacking—the most interesting of all. How did the primitive man look upon his discoverer? What was his criticism of the white colonial? What did he think of *him*? How did Europe, how did America look in the eyes of the man of color? To answer this was Jules' mission. He had his data almost ready. He had only to organize his pictures, and then he could begin to write. His hundreds of photographs had been carefully mounted on mats in the Museum, and the faithful Fröhlich had asked for the privilege of sorting them. Jules' idea was to present a survey of how the Negro, the Indian, the South Sea Islander had revealed their impressions of the European in the arts native to them—in wood, in stone or in bronze.

Of an evening, after the students had gone, Jules' steps could be heard as he paced the floor in thought. When Ziska had tiptoed off to bed and Tapir lay dozing on the straw in his kennel, I would sit alone in my room, writing letters to friends in distant lands or setting down my own thoughts. The West German Broadcasting Company had asked me to give a talk in March on the South of France. I held a signed contract for a fee which would enable me to satisfy an old longing for a first-rate camera, with which I expected to photograph the desert palms and the brownskinned water carriers of Africa and all the wonders of our future travels.

My window boxes were planted with cacti. Every plant had a special meaning to me, for with my own hands I had taken them one by one from the rocky soil at the foot of the Atlas Mountains and the beautiful gardens of the French Maritime Alps. It was divinely quiet. The soul of the room was my desk, built in the form of an altar, imposing, yet with traces of feminine caprice. On its big flat surface stood a large glass case, which held the many odds and ends that I had picked up in various parts of the world: an amber chain, a good-luck token of the Tuareg tribe, in its case of painted gazelle hide; little glass animals from Monte Carlo; a miniature gondola in silver and a bowl of unset precious stones, which a kindly old man had given me in Venice. My life was pleasantly occupied between work and the relaxation I found in the opening and shutting of drawers, in the feel of our soft rugs and hangings, in the

[11]

tones of our piano, in the pages of our beloved books.

When I felt myself growing sleepy, I would lock the front door and go upstairs. After a lazy bath, I would tiptoe across the hall and scratch softly at the door of Jules' study, like some spoiled animal begging for notice.

"Come in, Panther," he would call. I would curl up in an armchair, while Jules talked—half to himself and half to me—of the arts of the black folk of the African West Coast, of the pitiless clarity with which the Negro penetrated through to the weaknesses of the white man. After a time I would get up and suggest that Jules go to bed.

"Yes, yes," he would say, returning to his desk and taking up his pen.

"Good night, Jules."

"Good night, Panther." In an instant he was back in Africa.

I would lie against the pillows with the fragrance of his cigar in my hair, my thoughts dwelling on Jules and his work. A last rustling sound in the garden—Tapir making his rounds—and I would drift off into sleep.

We scarcely noticed the passing of the seasons, for when we were not traveling, our days were spent at our desks. Now and again friends made strenuous attempts to drive us out into the open, and sometimes we took flight to Buchensee, an hour's train ride from Cologne, where we had a small week-end cottage.

One afternoon, toward the end of January, Ernst Fresdorf (First Burgomaster of Cologne and deputy to Mayor Adenauer) and his family burst in upon us to take us skating. We could not well refuse. Delight in the crisp winter weather and a craving for pure, cold air, combined with our affection for our friend Ernst, persuaded us. We got into our gayest woolen togs, dug up our skates and went out.

The environs of Cologne are beautiful. We drove along the citadel walls, down the military road, past the ruins of the crumbling fort. A mild wind blew across the gray fields. High spirits and a childish glee at the prospect of skating had seized us all. When we came to the pond, we ran down the sloping bank, only to find the water flowing in a swift current, carrying blocks of ice. There had been a thaw on the little tributary of the Rhine; it was too late for skating. Cologne winters are short. Disappointed, we climbed back into the car and drove to the lake in the city park, only to meet the same disappointment there. Too late—the pleasures of winter were past. The children began to cry, and we carried them off to a café in nearby Lindenthal, to appease them with hot chocolate and cookies. Over the green and gold cups our spirits rose. We laughed over each other's stories. Ernst Fresdorf called for an evening paper, while Jules amused the children by telling them how to make an Indian head-dress. "First you get yourself a nice pile of eagle feathers. You bind the quills good and tight with narrow, colored thongs. Then, one by one, you stick them into a woven strip, but you must be very careful not to . . ."

He broke off sharply. Startled, we turned to follow the direction of his glance and saw that the expression of Dr. Fresdorf's face had changed completely. He was as white as a sheet. The newspaper rattled in his hand. Frightened, his wife arose to see what was wrong.

"What's the matter, Lotte?" he asked absently. "I am all right. But you mustn't laugh any more. That's all over. Let's go. Frightful times are coming. Hitler has become Chancellor."

The children looked at us wonderingly. Lotte and I exchanged an anxious glance. Jules got up abruptly and paid the bill.

Hitler? I thought, puzzled. Frightful times? Why? Another Chancellor? Oh, heavens, there have been so many Chancellors! What have we to do with politics? Fresdorf is out of his head.

The car raced home. No one spoke. When Ziska opened the door, Jules threw his skates into the hall, just missing Tapir, who had rushed forward to greet us. As I went upstairs to change, Jules called out to me:

"Do you know what we missed last week?" he said. "The birth hour of the Third Reich!"

I laughed. It all meant nothing to me. On Jules' reminder I got out the little card, the invitation of the banker, Baron von Schröder, which we had declined because we were not interested in political dinners and had too much else to do. ". . . requests the pleasure of your company . . . dinner in honor of His Excellency, Chancellor Franz von Papen, and Herr Adolf Hitler, of Berlin." Our indifference and contempt for events of the outside world had caused us to miss a momentous occasion, when Papen and Hitler had agreed upon Hitler's taking the Chancellorship, when the captains of industry had gathered in the house of the banker-baron to lend their blessing to the plan, when an era in German history was opened which was to cost us the little house, the large house and our Fatherland.

"Hitler," said I, uncomprehending. "Why, that's the man in the cheap newspapers. It can't be serious. It might have been fun to meet some of those Berlin people. But what concern is it of ours? Papen, or Hitler, or another; it's all the same to us. . . ."

This was the thirtieth of January, 1933. That night torchlight processions blazed through all the streets.

"We have a Nazi in our midst!" snickered Weiss, the old Museum attendant, a few days later, as he helped Jules off with his coat. "It's Fluss. He works like lightning. Only four weeks ago he was a Communist!"

The wonder-worker came out of the cloak room, as meek and servile as ever. He said nothing. In the lapel of his coat there was a little, shiny button, showing a swastika on a red

[14]

field. Jules smiled and walked past him up the stairs through the waiting room into the director's office, where his secretary, Fräulein Fasbender, was waiting with the mail.

As always during visiting hours, the waiting room was full of people. Dealers with wares from Malay temples, reporters, interested laymen with special questions, messengers with packages, book binders, boys from the publishers' with galley proofs, all sorts of people on all sorts of errands. They were seen and dealt with, each in turn. But after the tall door had closed behind them and the secretary had gone, it often happened in those days that a professional conversation took a surprising turn. Some of these Jules laughingly repeated to me at home, over others he shook his head, and some saddened him.

There was the case, for example, of Rodens, the little journalist, who had dropped in to ask for illustrations for an article he was writing. Formerly he had chosen topics like the corn granaries of the Negroes or Egyptian cosmetics. Now he wanted data on the "Negroidization of France," or the "Racial Inferiority of non-Aryan Peoples."

"Weren't you once a sensible man, Rodens?" Jules asked banteringly.

"A man like myself," answered Rodens soberly, "who did not fight in the War and furthermore has the bad luck to have black hair—though, mind you, I'm pure Aryan—a man like myself has to show that he holds the right principles, and the best way to do that is to hand in the right articles."

Principles, indeed! Why, this man had gone through school on money provided by a Catholic politician, had later taken part in the founding of a Jewish political bloc and only a month ago had suddenly discovered that he was a Socialist at heart and asked for admission into the Social Democratic Party. He kept in step with events. The swastika was the badge of his latest ambition.

He left. He was one of many who changed their views.

[15]

Others changed the color of their hair, turning blond in an afternoon. Our friends would come to the house, cautiously close the door behind them and ask: "And you? What do you intend to do?"

"Work," was Jules' reply. And then we heard the word that for years was to echo in our ears, repeated in every circle, in all our newspapers, in every office and club, among high and low, alike. "Co-ordination! Are you going in for co-ordination?" Change with the changing tide, they advised.

What did all this mean? What had Jules, what had any of us, to do with the gentleman in Berlin who filled the air with loud speeches and set uniformed troops to marching in the streets of all our cities?

Brown shirts darkened the shop windows, and brown ready-made suits. The prosperous scurried to their tailors to be measured for brown trousers. An official National Socialist paper declared: "For evening wear tuxedos and tails in brown are not only correct, but decidedly preferred." It was positively funny. Italy had her black shirts; we had brown. And Mussolini's Roman salute of the raised right arm was suddenly discovered to be the "German greeting."

Fortunately none of this nonsense was noticeable at the Museum—until the second swastika put in its appearance.

"There's a Nazi around," said the seminar students sarcastically. And there was. Scheller, of all people! While his classmates pored over their books, studied their atlases or wrote furiously in their notebooks, Andreas Scheller went about in high spirits. This was all the more remarkable because he was an inhibited and unhappy person. Much older than the other students, he was far below the youngest of them in attainment. The War had left him with a wooden leg, and he drew a pension granted for the duration of his college course. He was determined, therefore, never to take his degree. In the seminar he cut a half pitiful, half grotesque figure, and everyone felt under obligation to make up for the disgust aroused by his unattractiveness by being kind to him. As a matter of fact, that wooden leg of his was the only dependable thing about him. At least, it was straight. On that day in February when he openly acknowledged his allegiance to Herr Hitler's party, he was drunk. He announced that he had been a National Socialist for a long time. When reminded that he had never mentioned the fact before, he replied that in his heart he had been on the Chancellor's side from the very beginning.

Attendant Fluss and Student Scheller were the first of the chameleons to change color. Both were dissatisfied men who had nothing to lose—and perhaps something to gain. When they began to rant about their "Führer," the students and attendants flocked around them as though a Punch and Judy show were on.

"It's simply side-splitting to hear them!" laughed Weiss, shaking his pious Catholic head. In those days a Nazi was a suspicious character in Germany, and Catholic priests were forbidden to give absolution to any of that outcast crowd.

"Clowns, that's what they are!" exclaimed Schmitz. The two old attendants, who had worked together for nearly thirty years, wiped tears of amusement from their eyes.

"Well, have you got your brown shirt yet?" asked Fräulein Fasbender. "If I were you, I'd stick to my books."

Scheller pushed his glasses back on his bulbous nose, shrugged his shoulders and limped out to call on his sweetheart, a housemaid in the home of the professor of geography across the road. Echoes of laughter from two pretty girls followed him.

"Heil Hitler!" the blonde called after him hilariously.

"Heil him yourself," giggled the other.

It was not at all clear why a change of government in Berlin should cause such commotion in the streets of Cologne. The Rhineland is liberal in its views and has a lightness of heart unknown to the Prussian temperament. Her people love laughter and they love their wine. The time for merry-making and masquerade is the carnival season. Why anticipate it? Why shout so loudly and dress up? For politics? That was what the gentlemen in Berlin were paid for.

However, there was no escaping the noise. All over the town orators stood about, proclaiming the virtues of the new Chancellor as though he were a new brand of cigarettes. We began to notice that these masters of the advertising art talked an East Prussian twang, in clumsy Berlinese. They had been specially trained and sent out "to enlighten the people." Cologne was Catholic and democratic, and opposed to the screaming school of advertising. People laughed and went about their business. But at every street corner the "salvation of Germany" was dinned into their ears. Then hundreds of uniforms made their appearance. Brown, with the Austrian shako; these were the S.A. (*Sturm Abteilung*), the storm troopers. A warlike name. Those higher up were in black, with a flat service cap; these called themselves the S.S. (*Schutz Staffeln*). Even more warlike. The city was invaded by soldiers. It was vain to fight against the feeling of depression their presence brought, vain to keep cheerful by avoiding them. They were too many.

Small boys were given knives bearing the words "Blood and Honor!" to stick in their belts, and soon the papers carried the story of the murder of a boy of twelve by a younger playmate. "I wanted his uniform," said the eight-year-old murderer to the Judge. "He was my pal; no, I hadn't anything against him. But my father couldn't buy me a uniform. So I used my knife and got his."

This was going too far. It hurt, this frightful symptom of the danger which "the Movement" brought to the immature. The uniform stood for authority, no matter who wore it. True, among savage tribes, it is the carved and

[18]

costumed mask that holds the power of magic, not its nameless wearer.

The radio fulfilled a new function. New voices came from it, voices in fortissimo, members of the Party speaking for the coming Reichstag election, eulogies of the "Saviour," of the "Leader," titles bestowed upon Herr Adolf Hitler, of Braunau, Bohemia, by his heralds. Jointly with the conservative German National Party a "rule of national concentration" was planned. For the popularization of this idea the jovial Dr. Hugenberg was selected, and his powerful peasant's voice came over in pungent phrases. "I am Hugenberg. You call me 'the stubborn goat.' But it's all for your good. Now, listen to me!"

And the nation listened, because voting is a serious responsibility and because it was becoming a bit confused by the political uproar in the streets. Elections are exciting everywhere, but we had never had anything like this before. Is it decent to brand one's opponents as blackguards, to charge them with high treason? Is it a good thing to besmear the church doors with obscene daubs of paint, to deface synagogue walls with signs of "Death to Judea!" plastered over them? Is it Christian to hunt a poor old man, who lives by peddling mangy rabbit skins, through the streets with a placard forcibly tied round his neck reading: "I am a circumcised swine and I live by treason"? This was the kind of hooliganism perpetrated openly on Germans in the name of the gentleman now Chancellor of Germany, who carried over into the official government the despicable methods of his "Movement," unknown until now, except in the penny-squawker newspapers of the provinces.

The swastika appeared in dozens, in hundreds, in thousands, introduced to the Germans as the design of an ancient German sun dial. We had been familiar with it for a long time, having seen it among the insignia of Oriental princes and embroidered in porcupine quills on the moccasins of "non-Aryan" Indians. The black-red-and-gold flag of the Reich vanished in the confusion. In patriotic fervor elderly officers, corps students, old-maid piano teachers and reedy little nobodies hoisted the black-white-and-red flag of the Empire in its place, the over-zealous combining it with the swastika. Chaos reigned. Was the Kaiser returning? The monarchists rejoiced at the promise of "national concentration." Cologne took readily to the uniforms and the shouting, with a volatility characteristic of the Western temperament. The number of new flags, however, was astonishingly small. The entire length of the Siebengebirgsallee showed only four, all the others contenting themselves with the decoration of vines, flowers and hedges, which the sun and the soil had permitted to flourish even before Herr Hitler had brought salvation to the land.

The gentleman in Berlin who had himself announced with such blasting of trumpets aroused much curiosity. The papers blazoned his pictures. He did not look seductive; he did not look cultivated; above all, he did not look German. His personality was without a doubt unusual. The Munich Beer-hall Putsch of 1923 had given him a fleeting prominence. He had struggled with General von Schleicher for the Chancellorship. Under von Papen he had won out. Immediately after swearing allegiance to the Constitution of the German Republic he had done away with the flag of the Republic, substituting for it the Asiatic swastika. "Germany, awake!" cried his army of followers. Had Germany been asleep? She had gone through bad times bravely, hoping to conquer the economic crisis through hard work. And here was Herr Hitler, promising all things to all men. Who was he? An Austrian by birth. His friends had obtained German citizenship for him by making him a petty official in Braunschweig. He was said to be the author of a polemic against France called *My Struggle*. As the Chancellor determines the course of the German government, Germany's future was now to be determined by the dark-haired gentleman with the "fly" under his nose. As a matter of fact, his name was not Hitler, but Schickelgruber, as a Dortmund newspaper revealed in an excess of zeal for the truth. It was, by the way, immediately suppressed and confiscated. "Hitler" was merely the "brush" name of the gentleman. True, he had used a brush, in the rôle of house-painter's apprentice, which does not, of course, preclude the possibility of great political talents. Only this, combined with the extraordinary amount of advertising surrounding the man, was confusing. Meanwhile Herr Göbbels had presented his Führer with "the bona-fide coat of arms of the Hitler family" in bronze. Signs and portents are no trouble to a Minister of Propaganda.

It was doubtless wise to introduce the new hero to the people from the first under a name with a popular ring to it. How effective this was could be seen in the case of Il Duce. Therefore one heard "der Führer" on every hand—not a very original title, but less painful to our ears than the "Heil Hitler," which was now supposed to take the place of our "Guten Tag" and our dear old "Auf Wiedersehen." The prophets of old did not require any Minister of Propaganda to make them popular through such epithets as "most illustrious," "anointed" and "great-hearted." Buddha and Christ and even Mohandas Karamchand Gandhi made their names known to their people unaided. Here the case was otherwise. The hero was served up to his people as "recognized," and they had to swallow the dish, with Party troops on hand to assist in the operation. That Adolf Hitler ranks himself among the prophets and the gods, and not among statesmen, is clear from the command made on the occasion of his forty-sixth birthday: "My will shall be your creed." A god cannot speak otherwise, though the mild man of Nazareth, to be sure, was more modest.

Tense with expectation, we sat at the radio, waiting for HIM to speak. He had been advertised as a magnificent orator, a sort of Pied Piper of mysticism. The announcer introduced him in awe-struck tones.

He spoke with foreign r's and with diphthongs heretofore unfamiliar to German ears, this Chancellor of the German Reich. His hoarse voice was repellent, his Balkan dialect disgusting. He made frequent use of the word *"vernichtet"* (destroyed), and the guttural "ch" shocked our ears horribly, as he delivered it with a gusto that shook the rafters.

We tried to be objective, tried to forget the sound of the speech in its content.

Hitler talked about everything: the theatre, the church, the Jews, the Free Masons, the universities, the administration of the law, the art of governing, the education of the young. He talked about masters and servants, craftsmen and industrialists, workmen and teachers. All these persons and institutions were to be changed—from top to bottom. We heard announcements of the supremacy of the Nordic race. (Was it blond, like Herr Hitler? Slender, like Herr Göring? Truth-loving, like Herr Göbbels?) We learned of Jewish degeneracy and of the "fourteen years of ignominy." ("Foortain," Herr Hitler pronounced it.) We learned that National Socialism is not a political creed, but a philosophy of life. "For a thousand years," he yelled, "for at least a thousand years this philosophy will rule Germany." He was probably unacquainted with the ancient book that declared: "and a thousand years shall be like a day and a night . . ." When he insisted that Communism was a catastrophe which was on the verge of crushing Germany and that not only the German people, but all Europe—nay, the world—was indebted to him, Adolf Hitler, for staving it off, we could literally see him sweating with fervor. It seemed as though the microphone must burst from the impact of that shattering voice.

We listened with strained attention, following the loud, long speech closely. Suddenly Jules and I burst out laughing. We both remembered where we had heard those tones and modulations. Hitler's voice was the voice of that master comedian, Max Pallenberg, in the rôle he had played on his triumphant road tour—Zawadil, the Bohemian *Schnorrer*.

"A few more such speeches," said Jules, "and no one will vote for the National Socialists. Hitler underestimates the intelligence of the Germans. Confused ideas do not become convincing through being shouted in fortissimo."

Then we thought it was time to leave the perspiring orator to his own propaganda and return to our daily routine. We went on working at our pictures: "How the black man looks at the white man." We sat upstairs in the orange and blue room among our books. Tapir lay in front of the door, seeing to it that loud-mouthed intruders stayed outside.

III

We forgot Hitler, the more completely as it was the beginning of carnival. Our first invitation of the season was from the von Rautenstrauchs. "Evening dress, please," wrote our hostess, "and only the head is to be masked. I have no doubt the director of the Rautenstrauch-Joest Museum and his wife will find something most unusual. . . ."

Carnival, carnival in Cologne! On the eleventh of November of the old year it is solemnly inaugurated, then forgotten for a bit in the Christmas preparations, only to be revived after the holidays, holding sway until Ash Wednesday. Paper festoons hang on the trolley wires. At night the streets are filled with "parades." Postmen and opera conductors, milkmen and university professors, artists and seamstresses, all mingle happily together. They have nothing with them except a big drum and a couple of prehistoric umbrellas. These processions are the incarnation of the maddest and most innocent festival in the world. The traffic policeman is surrounded by a mob of singing merrymakers who won't let him go. Motor cars are stopped. Confetti-laden clouds send down flurries of snow that never reach the earth. No one interferes with the revelers. Rejoicing spreads over the Rhineland. Peasant women come in from the hills strumming guitars. Some of the crowd are in silk, others in rags; one flaunts a saucy peacock feather, another a cheap pasteboard nose. But all are equally happy.

Not even the political events of 1933 could dampen this time-honored festival in Cologne. Away with politics! They can wait till after Ash Wednesday. The carnival is on!

The National Socialist Party forbade anyone to wear the brown shirt during those feckless days, for fear of ridicule—

for ridicule kills, and above all in Cologne. Hitler was adulated elsewhere, but not in Cologne. There His Frivolous Majesty, King Carnival, was ruler.

The students snapped their notebooks shut, hunted up Apache shirts and flesh tints to disguise possible black eyes. The newspaper men went in a body to the *Fest in Rot* and half the radio staff forgathered at the *Decke Tommes* or at the *Hängematte*. It was a wonder that there were newspapers to read and broadcasts to hear.

For us carnival opened with the masked ball in the Rautenstrauch villa. They wished us to look exotic. With Jules the matter was simple. With his profile and eyes, he was easily transformed into an Indian. My case was somewhat more difficult. I spent a whole morning at the Museum, turning over harem veils and Egyptian draperies, South Sea shell ornaments, Japanese headgear and Eskimo pelts. Everything, just because it was genuine, looked unreal. I was altogether too European. After a long search I found something pretty and decided on it. On the evening of the party the hairdresser came and made us up—Jules as a Sioux Indian, with a crown of eagle feathers on his jet-black, oiled hair, and myself as an Amazon squaw, with my face darkened to a shade between olive and coffee, a wreath of gray and pink feathers in my hair and delicate little bracelets of bird's down on my tawny wrists.

The Villa Rautenstrauch was brilliant with lights and flowers. As we entered the drawing room, my Indian brave in full white tie and I in black lace, we were crowned king and queen of the festival. Around my neck hung the diamond "Trembal," so named after a swarthy jeweler of the East. I had inherited it from my grandfather, who had been Minister of State in Thüringen at a time when changes were not so rapid.

Dinner was served on plates of Delft. Across the table a medieval Venetian nodded to a tufted cannibal head. The compliments were extravagant, the wines exquisite. Over the coffee cups flirtations buzzed to the sound of insinuating dance music. It was dear old Cologne at its best, in all its cultivated charm, and we forgot that Germany had become a barracks, that the white doors had traitors behind them, never realizing that the elegance of our two-thousand-year-old city was soon to fall into the savage clutch of a foreign hand.

We left at dawn. The orchestra burst into a fanfare of farewell. A merry crowd accompanied us to the gate. No one on this evening had mentioned politics, not even Baron von Schröder, who was among the guests. The danger in Berlin simply did not exist. We could afford to ignore the arrogance of the Chancellor, for, thank heaven, we lived in Cologne, the peaceful Colonia Agrippina of two thousand years ago.

IV

At the peak of the carnival, when morning lectures at the University died away into nothing toward noon, when the library was deserted, when at night the streets rang with choruses clamoring "Coffee! Coffee!" until the stolidest of citizens left his feather bed to brew a cup of the appeasing drink, a note of gravity entered our lives, in the form of a solemn and unexpected honor. Ernst Fresdorf, First Burgomaster of Cologne, and Julius Lips, university professor and Museum director, were elected presbyters of the evangelical community.

On a cold Sunday we went to church. Lotte Fresdorf and I watched our husbands take the oath of loyalty to the community and the church at the altar. The windows fitted badly; it was drafty. We were deeply moved.

We sat together late into the night, talking of the new duties our husbands had assumed, of God, of human beings and of Christianity. Ernst Fresdorf had fully recovered from his panic over Hitler. "He may succeed in Berlin," he remarked, "but the Rhineland is another story. We won't stand for the thumbscrews. An automatic 'Führer principle' is impossible in Cologne. We believe too much in personality. Those who lack it have always lost out, and those who have it are not to be talked down by bombastic proclamations."

These were private conversations in a private house. What was going on in Berlin was still the private concern of the country. But what followed affected the world.

The calendar on the wall recorded the date as Sunday, February the twenty-sixth, 1933. What occurred on February the twenty-seventh, the world knows. That day made of Adolf Hitler a menace to the peace of Europe.

On that day the radio screeched indignation. The newspapers sweated special extras. People cried out in hysteria. The country was alive with rumors. It was true; it was proven. The Reichstag building was on fire, set ablaze by a criminal. The Communists had done it. Terrified by the figure of the Führer, they had committed one last act of desperation. Arson! All praise to our police. They had caught their man. He was a workman from Holland. He could be identified at once, for he had his passport on him when he committed the crime. Marinus van der Lubbe was his name. He admitted, the National Socialist Bureau of Information announced, that he had been affiliated with the German Communists and the Social Democrats. Their complicity was therefore regarded as proven. Ernst Torgler, the German Communist, had also been apprehended. He had heard that he was under suspicion and had gone to the police to clear the matter up. A Bulgarian agitator, Dimitroff, said to be the head of an international Communist conspiracy, was also imprisoned, together with his two countrymen, Taneff and Popoff.

A wave of fear ran over the country. What did all this mean? First the saviour, then the act of destruction. Had the Communists really been so insane as to believe that they could increase their votes by so criminal a deed?

Testimony by the firemen on duty, vows of vengeance from the new Minister-President, Göring, hymns of praise for the presence of mind of the S.A. and S.S. troops sounded in fortissimo over the radio. The entire Socialist and Communist press was instantly silenced on the ground that van der Lubbe had admitted to a connection with them. Both parties were forbidden to engage in speeches, election campaigning or any other activity. Their property was confiscated, their places of assembly seized, their presses and printing machines turned over to the Nazi press.

Under the shadow of this crime Germany went to the polls after a final declaration by the Führer of what he had done for the country. Now he could proclaim that he had saved Germany not only from past ignominy, but also from the clutches of world Communism. At the same time he was not sparing of promises to all social classes. Small industry was to be stimulated, the "thralldom of usury" was to be broken, rents would fall, but property owners would profit thereby. The painters would sell their pictures, the butchers their sausage, the brewers their beer. The peasants would grow rich, the soldiers be armed, students be given appointments and the apprentices would become well-to-do masters. And, above all, unemployment was to cease. Unprecedented economic expansion and increase in foreign trade were to bring wealth to all, to the big business man and the manual laborer alike. Christianity was to be honored, Communism wiped out and peace to triumph. Vote for the rule of national concentration!

The petty bourgeoisie, with the crime of the Communist burning of the Reichstag building sounding in their ears, heard this. The tenants and the landlords, the brewers and the peasants, the soldiers, the students, the apprentices and the unemployed heard this. And the next day they went to the polls.

The Communist Party was outlawed. The Socialists were allowed to vote, although because of the Reichstag fire their votes were not included in the count, and the opposition could learn the exact extent of their numbers. The old officers and conservatives voted black, white and red, and therefore for "national concentration." But Hugenberg, the chosen mouthpiece, was one of the first to fall. It was apparent that the "national revolution," as it was suddenly called, was incorporated solely in the person of Herr Adolf Hitler, the Führer and the Saviour. Let us not forget that even in this election the National Socialists were numerically in the minority. The burning of the Reichstag

[29]

building, with the consequent suppression of rival parties and the exclusion of opposing votes from the count, made the German Reich National Socialist.

In Bavaria and the Rhineland, traditional centers of Catholicism and of democratic freedom of thought, people were astonished and dismayed.

Here the National Socialists were openly in the minority. Here even after the election no one took them seriously. "Here, too?" we asked in consternation, when the faked returns showed the "overwhelming victory of the National Socialist Party." Yes, here, too.

Innumerable newspaper articles hailed the victory of Hitler's party. Radio speeches resounded as they never had before. It was as though drunken men made maudlin celebration of an imaginary triumph. The "circus" had arrived —would the "bread" follow?

The manifestation of this triumph stirred uneasy doubts in many unsuspecting minds. It had gone off altogether too smoothly, like a well-rehearsed scene on the stage. The sensational appearance of the Führer, the exposure of a monstrous Communist crime, the suppression of the numerically largest parties of the opposition, a sweeping victory in the face of a small minority.

It all lacked the dignity expected of a civilized government. It was all too loud. Every man outshouted his neighbor, but the loudest voice of all was that of the gentleman from Austria. "I have conquered!" In Germany such sounds had never been heard, not even in the political arena. The people could only listen in dumb dismay. For the time had come when one could no longer speak or act independently, but must listen and obey.

The front page of every newspaper was full of the wild rejoicing of the victors. The second page, likewise. The third was crammed with new laws and decrees. The most sensational of these was the so-called *lex Lubbe*, a law declaring arson punishable by death. It was the first of an endless series of retroactive laws, deliberately framed to fit deeds already committed and then applied. An excellent weapon for the suppression of undesirable individuals and groups. The rest of the paper was filled with revelations of the past "fourteen years of ignominy" and the "corruption of the previous regime."

The torchlight processions rushing through the streets came to an end. Not so the exposures of the shocking corruption of those who only yesterday had sat in high places.

Corruption! The first attack was upon Mayor Adenauer, a man who held four honorary degrees, president of the Prussian Diet, holder of many titles and honors, a power in the Catholic Church, the most important force in Western Germany, a man of international reputation and an Aryan, a man whose civic career had brought added fame to the famous old city of Cologne. This man—if one was to believe the newspapers—had misappropriated public funds, had supported Marxism and had ruined Cologne through his crazy mismanagement of the city's finances. The flowers on his desk cost 36,000 marks yearly; the mushrooms at his dinner parties cost as much as the running of the University. And already one could hear the mutterings of thousands of street cleaners, of petty clerks, lobbyists, silly women and worthless nobodies who had once been turned down: "Adenauer! I always knew it!"

Corruption! The next to be attacked were the president and vice-president of the government-board, the president of the Chamber of Commerce, hundreds of petty burgomasters in the provincial towns, teachers, people in positions of confidence, musicians, secretaries. Corruption! Note well, the entire system was corrupt. Look at the people before whom you trembled yesterday. They caused your poverty by their mismanagement. See them fall! The Führer is putting things in order, tin gods do not stand in his path. Away with all party interests, for the National Socialists are taking hold! Away with the men of yesterday, every last one of them!

Away with Ernst Hardt, the director of the West German Broadcasting Company. He had been brought up in the cadet corps of Potsdam; he was the author of *Tantris der Narr*, one of the most charming books on the Tristan saga; he was known all over Europe; his art and his personality had brought the Broadcasting Company prestige and distinction. All this was of no account. He was worse than a Jew; he was in the service of Jews.

Away with Szenkar, the opera conductor. An authority on Bach, is he? A swine of a Jew. Corruption!

The director of the Museum of Industrial Art has a Jewish wife. Away with him, he is tainted!

Away with the musicians, the actors, the interpreters of "asphalt intellectualism." * We do not need intellectuals; we are marching. Germany, awake! Death to Judea! Heil Hitler, our great soldier! The new German is born. He is a National Socialist. He is taking office everywhere, and on him the face of the Führer shines. Everything is to be different. Such was the dawn of the National Socialist revolution.

Mayor Adenauer fled to the old monastery of Maria Laach, and Prior Ildefons spread his powerful hands over him in protection.

Remarkable scenes occurred in the Cologne prison, Klingelpütz, which was hardly equal to the sudden increase in the number of criminals. One morning three of the new inmates met in the shower bath. One was the president of the Department of Labor, another a departmental vice-president, the third a Jewish banker. At first they were embarrassed by their nudity. The last time they had met they were in full evening dress, attending a banquet. Timidly

* A term of opprobrium applied to city intellectualism. Asphalt art or writing is placed in opposition to Blubo art, Blubo standing for *Blut und Boden*, blood and soil, synonymous with the highest praise.—Translator's Note.

each asked the others why they were here. And all three answered with a shudder: "Corruption!"

Briefly, the facts were these: in eighty per cent of these cases of "corruption" there was never any trial. Eighty per cent of these accusations were unfounded, trumped up for the sake of publicity. Of the other twenty per cent, which did come up in court, the majority of those accused were acquitted. As for the others, either the indictment was quashed, or a verdict was given on a basis which no one was permitted to know. Under this persecution the German people cowered, rigid with terror, like a rabbit before a huge snake. No one dared to speak. Men were happy if they could save their skins, happy not to be noticed. In those days of February, 1933, the German people had not yet learned what they know now—that the National Socialist does not know what truth is and does not want to know. At that time they were not aware that these charges of "corruption" were part of the "propaganda and enlightenment" of the people, invented by Herr Joseph Göbbels who achieved a ministry of his own as a reward. On June 19, 1933, he himself declared this propaganda an art and asked the German people: "Did the National Socialist Movement really come into power by virtue of its ideology, or was it through propaganda?" He himself answered: "The nation was conquered not only by ideas, but by the methods with which these ideas were presented. What would our Movement have been without propaganda? And where would our State be today, if a really creative propaganda did not even now lend it a spiritual aspect? Is it any reflection upon Art to place it on a level with the noble art of 'popular psychology,' which, more than anything else, rescued the Reich from the abyss?" These are candid words.

It was this "noble art of really creative propaganda" that thought up the catchword "corruption" and the short-lived legal farces based on it. In those days a charge of corruption still counted as a disgrace, still had a far-reaching effect. The Minister of Propaganda owed this effect to the integrity of the old German legal system and its reputation for justice. One believed in the "noble art of popular psychology" because it took months for the German people to realize that in the name of "positive Christianity" the National Socialists had let loose upon Germany a Pandora's box filled with hatred, heathenism, barbarism and suffering. Today there is no such thing as corruption in office, since all offices are held by National Socialists!

V

The rumors, doubts and anxieties which had disturbed all the intellectuals in Cologne had also had their effect upon us. We withdrew completely into ourselves and worked—until panic knocked at our door, too.

One evening Lotte Fresdorf appeared at our house in a frantic state. Jules was not at home. I was shocked by the change in the woman. In hysterical whispers, she implored my help. That day her husband had gone to his office in the Rathaus as usual, and since then had disappeared. He had not returned for luncheon, and Lotte had rung up his office. There was no answer. She had hurried to the Rathaus; she could not get in. In the evening a car drove up to their door. Three men got out, two policemen and her husband in handcuffs. He only wanted to get his things for the night, he stammered; they had been kind enough to allow him to do that. Then they drove away with him again. Now, after three days without news, she had discovered that her husband was a prisoner in the Klingelpütz. She had come to get me to help her with a mad plan. She would go up to our bathroom and cut the arteries of her wrists. I was to call the prison and say that Frau Fresdorf was dying, that the Burgomaster must be brought to her at once. Meanwhile Jules was to have a car ready. He was to seize the prisoner and take him away by force—simply kidnap him. It didn't matter where they went. She could arrange everything.

I succeeded in getting the raving woman to take some soup, into which I poured a sedative. Ziska went to the Fresdorf home to look after the children. Lotte stayed with us. I managed to dissuade her from her insane idea. We sat up with her at nights, and the doctor gave her morphine. Dr. Fresdorf was kept in the Klingelpütz only a few days. Then he was transferred to a penitentiary near Trier. There was no trial. Nor was it known of what he was accused. But the newspapers were better informed and cried out: "Corruption!" All of a sudden Fresdorf was released. He and his family moved to another quarter of the city. He neither wrote letters, telephoned nor received anyone. He had become a Nazi. He was thus assured of a pension, and there was no more talk of "corruption." A few weeks before, he had said in our house: "We believe too much in personality. Those who lack it have always lost out, and those who have it are not to be talked down by bombastic proclamations." Prophetic words!

These weeks were decisive for one's character. It was a strange time, when even the man who had no interest in politics was forced out of his indifference. Politics? It was not a question of politics. It was a question of strength, or weakness, of loyalty or betrayal. The Fresdorf case was one of seven among our acquaintances—the six others had a sense of honor. Our then chief at the Rathaus, Commissioner of Culture Meerfeld, served a term in prison. He was nearly sixty, and his eye trouble increased so while he was in prison that they released him. He was not a Jew and not a Communist, but a pious Catholic. What was his crime? "Culture bolshevism." He fled to Switzerland, but soon returned, half starved and homesick for Germany. Now he lives in a small town in the Rhineland, in constant fear, without money or help or advice from any of those who formerly courted his favors. Loyalty is the mark of honor, says Hitler.

Of five other cases, involving the destruction of homes, the mistreatment of an old woman, theft, threats and revenge upon a child of two, I cannot tell here. These people are compelled by circumstances to remain in Germany,

[36]

and my account would injure them. I can only say this much—these victims were neither Jews, nor Communists, nor criminals of any sort, merely German citizens who had the courage to be honest.

While many of our friends were suffering in this way, while bands of storm troopers entered their houses unchecked by the police, things at the Rautenstrauch-Joest Museum went on as usual. There was no swastika hoisted. No screaming voices invaded this home of science. The work went on. Fluss and Scheller wore their Nazi insignia, but otherwise remained as they had always been. How delightful to enter this great house, to lose oneself in work and forget the outer world! But how long would this heavenly isolation last? How long would it be permissible to withdraw quietly? The new State was not content with tolerance and the quiet fulfillment of one's duty. It clamored for "totalization," for active participation in the development of what it called "National Socialist culture." As a civic institution the Museum was under the control of the Municipal Council, and this in turn was governed by the Ministry of the Interior in Berlin. But the old Rathaus of Cologne had become the local center of enthusiastic propaganda for National Socialism. No one knew what turn matters would take. Something had to happen.

An early indication of what was to happen came in the form of a letter from the Chief Magistrate of the city.

"TO ALL OFFICIALS AND EMPLOYEES OF THE CITY OF COLOGNE:

"You are hereby informed that Mayor Adenauer has been granted leave of absence, by order of the President of the Government Board. His Excellency has temporarily appointed me acting Mayor of the city of Cologne. By the same token Herr Ebel has been assigned to the administrative duties of Herr Fresdorf and Dr. Meerfeld. I shall expect all employees of the city of Cologne to perform their tasks in the spirit of the old Prussian sense of duty. Though it is far from my intention to interfere with the freedom of thought of any individual, I emphati-

cally demand a capable civil service which is willing to work eco-
nomically, wholeheartedly and responsibly for our sacred city
and for the welfare of our glorious German Reich.

"Heil Hitler!

"RIESEN"

Who was Herr Riesen? We had not met him socially.
He had been a clerk in the banking house of Louis Hagen-
Levy, and there his face had grown round and smug. He
had made an advantageous marriage with the daughter of
a textile manufacturer. Today he was Mayor of Cologne.
Had this been arranged at Baron Schröder's, along with
Hitler's Chancellorship? Formerly Herr Riesen—living on
Jewish dividends—had been a very modest light, absent
from the parties illuminated by Dr. Konrad Adenauer's wit.
Obviously he could not count on the response to "national
concentration." He made no mention of it, relying on the
force of tradition in the older ideology. At that time there
was still a degree of risk in invoking the popularity of the
gentlemen from Bohemia and the "national revolution,"
at which he had hinted, however, by closing his letter with
the prescribed "Heil Hitler!"

When Jules got this letter, he felt that the time had
come to leave the silence of the little house and the work
of the large house and look into things for himself. He decided to go straight to the Rathaus, to find out just where
the Museum and its staff stood.

A row of well-padded limousines stood in front of the
Rathaus, flying pennons decorated with the swastika. Third
Reich novelties. In the lobby of the Division of Culture a
young man in a brown shirt did the honors, happy to
escort the director of the Rautenstrauch-Joest Museum to
the Burgomaster in charge of theatres, schools, museums
and, in fact, all the cultural institutions of the city of
Cologne. His name was Ebel.

This well-upholstered individual was better fitted for the

[38]

rôle of Falstaff than of Caliban—certainly not at all for the rôle of cultural arbiter. He was one of those wine-sippers so frequently met in the bowling clubs of the Rhineland, who do no harm as long as they sit in the dim light of the rathskeller. That thirtieth of January had transplanted him to the limelight of public office.

Perhaps he had some notion of what a museum of anthropology was. As an employee of the Hamburg-American Line, Ebel must have heard something of far-off countries and their inhabitants, if not personally, then by correspondence at least. After the close of his career with the steamship company, he had completed his modest education writing bills of consignment at the railway freight yard. Like other malcontents he had attached himself to the National Socialist Party, recognizing in it the chance of a lifetime. The moment Dr. Meerfeld was imprisoned, Ebel had jumped straight into the Division of Culture at the Rathaus. There he sat, signing his name to things.

Brown-shirted and embarrassed, he stood in the doorway of his office and greeted Jules with a loud "Heil Hitler," to which Jules replied, "Good morning." This was the first time since the establishment of the Third Reich that Jules had appeared in the lion's den. He had come to ask a few questions, but in no time at all he found himself involved in a strange conversation. He had no interest whatever in the perspiring upstart before him. The essential thing was to keep the Museum free from politics. It was for that he had come.

Ebel had braced himself to meet the arch-enemy, an intellectual, and showed himself most agreeably surprised at finding before him a pleasant young man, tanned and quite unspoiled by his travels. At first they fenced a little. As long as they talked about the War, all went well. They exchanged anecdotes about their respective regiments, except that Ebel wanted facts and figures. "Volunteered at the age of eighteen, did you, now? And at what hospital did they patch you up?" Becoming more and more personal in his questions, he inquired in detail about Jules' home in the Saar and was immensely interested to learn that both he and his wife were "descended from good old German families." Then the talk turned to science.

"Tell me something about this nigger business," said the Commissioner of Culture. He was charmed with his visitor, whose call he had obviously dreaded. "Men like you are just what we need," he exclaimed heartily. "We count a lot on the co-ordination of the director of our Museum. His backing will show that we know what we are doing, that we think before we speak. It will give scientific support to our program. Splendid!"

There was a pause, each weighing his purpose. Jules, the maintenance of independence for the Museum and for himself; Ebel, the capture of the professor and his institution. What a feather in his cap that would be! After a few moments of awkwardness, the Burgomaster broke the silence.

"Yes, you can serve us handsomely. It's settled then. I count on you for some mighty effective propaganda."

"Propaganda?" echoed Jules. "But, the Museum is a scientific institution."

"From now on," was the reply, "all our museums must have as their main object the business of propaganda for the National Socialist State."

A heated argument followed. On points of rhetoric the Burgomaster was worsted. But he succeeded admirably in revealing to the director of the Museum the vacuum that calls itself the culture of the Third Reich.

Science? According to Herr Ebel and his party doctrine, that was the urge to supply a show of logic as a foundation for insane notions. A museum? An institute of propaganda for race theories spawned in the addled brains of eccentrics. A university professor? A nodding image, controlled by orders from above. A museum director? Advertising agent for the Third Reich. A lecture? Whatever the subject, a

[40]

dissertation on the supremacy of the white race over the colored or the Jewish. Like a gramophone record, Herr Ebel ground out the sayings to which he owed his career. The collapse of a nation and the end of a liberal era were to him a Führer State destined to last a thousand years. The revival of Germanism was death to Marxism. The upheaval of all science was to him the dawn of a new cultural age. The spirit of Widukind, the spirit of Potsdam, to him subjection to one man's will. "Blood and the soil" from now on, as opposed to "mental acrobatics."

It was not, of course, the simple-minded Ebel speaking. The Master himself, or Herr Rosenberg of Riga, or Cairo-born Herr Hess, or any wearer of the brown shirt and the swastika would have expressed himself in exactly the same words. The formula had been found for one and for all. A thousand human megaphones repeated what had once been shouted into the microphone at Berlin. Ebel merely recited what he had learned by heart. The very monotony of his voice showed how the lesson had been hammered into him. The only choice lay between crawling in the dust and a flat "No."

This was apparent to Jules, as the Commissioner of Culture delivered his lecture on the new ethics, overwhelmed him with flattery and finally stretched out a huge right hand to welcome him into the new order.

"And be sure you write an article for us, Herr Professor," he added, "*Adolf Hitler and Ethnology* or *How I Found the Führer*. I will see that it gets published in all the newspapers right away."

Instead of answering, the director of the Rautenstrauch Museum asked the ex-freight-clerk now standing before him as the Commissioner of Culture in the Rathaus of the city of Cologne three questions: "Am I obliged as the director of the Museum to become a member of the National Socialist Party?"

Herr Ebel answered in the affirmative.

"Are my appointments regarded as political rather than scientific?"

Herr Ebel answered in the affirmative.

"Do you as Chief of my Division require that I as a scholar and museum director employ my name and my science in active propaganda for National Socialism?"

Herr Ebel replied in the affirmative.

"Then I see what I must do," said Jules. "Good-bye."

"Your hand, Herr Professor. I must by a handshake cement . . ."

But he was already alone. A door had banged.

As we had kept away from politics, politics came to us. The mountain to Mohammed. It already stood in the center of our little house, and we knew that we would rather perish than climb it.

We still had faith in the University. But a new president had been appointed, a young man who boasted a brown shirt and a swastika—in place of a degree—a young man who took precedence over an entire staff of scholarly men, who heretofore had been responsible solely to the Ministry of Culture. The lips of these professors—so skilled in the art of dialectics—now murmured "mein Führer"; their hands—so accustomed to recording the results of research—now signed their letters "Heil Hitler."

And now an odd thing happened. The composers, the painters, the distinguished men of law and literature who had been so sought after socially were examined with an eye to the color of their hair and the shape of their noses. A study of their "racial features" determined their desirability as guests. One's complexion and one's profile became subjects of frantic interest. Such were the standards and the values imposed on Germany by Adolf Hitler upon the inauguration of his "thousand-year reign."

One afternoon I was sitting at home drawing vignettes for the next Museum program. Tapir lay at my feet gnawing at a tennis ball. We heard the garden gate open, then the front door. Tapir's eyes turned a deep black and began to burn. Jules had arrived. Tapir flew to greet him and jumped repeatedly at his master. Then he stood still, waiting to be stroked. But Jules paid no attention to him. He looked at me with the serious glance with which he had looked at the girths of our pack-mules in Africa before trusting them with any weight. He looked at me as one looks at a man who has just lost his last dollar, wondering how he will face the future. He looked at me as an older and wiser companion looks at an untried youngster. Something new was about to enter my life, and he wondered how I would take it. I sensed this somehow. I sent Tapir into the garden, dropped my work and pushed an armchair toward Jules. I moved close to him, and we sat there smoking. Jules' glance wandered over the familiar room.

And now for the first time the world as it had become since the thirtieth of January came home to me. Jules spoke of Ebel; he spoke of the University, of the theatre, of books and of our aim in life. It was no longer right to close one's eyes and seal one's doors. We were people of our times. We must look facts in the face.

There was no longer a Museum; there was no longer a University. There were only institutions of propaganda, brothels of the spirit. There were no longer any independent scholars—only tools of the new system. The walls of learning parted and I saw the horrors behind them: soldiers and bayonets, falsehood and force. We still sat in our own house. But the Siebengebirgsallee was no longer Cologne, and Cologne was no longer Germany. An earthquake had engulfed our country, and we had sunk back into the Middle Ages. Barbarians governed us, ordering us to become barbarians. Armed men gave orders, and their orders were to shoot. A muzzled dog on an iron chain; this was the spirit permitted and encouraged by the Third Reich. God was to be done away with—He was no longer needed. A man had come to play at destiny. One had to raise one's right hand, to say "yes" and to obey. Books were to be written to prove doctrines as dictated. We were no longer to travel in search of foreign cultures, for Germany had become the hub of the universe, with the devil at the wheel. In Berlin sat a spider in the center of its web, determining what form God and science, honor and conscience were to take from now on.

"Everything for Germany," exclaimed the spider, "and I am Germany." The spider, of course, was not a German. "Right is what serves the German people," exclaimed the spider, "and I am the German people." The Ship of State steered as the creature commanded. POSITIVE CHRISTIANITY was emblazoned on its sails, but it turned aside in its course from spire and cross, from faith and truth.

"Resurrection of the spirit." The words sounded shrilly from the amplifier, and the burning of books had already begun. The arch enemy was the intellectual, the man who dared to use his mind to think. But he could easily be cowed. He was given the choice between hunger and obedience—and behold, he submitted at once.

The birds all shed their wings and let them fall into the fire and crept to the food trough beside the caterpillars. The butterflies changed into crawling insects and ate with the snake. The crickets ceased their chirping and scurried to join them. All the free, gay, flying creatures of the air discarded their colors, their songs and all their blessed gifts, to court the spider's favor. They had been threatened with hunger. The spider itself could not fly, but no one noticed this. Was there not one among the creatures that would continue to soar, for the sake of their freedom and because God had created them for flight? Would they all slink into the black hole that gaped for the soul of Germany? All?

There was silence in the room. We heard Ziska's voice in the kitchen, talking affectionately to Tapir. Suddenly Jules said: "And what do you think about it, Panther?"

[44]

There could be only one answer.

I got my little typewriter and we wrote two letters, one to the Minister of Science, Art and Education in Berlin, the other to the Prussian Minister of the Interior to whom the University and the Museum were respectively responsible. Both letters were short and clear. They requested an immediate leave of absence for Jules as professor of the University of Cologne and as director of the Rautenstrauch Museum. We sealed the letters and sent Ziska off to the post office with them.

When we were upstairs in Jules' study, Ziska came in with the registered receipts for our letters. She stood there before us in her simple black dress, our trusted little maid, so well deserving of our faith and our affection. She had nursed us in illness. She was the friend of dogs and squirrels and flowers. She was an admirable cook—and an admirable human being. And now we were obliged to break the news to her.

"Just a minute, Ziska. We would like to . . ."

She stood there hesitating and blushing. Simple people are easily embarrassed. She looked at us intently. Tapir lay on his back on the floor with his paws in the air. He began to snore.

"Ziska, I am so sorry. We must give you notice."

Her mouth fell open with fright. Her eyes filled with tears.

"I will try to do better," she said in a low tone. "I can learn anything. I can . . ."

"Oh, no, Ziska, we are not at all displeased with you. Only from now on our life will be different, uncertain. Professor Lips has just asked for a leave of absence."

"Are you going to Eze, Frau Professor? I have stayed alone before."

"No, not to the South of France, Ziska. We are going into uncertainty. You see, it does not suit us to say 'Heil Hitler.' There will be hatred and revenge."

"But our Museum?"

"That won't be 'ours' much longer."

"But, you can't do your own work!"

"I must, Ziska. Who knows whether our salary will go on?"

"But we aren't doing any harm. We work, until late at night! The exhibitions! Why, the students won't permit such a thing! Can the Nazis . . ."

"We aren't sure of anything. That's why we must let you go, Ziska. You need your money."

"I'll stay without wages. There will be enough to eat, I'm sure!" Her cheeks were quite brilliant now. She had dried her tears. The world had attacked her. She was through with the world, little Ziska Zendrich from the orphanage.

"You will find another good position."

"Oh, no, Frau Professor."

"You have been with much richer people; why do you like to be with us so much, Ziska?"

She came a few steps closer and said with dignity, "It's the way you treat me—like a human being."

I was deeply touched. I could find nothing to say.

Jules came to my rescue. "Is that it?" he asked, smiling. "So you have felt that way. Good, Ziska, you put things well. If that's the case, why don't you sit down?" He pushed the big blue velvet armchair toward her. "As long as we stay, you shall stay, too." He gave her his hand and so did I. Tapir woke up at once. When there was affection in the air, he was always alert to get his share.

"And what about you?" said Jules, patting his head. "Will you stay, too—without money or bones or tennis balls?" Tapir yawned in reply.

"Then we four will stick together. Perhaps this is the 'partnership of the people' the Nazis are advocating. Outside the storm rages, but within doors all is well."

As long as we remained in the house together, we were

deprived of nothing. Ziska had her wages, Tapir had his tennis balls and bones and we had peace and freedom. Outside the storm raged on, but within all was well—as long as we could remain faithful to one another, Jules and I and Ziska and the dog.

Emotional crises are quickly over. Tapir raced about in frolicsome capers, and Ziska chattered fussily of trivialities. Life was gay once more. On an impulse Jules and I decided to go to the carnival, not to a fine villa with a string orchestra and everyone in evening dress, but to the good old *Decke Tommes*. This was a mid-town pub, where taxi drivers met to drink their "corn" and eat their sausage. During the carnival the dingy pub became a fairyland of nonsense. Its walls were covered with slap-dash paintings, depicting scenes of orgy in violent colors; little private booths were hung with paper serpents; brass bands tooted and blared and the roof rang with laughter and merry-making.

The bohemian crowd had discovered the *Decke Tommes*, and it had become the haunt of stage and radio artists, of painters and writers. Their pockets were empty, but their hearts were full. Their clothes were sometimes shabby, but not so their wit. The future might be uncertain, but who cared for that? They lived for today, and today held no terrors. The *Decke Tommes* was an exclusive place, far more exclusive than any of the high-class night clubs, which were open to anyone who could pay the cover charge. Only a few of the University staff were admitted. We were among the lucky ones. So was Herbert Kühn, a young professor of archaeology, who at that time was still more devoted to his charming Jewish wife than to his later love, Nazi propaganda. There was another colleague of Jules' on the favored list, whose life has likewise since been uprooted. He and his wife were an incredibly hilarious pair. No one in the world would have dreamed that he had ever heard of mathematics, much less specialized in the science. Such people were welcome here, none of them rich, none

[47]

of them smug, but all of them alive to laughter, all true sons of Father Rhine.

Jules wore wide, black velvet trousers, a red silk shirt, a sailor's kerchief embroidered with anchors and long, swinging earrings—just the sort of clothes for the *Decke Tommes*, where one is apt to find himself sitting on the steps or the floor. I went in Chinese costume, high-arched eyebrows, light yellow trousers, pointed hat hung with little bells—though no one heard their tinkling with four bands going at once and an unceasing outcry of hi-de-hi!

The hero of the evening was Karl Heil, manager of the West German Broadcasting Company. He was the guiding spirit of the carnival, as warm-hearted as he was brilliant, as sincere as he was capricious, as fine a fellow as ever lived. He had come dressed as "Mackie Messer," the Irish ne'er-do-well of the films, in a crumpled over-size tuxedo topping his flapping bathing trunks, with a battered opera hat and bulging leather gloves as finishing touches. I was flattered when he asked me to dance with him, and we romped through the room hilariously.

At the buffet we ran into Professor Kühn, but his charming little Jewish wife was nowhere to be seen. He was dressed in the handsome white silk robe of a maharajah, much too fine for the *Decke Tommes*, and looked drunk. "I am becoming an Aryan, an Aryan, an Aryan, and my little Rita is, too!" he bawled, to the tune of the latest waltz. Close behind him stood a young man, so ordinary in appearance that his presence here seemed altogether wrong. He had a pencil and a notebook in his hand. He never took his eyes off Professor Kühn.

"What's he up to?" I asked Karl Heil. He went up to the lad, pushed him through the dense crowd of dancers and out of the room.

"I have already ordered him out three times. He is taking notes. A swine of a Na . . ."

"Hush, Karl, hush!"

Some remarks are dangerous even at carnival time. I sought out Jules and we left the party at three in the morning. An hour later twenty-three people were arrested at the *Decke Tommes* for remarks hostile to the State. Karl Heil was among them, taken on the charge of "communistic propaganda."

On the same carnival night in Cologne Robert Görlinger disappeared. He was a town councilor and University trustee, a patron of art, a man of reputation with tremendous influence in Berlin. The last time he was seen he was dancing at the Artists Club run by Alfred Heinen, who is today starving in Amsterdam. Görlinger vanished. Many people thought he had been murdered. Others could not believe that this strong-willed man, who was equal to any emergency, could have been crushed in the avalanche. Months later we found that he had taken refuge in France, in Besançon, where he sold chocolates from a pushcart in the railway station, incidentally impressing all who came his way with his fluent and polished French.

Not one of the leaders of all this gaiety has ever appeared again at the *Decke Tommes*. It was like the fairy tale in which a single word breaks the charm and turns everything to ashes. A gray world was suddenly revealed to us—no, a brown world!

On March 28, 1935, the eight leading carnival associations, representing the oldest popular tradition of the Rhineland, filed a formal protest with Burgomaster Ebel against the injection of politics into their festival. They repudiated the censorship of all carnival speeches demanded by the National Socialist Party. They cited the presence of "masked political spies," and entered a bitter complaint against the interference of the State in matters concerning local customs of the Rhineland. Their protest was ignored. The State put through its program. The Cologne carnival has been "co-ordinated."

Carnival balls are still held at the *Decke Tommes*. But

there are no bright paintings on the wall; the witty voices have been silenced; the jovial laughter has ceased. The costumes are more expensive, the wines finer, and the conversations such as spies may hear. Two priceless things have been extinguished: the freedom of the mask, and the gaiety of a childlike people whose hearts beat warm and wild with the joy of living.

PART TWO

VIVACE—STRUGGLE WITH THE LEMURAE

Behold, how they cower, all shrunken with fear
Like startled storks, when a rat rustles near.

Jean Giraudoux

I

THE ANSWER TO JULES' APPLICATION FOR
leave of absence did not come from the Minister of the
Interior at Berlin, but from the Cologne Rathaus. It was
signed by Ludwig, one of the new men, who, like most of
them, held only a temporary appointment. The letter consisted of a single sentence, to the effect that the requested
leave was granted until further notice. There was no reply
from either the Minister of Culture or the University, so
Jules was obliged to go on with his teaching for the time
being.

One afternoon there was a telephone call—Herr Ebel in
a state of excitement. Only later did we notice that under
the Third Reich compromising matters were settled by telephone, for fear that documents, being publishable, might
serve to expose the tyranny of the new regime to the outside
world.

Herr Ebel was humorous enough to appeal to the director
of the Museum for advice as to his successor. He actually
implored Jules to let no one know of his leave of absence
until a "substitute" had been found, to say nothing about it
to the students or the staff. Ebel appealed to him to stay at
his post "until the worst was over."

"We can't shut up shop! Why the devil are you taking a
vacation? I don't know anything about your damned anthropology! At least get me one of your damned anthropologists to take over!"

Jules promised, for the sake of the Museum, to consider
the matter. He obliged the fat Commissioner by keeping
silent. Not a soul knew the next day that he had come to
say farewell.

He entered the seminar; the students shot up from their chairs. He looked at them with a mixture of hope and pain. These were the coming German anthropologists. These men were to carry the banner of science, with the swastika flag leading the way.

How could they meet their trust? For theirs is a science which does not deal with research into German origins as prescribed. Its scope embraces the cultural history of all mankind. Its origins lie among the primitive peoples of all the continents of the world.

There they sat: Baumgarten, the sick lad from the provinces, whom we had nursed back to health after a desperate illness—Niggemeyer, the tall chap, whose aspirations were so high—Scheller, the eternally dissatisfied, in a brown shirt —Melchers, the most cultivated of the students—Schmalenbach, the adolescent aesthete—conscientious little Maurer and that kind-hearted imp, Krings—young, golden-haired Renate, the co-ed, of whom we were so fond, and the intellectual little Catholic priest, zealously preparing to carry his faith to a waiting world.

Among them all, Fröhlich's polished personality stood out. He was always immaculately groomed, always on time, always receptive, always docile. If I went away, Fröhlich unfailingly came to my train with a sheaf of roses. If Jules wanted help of any kind, Fröhlich came forward with a rush.

These were the more mature students, who were working on their theses. How would they all react? How would they fare without the guiding hand of their teacher? What would become of their studies? How steadfast were their vows of loyalty to their young professor, at whose house they had so often been welcomed, whose aim in life up to now had been to round out their understanding of the world, to make them into men, scholars and Germans?

Jules went back to his office, and sent for Fröhlich and Scheller separately. He asked them both to come to our house that same day, Scheller in the afternoon, Fröhlich in the evening.

Then he took a few things from his desk, packed his brief case, washed up, put on his coat and hat. Once more he opened the door into the library, where his own volumes stood among the Museum's books. He did not look at the Javanese image, nor at the blue walls of the director's room, the wall paper of which we had selected together. The stenographer wanted to ask a question, but he hastened by her and walked down the broad staircase, past its guarding lions. Weiss came up from the cellar to report that he had got out the African film. Jules whistled for Astor, the watchdog of the Museum, and a magnificent German shepherd dog bounded up to him the instant the door was opened. Jules stroked his head. The dog and the man looked into each other's eyes. The attendant, Fluss, was poking about in the cloak room.

"Good-bye, Weiss," said Jules, with a last look at the honest old fellow. Then he turned and went.

Scheller appeared punctually at our tea table in the study. He seemed ill at ease, shifted his wooden leg awkwardly and tried hard to make himself agreeable. He had none of the spiritual grace that lends dignity to physical affliction. When in pain he took morphine; and when he could not resort to the drug, he was ill-tempered and gave full vent to his inferiority complex in suspicion and arrogance. He had a misshapen skull with a low forehead, wore enormously thick glasses and had a cracked voice. His ugly sensual mouth was the gateway for many inane utterances. As a student he was far from satisfactory. But once the poor wretch had broken down and wept before his teacher. His misbegotten soul—which was far more deformed than his unfortunate body—had crawled forth and begged for deliverance, for help, for salvation. In memory of that despairing hour Jules protected the man and tried to assist him. To me he was unendurable.

[55]

Our conversation that afternoon revealed that Scheller had recently come to realize that he was an ardent Nazi, a "hundred percenter." He admired the Führer and boasted of new and influential acquaintances, talking with an emphasis that was entirely foreign to him. What was the source of his self-confidence? A sense of importance? Morphine? Revenge? The opportunist's readiness to accept any code that might be handed out, for the sake of a possible chance at power, of winning some advantage?

His thesis was still unwritten. He delayed it deliberately, for his stipend was only to last until his graduation. He spent most of his time in drinking and in limping about the streets.

Jules had not told me why he had invited Scheller. Because I could not endure him, I tried to welcome him with housewifely hospitality.

"You have been working on your thesis for six years now," said Jules. "Don't you really want to get on?"

"Why, you know, Professor, my pension . . ." replied Scheller, thinking of his plan to prolong his piddling little study of the musical instruments of New Guinea into the years of his old age.

"The pension is all very well," replied Jules, "but why not try for a job? That would not be so bad."

Scheller raised his head with a jerk. In his excitement he smacked his lips. He nervously crumbled his cake, waiting tensely to hear more.

"They are looking for an ethnologist . . ."

"But I haven't my degree."

"For the position in question the one requisite is to have the right badge in one's buttonhole."

Involuntarily we glanced at Scheller's coat lapel—even he looked down at it. And there it was—the right badge. Its pattern had been known in Asia for two thousand years before Christ. Under Hitler it had become familiar to the modern world as the swastika.

Jules cut off the tip of a fresh cigar and lighted it, enjoying his first puff in silence, his eye fixed on the vanishing line of smoke. He went on in a light conversational tone:

"The position I should like to offer you is the directorship of the Rautenstrauch-Joest Museum."

I felt as though a blow had been struck at my heart. I should be lying if I were to describe the impression Jules' words made on his pupil, for I never saw it. I literally had not the strength to look at him. Nor did I look at Jules. I did not understand. I could not understand the humiliation he was inflicting on himself and on the noble house on the Ubierring. I was beside myself. I understood nothing—at that time.

Then I heard Scheller ask: "How much money would I get?"

I don't know how I held my temper. I was more angry than grieved. Scheller! That dirty clumsy clown, that idler who lived by cheating, that denouncer of his classmates, that brand-new Nazi convert!

Jules referred him to Commissioner of Culture Ebel, saying that Scheller might use his name as a reference, that he was taking a long holiday and thought it important in view of the present circumstances that the Museum should be in National Socialist hands.

Did I still not understand? No! I flew down the steps, calling for Tapir, as though his were the only untainted name left in the world. I hurried to the kennel, where I poured forth all my grief and bewilderment.

When Fröhlich came in the evening, Scheller had long been gone. I had changed into a dinner frock, and was refreshed and calm. Fröhlich was his usual immaculate and deferential self. He was in a cutaway. He had brought me some flowers.

Jules told him that he was taking a holiday and that Scheller would probably be his successor. The student

[57]

showed not the least surprise at the decision of his teacher, but as though he had not heard right, he kept on repeating: "Scheller? Scheller?"

"Under the circumstances," said Jules, "it is best to have a National Socialist in the post. I know none more typical than Scheller. Of course, the formal appointment must come from the city, but I wanted to let you know at once. In view of the close association between us and of the many evidences of your devotion and loyalty as my assistant, I did not want you to hear of the change through the newspapers. I wanted to talk the situation over with you and get your reaction."

"Reaction?" Fröhlich seemed disturbed at the word. "Well, of course, Herr Professor, I am your personal assistant, selected by you for the post, but I hardly see how your desire for leave of absence affects me. After all, mine is a Museum assignment."

"Well," said Jules, "it had occurred to me that you might possibly like to take a short leave, which would not commit you in any way—just to see how things develop. Your salary is in any case secure for several months."

"Leave of absence? But why?"

"Because, as one in close contact with me, your fellow students may feel that you reflect my point of view to some degree, and there may be some who look upon you as an adherent of mine, with similar ideas . . ."

"What ideas, Herr Professor?"

"Certainly you have worked long enough with me to be familiar with my ideas of the purpose of science, with my view that it is only absolute fidelity to truth that gives meaning to research. This very truth for which we have striven all our lives now seems to me endangered by recent political events. It is therefore that I have decided to entrust the Museum temporarily to a substitute. I have discussed the matter with the city authorities and hope that the Commissioner will meet my wishes."

[58]

"But why Scheller?" exclaimed Fröhlich. "Why that blockhead of a Nazi . . ."

"You must be more circumspect in your speech," said Jules. "Some people have no sense of humor."

"But we are only intended as cannon food for future wars," cried Fröhlich in a frenzy. "A sounding board for all their heroic outbursts. A new target! Students to the front! Cannon food! Hitler himself won't go into the trenches. It's us he's driving in, us!"

Such words were unbecoming to a young student, Jules reminded him, and, furthermore, as an officer he did not want to hear them. It was not Hitler's ideas that were under discussion, but the freedom of science, the future of the Museum and a clear, unequivocal decision.

"Decision?"

"Yes, decision! The question is whether you take your stand with me, or with the man who may prove to be either a pawn in an uncertain gamble or perhaps really the bearer and defender of new doctrines that will endure—which would be a pity as far as the Museum is concerned."

Then came a curious question. How long did Jules think the Hitler regime would last?

"It is not the duration of Hitler's rule that concerns us, but the nature of it. One must either accept or repudiate it. You must think it out clearly. After all," he smiled, "I have been trying to teach you just that—to think clearly."

"I am to tell you now?"

"Yes."

Fröhlich raised his head, tightened his cravat, moved his tortoise-shell spectacles nervously up and down and finally looked over toward me. I had been perfectly silent.

The pause grew painful. Fortunately, Fröhlich was a master of the social conventions. He got up, pulled his coat into place with an easy gesture, adjusted the creases of his trousers and came gracefully toward us.

"Herr Professor, Frau Lips, I thank you for the honor

that you have done me by taking me into your confidence. You expect an answer from me. I will give it to you tomorrow morning."

He kissed my hand, bowed, clicked his heels and left the room slowly, keeping his back turned toward the door in the manner learned at dancing class.

"Yes, my dear," said Jules, "that's how a traitor does it. Did you see his parting glance at your flowers? Wasted money, is what he thought, wasted money."

"I should never have expected that of Fröhlich . . ."

"Well, you see, a practical course in psychology is now beginning for us."

At nine o'clock the next morning the telephone rang. Might Herr Fröhlich speak to Professor Lips? He informed Jules that he saw no reason for allowing his chief's personal decisions to affect his own work. He was employed in the Rautenstrauch-Joest Museum and was paid by the city of Cologne.

"Thank you, Herr Fröhlich. Good luck to you. Good morning."

"Heil Hitler!"

He had a capacity for adjusting himself, had Fröhlich— that we must admit. Within a week, he had donned a brown shirt and took active part in the plundering of the home of former editor and Alderman Beyer, when the piano was smashed to splinters, the chairs ripped to shreds and a number of works of art stolen. Herr Fröhlich succeeded in appropriating an old silk prayer rug, which he hung up as a trophy of the occasion on the wall of his study.

II

On the fourth of April the official announcement of Professor Lips' leave of absence was sent to the press. It caused something of a stir. There were various reactions. Our telephone rang incessantly, for the news seemed almost incredible to the editorial offices. Neither of the famous old Cologne newspapers (the Catholic *Kölnische Volkszeitung* and the conservative *Kölnische Zeitung*) failed to stress the fact that Professor Lips was being replaced by a man whose chief merit was his membership in the National Socialist Party. But the official party paper for Western Germany, the *Westdeutscher Beobachter*, made the announcement in such an extraordinary way that it is worth quoting: "The director of the Rautenstrauch-Joest Museum has been granted indefinite leave. Party member Andreas Scheller has been temporarily appointed in his place. Thus an authority on anthropology has taken over this position."

It was obvious that the hand of the censor was at work. Acting upon a hint from Berlin, all the announcements neglected to state that Lips' leave of absence had come at his own request. "The authority on anthropology" and the disappointed Commissioner of Culture had put their heads together and framed the story so that the uninitiated would think, "There must have been something wrong!"

"You're Jews, aren't you?" the butcher asked Ziska. "We only sell to Aryans now. Go somewhere else." A neighbor, whose Boxer had won second prize at the recent dog show to Tapir's first, sent a message to me saying that doubtless this had been due to "the usual skulduggery of the Jews, as was evident from the expulsion of that non-Aryan Lips from the Museum."

[61]

The slime of defamation which was spreading over Germany had already reached our doors.

I turned over several pages of my diary, drew a thick red line across them and as the heading for a new chapter in our lives wrote: *The Interregnum.*

With the exception of Fröhlich and Scheller, no one at the Museum was prepared for the news of their chief's departure. It was a shock to them to read the announcement in the papers. It seemed to them impossible. They expected, as a matter of course, that pressure would be brought to bear. They knew perfectly well that they would be "invited to co-ordinate," if they wanted to keep and reinforce their positions. But that their director, a man who possessed all the qualities so suddenly at a premium, a favorite in Cologne's most conservative social circles, one of the ranking editors of the *Koloniale Rundschau*, that he of all men should rise up and utter a categorical "No!" instead of the universally eager cry, "Here I am!" It was incomprehensible. It was hard for those who meant him well, particularly for the weak among them.

But who was strong in those days? Our thoughts turned to the men whose standing in the intellectual field pledged them to echo that "No." Let us not speak of the unfortunate Jews among them, for the moment paralyzed with fear for their future. But what of our university presidents, our composers and conductors, our acclaimed authors, of all those representatives of the long-established German culture, now so suddenly imperiled? If all our learned men, all our artists and musicians and dramatists and essayists and thinkers—down to the last poetaster and fiddler, down to the humblest amateur—had boldly made a stand on the thirtieth of January, 1933, uniting in a common protest against the crime perpetrated against German culture, then the gentleman from Bohemia could never have plunged our country into the ruin that now engulfs her. Germany could never have been degraded into a nation bristling with bayonets, a nation that persecutes its churches because it no longer feels the need of God; a nation that brands some of her greatest physicians as "ritual murderers," substituting for them untrained quacks; a nation that throws the works of its masters of music and poetry and science on the rubbish heap, while the world makes mock of her and the guardians of the soul of Germany shed tears of despair; a nation whose children, before they can say their letters, chant songs of hate against France; a nation whose mothers are advised to seek courage for their impending birth pangs by gazing at portraits of the criminals held up to them as "heroes," hung in the place of honor in their homes.

Where were Germany's great men? Our eyes turned toward Gerhart Hauptmann, before whom, on the occasion of his seventieth birthday, an entire nation had bowed in homage, paying unprecedented tribute to his genius. With tears of emotion and gratitude, he had clasped the hands of men whom the thirtieth of January had altered into "traitors to their country." What would he do? What would Rudolf Binding do, and Richard Strauss, and Furtwängler, and what would our revered anthropologists do?

One and all, they became apostles of the creed of race. They were "Aryans," and it was easy for them to keep their nests feathered. They had only to raise their right hands at the proper time. They did not see that they were falling into the hell of hopelessness, that they were burying themselves alive, dooming themselves to a death from which there is no resurrection. This is what the great men of Germany did in the days when heroic words were sounding in the streets, in the days when real heroism demanded only the utterance of a single little word, a word one never heard—the word "No"! With the great men pointing the way, what were the small fry to do?

Well, one day Scheller appeared at the Museum, student Scheller, he of the wooden leg and the soiled clothing, the oldest and the laziest of the class. He came with a document signed by Commissioner Ebel and asked to examine the books and records of the Museum. He had a desk and chair arranged in the waiting room. He did not yet dare to penetrate behind the tall door. There, a golden Javanese god stared blankly down at an empty chair and an empty desk. Scheller remained outside, rustling the papers. He had his orders. He was looking for traces of "corruption." He asked to have every bill explained. He read every letter. When he came and when he went, he called out "Heil Hitler!" and weak arms were raised and willing lips were opened to attest to their subservience.

Attendant Weiss buried himself for days in the photographic laboratory. There he was secure against Scheller, who avoided the stairs. Weiss, they say, sat on the cases which we had brought back from Africa, shaking his head in silence.

Attendant Schmitz, the jester, the chatterbox, spent all his time in the cellar. If anyone addressed him, he ran away. These old-timers had their principles.

Fluss, on the other hand, who had only been in the Museum a year when all this occurred, Fluss, the ex-Communist, the second brown shirt after Scheller in the Museum, announced his Third Reich qualifications loudly and plainly. He now hurried obsequiously to Scheller, to help *him* on with his coat.

In the ante-room spinsterish Fräulein Fasbender hovered about Scheller, whom she loathed, handing him whatever he asked for. Of a sudden he was no longer ridiculous to her. She shook in her boots for fear of losing her position, for the day of woman's rights was now over. Her Catholic heart rebelled against the heretic. Her mind refused to think. Therefore her tongue and her hands were all the more zealous in serving the new master.

There was no work done for the Museum. Letters went unanswered. Scholars stayed away, for each had his own problem. The whole great house was silent with a quiet which it had never known before. Who indeed could have found time for study of the culture of foreign lands in an epoch when our own culture was being brought to burial, with the drums beating dismally?

We vegetated during the interregnum. We watched eagerly for interruptions from the outside. The day the morning papers headlined the announcement of Jules' leave of absence, Fluss came up to the garden gate on his bicycle. He had brought a slip of paper, which he refused to give to Ziska. He insisted on seeing the professor in person. The professor could not be disturbed, and so I went to the gate. Fluss called out "Heil Hitler!" I looked at the slip of paper. It was a receipt, signed by Scheller, for the key to the Museum toilet. The key was still in the possession of the director and was to be handed over at once. I wanted to take the receipt and get the key. "No," exclaimed Fluss, "first the key!" I brought it to him. There were five duplicates hanging on the Museum keyboard. He gave me the receipt.

I was called to the telephone. It was the West German Broadcasting Company calling. I was requested to cancel my broadcast on Southern France. The name of Lips was just now not popular with the radio audience. Many believed that we were Jews. When things cleared up, the matter would be brought up again. There was nothing to clear up, I replied; everything was perfectly clear. Would I care to speak under a pseudonym? Oh, no, my husband's name was mine. They expressed their regrets. They would return my script. I asked them, since my talk had been definitely accepted, to send me the fee. This was impossible; contracts unfortunately were no longer valid. Surely I would understand. I did understand. Good-bye to my camera. Oh, well, what of it? I should probably never again walk beneath palm trees, or have a chance to photograph the shores of the Mediterranean.

We went walking on the Ring, the main street of the inner city of Cologne. Among the familiar columns of marching men, whose uniforms and trappings from day to day were more and more differentiated, we met a curious conveyance. It was a truck belonging to the Department of Sanitation, but there were not many barrels on it. It had quite another load, and a comical load, at that—a group of men, looking like a flock of frightened ravens. They wore flowing black robes, some had portfolios under their arms, others wore judicial caps. They carried poles with placards attached, bearing the words "Down with Judea," "Germany, awake!" "The Jews are a curse to our country!" With them was a group of half-grown boys in brown shirts whose task it was to hold the placards upright, so that they could be read. They sang the Horst Wessel song. Who were these men? A new troop in a new uniform? No, they were—as the inscription on the truck informed us—Jewish judges and attorneys. Under the very eyes of the "Aryans" there on trial, they had been dragged from their desks in the law courts, to be driven through the city streets in ignominy.

Decidedly it was best to stay at home. It was advisable not to turn on the radio, so as not to hear the voice so reminiscent of Pallenberg in the rôle of Zawadil. It was also wiser to look as little as possible at the newspapers. Most of those we had been in the habit of reading were now forbidden. The *Westdeutscher Beobachter*, however, a sheet scarcely known in Cologne, had moved into the premises owned by the *Rheinische Zeitung*, which had been seized by the Nazis, and there, on "transferred" presses, in the excellently lighted halls, also "transferred," came out in editions thirty times its original size. A particular importance attaches to the *Westdeutscher Beobachter* as the official organ of the government for the entire Rhineland. For Hitler's press clarioned the principle of the authoritarian state, "I am the Führer, thy god, and thou shalt have no other Führer than I," as loudly as did his own voice. Not everyone

[66]

in Germany was so fortunate as to hear the voice of her saviour every day. It was a good idea therefore to learn the ten commandments, as revealed by Herr Ley, a man who stood high in Hitler's confidence. The first of them was: "We salute the Führer in the morning, and in the evening we give thanks to him for awaking us to new purpose and activity in life." And those who lacked sufficient fervor for such a prayer had only to consult the *Westdeutscher Beobachter*.

If one stayed at home, it was as well not to go near the telephone. But who can successfully withstand the incessant ringing of a telephone bell? Mysterious calls took place. Anonymous "friends" advised Jules to co-ordinate without delay. Others called up without giving their names, satisfying themselves with asking the maid to deliver messages of abuse. Threats did not come until later.

At times after dark there were visitors. There was a university colleague of Jules, a quiet, hermit-like, scholarly man, whom in former times we scarcely ever saw. This man came to see us and told us warmly how delighted he was with Jules' stand, how much he wanted to assure us of his sympathy. The professors who kept their mouths shut for fear of losing their positions were scoundrels, he said. However, he asked us to be good enough not to mention his visit. After all, Jules was on leave of absence, and one must watch which way the wind blew. He himself would prefer to act as we were doing; but what would become of him? Cologne was such a beautiful city. Then he left, looking anxiously about, conscious of having done a heroic deed.

The belief that our house was a citadel of peace was soon disturbed. Besides the radio and the newspapers, which one could banish, and the telephone, which one could ignore, other interruptions of the quiet of our life soon made themselves felt. There was a trick of ringing at our garden gate at night that put an end to sleep. Every three-quarters of an hour from midnight until five o'clock the bell would ring

[67]

for three solid minutes. We plainly saw a figure at the gate, when we looked down from the balcony outside Jules' bedroom. Since the ringing occurred regularly three times a week, we prepared to rout the enemy. The next time he appeared, Tapir was at the gate, his eyes flaming. I turned on the hose and shot a stream of icy water out of the cellar window onto the uniformed figure, and Ziska hurled chunks of coal at it as it fled. That was the end of the nightly bell-ringing.

In addition to such childish pranks it was curious to see what absurd attempts were made to meddle in our lives. One evening a well-dressed gentleman suddenly appeared at our house, introduced himself as an ethnologist, come to Cologne for a short stay, and mentioned the name of a friend in Berlin who had sent him to call on Jules. This visitor, whose utter ignorance of anthropology was soon apparent, asked Jules in a casual manner to tell him the details of his "over-hasty request" for leave of absence. Nothing was irrevocable; people like Jules were needed in the new State; God knows they were not seeking old men with long beards. Young Aryan scholars, soldiers who had fought at the front—this was the type that was wanted. Jules was exactly that sort. Why on earth had he applied for leave? Not only could he hold his post for life; but from the financial angle, it was full of promise. Meritorious scholars would be paid according to their merits. There was a demand for men of reputation, of youth and of forcefulness. Jules would soon see the foolishness of his decision. Moreover, he stood alone. Who else in Cologne had been mad enough to refuse to co-ordinate? He would see, he would see. . . .

We listened to this man and we listened to four others, who under various names and pretexts penetrated into our home to offer us open bribes. The sixth we did not receive. Ziska managed this splendidly. Our caller stated that he was an ethnologist from Paris, that he was passing through Cologne and had messages for Jules. Ziska was inspired to ask him the name of the director of the Trocadéro. She knew Dr. Rivet well, for he had often been a guest in our home. The "ethnologist from Paris" was unable to answer. Tapir sent him flying in half a minute by thrusting his demon's head through the bars of the garden gate, while Ziska remarked: "You had better go. Our dog is non-Aryan."

These early incidents of the interregnum were only funny. Later on they become more frequent and more dangerous. For the time being we were unemployed. Leave of absence of course meant nothing. Either Jules would be assured of freedom to teach and freedom to fulfill his administrative duties according to his conscience, or . . .

What that "or" stood for we did not yet ourselves know. We only knew that when the day of reckoning came, we would say, in the words of Zarathustra: "Praised be that which makes us hard."

III

Early in 1933 the law concerning the "re-creation of the professional civil service" was enacted. It provided means for the dismissal of life appointees wherever necessary "in the course of national regeneration," classifying the cases in the following major divisions: men whose "education was insufficient for their position"; "non-Aryans"; the "politically unreliable"; and those who were "not fully co-ordinated." These last were removed from their posts, but received a barely adequate pension. From then on the papers published daily lists of councilors, actors, judges, professors, musicians and teachers who were dismissed in accordance with one or another paragraph of this eminently practical law. In many cases the individuals affected were old and helpless. They had not been able to save any of their scanty earnings and had consoled themselves with the certainty of their old-age pensions. In our street there was an old primary school teacher who broke down and wept as he told us his story. He had been dismissed as politically unreliable, because he had once taught in a liberal school. He was a harmless botanist who had spent his life counting antherozoids. Who was going to bother about him? Two months later we learned that he had hanged himself.

Since we had no idea what the future might bring to us, we began first of all to put our papers in order and to return material which had been entrusted to us. In Jules' desk there were a number of manuscripts which had been sent him as editor of the scientific periodical *Ethnologica* by various colleagues. It was important to return these papers. It was Jules' duty to see that they did not fall into the unscrupulous hands of politically minded students. Jules did not know what would become of *Ethnologica*, and therefore the manuscripts of distinguished colleagues made their way back to Cambridge and Brussels, to Harvard and to Paris. It did one good to arrange one's affairs with the same precision and clarity with which our human relationships were ticketed under the new system. Circumstances labeled our acquaintances as traitors, weaklings or comrades in the fighting ranks. Automatically they took their places in one of the three categories. For instance, there was Eugen von Rautenstrauch. During the weeks of strain and uncertainty we had quite forgotten him. One day he telephoned, almost overcome with timidity and anxiety. He must talk to Jules at once. Were we crazy? Had we forgotten the Museum? Who in the name of heaven was Scheller? Naturally, he could not express his deep concern over the telephone. He was going to ask us to tea soon. He was completely at sea. He was leaving no stone unturned. He had just come from the Rathaus. That Eb . . . No, no, he would say nothing. The whole world had gone mad. In the middle of the conversation he hung up. We have not been to tea with him since then.

I tried to talk to Jules as little as possible about what was going on in the Museum or about our future. He, too, never spoke of these matters, but I felt that he believed in victory, in his reinstatement under conditions compatible with the honor of a German scholar. He realized, of course, that his enemies would oppose him, but he considered them sufficiently honorable to admit in time that one man of character was worth more than a hundred co-ordinated jellyfish. He was naïve enough to imagine that a movement founded on lies could be countered by sincerity and objectivity.

It was only on these grounds that this choice of Scheller as his successor could be explained. Scheller was a National Socialist to the marrow; a megalomaniac, a materialist, a malcontent. To expose such an appointee so that even the ruling powers could see his ineptitude—this was Jules' object in naming Scheller to take his place. It was a clever way of making one's point through subtlety, but Jules forgot that the Third Reich is not equipped to perceive subtlety.

But our relation to the large house on the Ubierring was too close, was too much a part of our lives for us to cease to be anxious about it. We worried about the Museum as one worries when a loved one is in the hands of an incompetent physician. And doubtless Eugen von Rautenstrauch worried too, but after a fashion peculiar to himself. He wanted to know that the institution he had founded was in good hands; he wanted to see exhibitions put on; to sit in the front row at impressive functions. Who was Scheller? A mere student, a man without a degree, a dabbler who had published nothing, an oaf without the slightest social grace. But Scheller wore that dangerous little badge in his buttonhole, that all-powerful emblem.

The almighty power of this badge soon began to make itself felt. A letter came from the city of Cologne written by Commissioner of Culture Ebel to the University, which had forwarded it for Jules' information. It was to the effect that as Professor Lips was taking a leave of absence it was impossible for him to hold his seminar in the Rautenstrauch-Joest Museum. It requested the immediate transfer of the seminar to the University and emphatically forbade Professor Lips' appearance in the Museum lecture room during the term of his leave. Below the Commissioner's signature was a memorandum: "Approved by Acting Director Scheller."

That day a notice was posted on the Museum bulletin board saying that the seminar in ethnology was closed until further notice. It was then that Scheller moved into the director's office. The golden Javanese god was put away. In its place was set a photograph of the man whom Scheller believed to be his leader.

[72]

The first of April of that year brought a blush of shame to the cheek of every decent German. That day the official announcement of the boycott of the Jews was made. That day the Nazis photographed all "Aryans" who entered Jewish shops. That day obscene words were painted on shop windows, and defenseless merchants were covered with abuse. "The Jews are a curse to our country!" How many of these firms had been established in Germany for centuries, contributing to the development of German commerce at a time when the foreign ancestors of Herr Hitler had been blissfully unaware that their seed was destined to provide Germany with a saviour.

Crowds thronged into the business section of the city, avid for a share in the excitement, divided between abandon and revulsion, craning their necks for a glimpse of the yellow patches, revived from the days of the Dark Ages, that disfigured the signs of so many well-known shops. "So they are Jews, too," said the mob. That was the object of the whole thing. Storm troopers watched to see that the placards were not removed. The proprietor of a large department store, known as a Maecenas of the arts, a zealous supporter of modern music, a noted aesthete and philanthropist, was imprisoned by two of Hitler's soldiers in the entrance of his own store and forced to wear a placard reading: "Don't buy from a Jew!" Can atonement ever be made for such barbarism? We were sick with disgust.

However, the Ministry of Propaganda itself, although the festival went off brilliantly, does not appear to have been entirely satisfied with its moral effect. Though it was announced that the performance would be repeated at regular intervals, it has never recurred. Other anti-Jewish demonstrations, much more cruel than this, were staged, but they were never again authorized and were officially censured as over-zealous, spasmodic incidents. Of course, the stimulus in this direction was always supplied by the government, but it no longer wished these incidents to be regarded as

[73]

official. Perhaps that degrading first of April was responsible for it. For I know of many "Aryans" who deliberately patronized the very stores that had been attacked by those sewer rats. I myself posed before the camera of one of the watchdogs on leaving one of Cologne's oldest silk shops, after thanking the proprietor for the excellent service I had received at his hands.

And so the official boycott of the Jews came to be forgotten. The Nazi government had other things to do. One of the most important of the new activities of this spring began on the twenty-sixth of April. We were only to recognize the historical importance of this day later on. How alarming it is for the inhabitants of any peaceful country to hear of the creation of a secret state police! But for Germany the birth of that invisible monster ushered in an era of incessant menace, of stealthy persecution. For ever since that twenty-sixth of April we have had not only a police and a judicial system such as other countries have, but a third power looming overhead—a judge who knows no justice, a dragon that thrusts forth its claws in the dark, blindly seizing whatever victims are offered to his clutch by his minion of the moment, his spy.

Many Germans overlooked the matter-of-fact announcement in the newspapers in which the formation of the secret state police was reported. Only a few brief paragraphs sufficed for the death-blow to the peace and privacy of the simplest citizen of the land. "The newly created branch of the government is authorized to seize and confiscate printed matter, to control the rights of property and liberty of person, of assembly and organization, and to examine all postal, telegraphic and telephonic communications."

We paid no attention to this. We were Germans, not enemies of the State. However, it was not long before we learned what might be expected of the "Gestapo" of the Third Reich.

The University still delayed answering Jules' request for leave of absence. In spite of all our attempts, we had not been able to get a reply from either Berlin or Cologne. Instead, there arrived in May the questionnaire which all state and city officials were required to fill out, under oath. Those absent on leave were to do so as well. They were investigating the "qualifications" of all men in any position of influence in respect to politics, race and religion. The University also sent out a questionnaire. It was addressed to all certified German professors and showed that the Third Reich had no interest in their scientific training or in their publications or in their lecture courses, but only in their participation in the World War, time of service, the number of their regiment, their rank and decorations, and finally the "race" of their four grandparents. One scientist whom we knew answered by the simple zoological classification "the race of man," and he was put under protective arrest on the charge of "insult to the Führer." Jules filled this questionnaire out with alarming thoroughness, and it was only then that I discovered that he held two war decorations.

On the second day of May there came a telegram from the Minister of Art, Science and Education in Berlin. After long consideration, he had acted upon Jules' request for leave of absence in accordance with Paragraph Four of the law for the "re-creation of the civil service." It ran thus: "Civil servants who have failed to show by their political activities up to the present that they are prepared to support the National Socialistic State unreservedly and at all times are subject to dismissal."

Unreservedly? At all times? Certainly Jules had not offered any such evidence. Now at last he was released from both posts. We tried to feel free, but we were not very successful. In certain respects, at least, Jules was free. He was not obliged to prostitute his learning to the promulgation of that famous racial theory; he was not obliged to adopt the coward's greeting; he could choose the color of his shirt;

he need have nothing to do with executives who busied themselves with toilet-room keys and letters of intrigue.

Yes, we were free. An animal in the zoo is free when the door of his cage flies open; but where can he go? A dog who has broken his chain is free; yet he finds no shelter except in his old quarters.

Heretofore, we had been in contact with passing events through our personal experiences; from now on they filtered in by letter. Like summer tourists on a rainy day, like invalids, like prisoners, we watched for the postman. Three times a day at stated hours we listened for the bell of the garden gate. When no letters came we were uneasy; when they did come our nerves quivered until we had read their contents.

We were alone in Cologne. Jules' family lived in the Saar, mine in Leipzig. My father wrote demanding immediate submission. The spirit of new Germany dictated it. At least Jules must at once join the "Steel Helmets, the League of the World War Veterans." My mother urged us to change our minds. We would starve. Why, everyone was adjusting himself; everyone had a brand-new brown shirt in his wardrobe.

Another letter came from Scheller: "You are hereby requested to deliver, not later than Monday morning, the eighth instant, all Museum property now in your possession, all books, photographs, etc." We got the letter too late, for we had been in Buchensee in our little week-end house which we called "Petit Eze" after the spot in Southern France which we loved so dearly. There one does not read letters; one digs in the flower beds.

Scheller wrote again. This time Wednesday, the tenth, was fixed as the final date. The tone of the letter was impertinent, its contents ridiculous.

Jules replied that he had looked for the books belonging to the Museum, but our library was a large one. It would be a good idea to send Weiss over, as he was familiar with the books and could readily select them. He had no photographs belonging to the Museum. But all his African films, all his scientific textbooks and much reference material owned by him personally were at the Museum. "If you want anything, just come to me," Jules wrote; "it is, of course, to our mutual interest that all matters pertaining to my connection with the Museum be settled in proper form."

Scheller's answer insisted on the date set. Weiss could not come to us. As for any personal possessions now at the Museum, he desired an accurate list of them, also by the tenth of the month.

These possessions which the Museum was so energetically claiming consisted of thirteen books, six photographs—we found we did have that number—and an aquarelle. I packed these in a little box and drove to the Ubierring. Ziska offered to go for me, but I refused. This was a task which I would not allow anyone to do for me.

I opened the heavy Museum door. Fluss was seated at the table in the cloak room, smoking. He did not greet me, but stared as I walked up the steps. Fräulein Fasbender was in the waiting room; at sight of me she turned scarlet and disappeared into the director's office. There was a pause. So this was how the Museum received its callers—like frightened little provincials when company comes.

Where was the writer of those imperious letters? All the doors were open. One had the feeling that there were a dozen pair of eavesdropping ears cocked for the least sound. Where was Weiss? Maria Fasbender returned with a message from Herr Scheller. Would I please come in? She pointed to Jules' office. I did not budge. I replied that if Herr Scheller could not come out, I should like her to be kind enough to give me a receipt. This was not necessary. Even as I spoke, I heard the tap of the wooden leg.

Scheller's face too was very red. Everyone in the place looked flushed, though it was not in the least warm. I opened my box and we bent our heads over the things I had brought, checking them against the list. Nothing was missing, and he signed the receipt. I turned to go.

"And what about your things?" asked Scheller.

"Oh, there's no hurry," I replied. "My husband will need them again when his leave is over. That's understood, of course."

Snap went my box. Scheller escorted me out in a flurry of politeness. The tables were turned. It was only when we were out of sight that he had the courage to write impertinent letters. He picked up my box and limped down the steps with it. Fluss sprang to his feet, a slave before his master. At the door Scheller handed me the empty box. He bowed. His face was still red. He even went so far as to murmur, "Remember me to . . ."

"To whom?" I asked. But he could not utter the name. Fluss grinned.

IV

We forced ourselves to forget the world of marching boots, concentrating our thoughts upon the mentality of the black, red and yellow races and the sharpness of vision with which they looked at Europe. Jules opened his immense collection of photographs, and we feasted our eyes on the perfection of the bronzes from Benin, the delicate netsukes from Japan and the ogre-like figures of the Nicobar islanders.

With scientific work made impossible through Scheller's closing the doors of the Museum and the reference shelves to him, Jules set to work on a popular article on the material at hand, which he called: "How the Black Man Looks at the White Man." It covered three full pages in the Cologne *Illustrierte Zeitung* of May eleventh, the very date on which Germany erected wood piles and threw books onto the flames.

The next day the *Westdeutscher Beobachter* published a paean of victory under the stirring title: "Down with the un-German Spirit!" No less stirring in style was the grandiose report of the ceremonies attending the burning of the books.

"At the midnight ceremonies observed at all the schools of higher learning in Germany, where the public burning of subversive literature took place, the books were cast into the flames with the following incantations:

"*First Herald:* Condemning class warfare and materialism! Upholding the partnership of the people and idealistic code of living! I consign to the flames the writings of Marx and Kautsky.

"*Second Herald:* Condemning decadence and moral disintegration! Upholding discipline and tradition in family and state! I consign to the flames the writings of Heinrich Mann, Ernst Gläser and Erich Kästner.

"*Third Herald:* Condemning vicious disrespect to the State and political treason! Upholding loyalty to the nation and the State. I consign to the flames the writings of Friedrich Wilhelm Förster.

"*Fourth Herald:* Condemning the corrosion of the soul by the exaggeration of the dangers of war! Upholding the nobility of the human spirit! I consign to the flames the writings of Sigmund Freud.

"*Fifth Herald:* Condemning the falsification of our history and the slander of our heroes! Upholding reverence for our past! I consign to the flames the writings of Emil Ludwig and Werner Hegemann.

"*Sixth Herald:* Condemning an anti-national press characterized by pro-Jewish and pro-democratic policies! Upholding conscientious participation in the task of national advancement. I consign to the flames the works of Theodor Wolff and Georg Bernhard.

"*Seventh Herald:* Condemning the literary betrayal of the World War soldier! Upholding the education of our people in the spirit of reality! I consign to the flames the writings of Erich Maria Remarque.

"*Eighth Herald:* Condemning the obscurantist adulteration of the German language! Upholding the nurture of the nation's most precious possession! I consign to the flames the writings of Alfred Kerr.

"*Ninth Herald:* Condemning insolence and presumption! Upholding respect and reverence before the immortal German national spirit! Consume, O flame, the writings of Tucholsky and Ossietzky!"

And the flames did as they were bid. They consumed the paper, the leather, the linen and the printer's ink. From the ashes rose the ominous Eumenides. They brood over Germany, the nation of poets and philosophers.

A friend in Berlin, who to this very day is secretly and untiringly working in the Ministry of the Exterior for the survival of the old German culture, was present at the burning of the books in the capital and saw the tremendous woodpile on which mortals thought to destroy what is immortal. There stood Göbbels, a raging demon, revenging himself on all the publishers who had rejected his writings in the past and on all the authors who had ignored him—Göbbels, a frenzied dwarf illumined by the fire, gesticulating and ranting. Who was this high priest who imagined he could destroy the spirit of the German people? In the background storm troopers unloaded trucks piled high with books, consigning them to the flames. But many a trooper was seen stealing away into the night, a packet of books in his arms.

The German people were ordered to carry out the same *auto da fé* in their own libraries and to rid their shelves of forbidden books by burning them. Death by fire to them all; not only to Engels, Marx, Hegel and Lassalle —death by fire to Einstein as well, to Freud, Hoffmansthal, Schnitzler, Wassermann, Kerr, Werfel, to Emil Ludwig and to Heinrich and Thomas Mann. Death by fire to the decadent poet who gave us *Die Lorelei*, that dog of a Jew, Heine, whose poem still stands in the German school books, though marked, "author unknown." Away with those trashy Semitic songs of Mendelssohn (*"Leise zieht durch mein gemüt"*) and the *Midsummer Night's Dream* music. What need have we of that? Haven't we the new music written by a brown-shirted, "pure-blooded" composer, Julius Weismann by name, at the command of Göbbels? The new poet Herman Burte was ordered by the State to write another text to Händel's *Judas Maccabaeus*. He did so, calling it *The Hero in Time of Peace* and dedicating it to the men who fell in the World War.

With a general conflagration going on, certainly the students must have a share in the fun. At every university in Germany they built their high "posts of infamy," as officially ordered. "Every student body shall erect a post of infamy at its academy. It should be a thick tree trunk, somewhat above the height of a man. It shall serve as a pillar of shame to which students will nail un-German and unscientific writings, as well as all other utterances of those who, by their participation in activities defamatory in character, have forfeited their membership in the German nation."

The students were provided with speedily published lists which instructed them exactly as to what was meant by "un-German and unscientific." At the same time lovers of the new terminology were introduced to another concept by which they could measure the quality of an author's work. The phrase "asphalt literature" was defined.*

"This form of literature is represented predominantly, though not exclusively, by Jews. However, not every Jewish author is an asphalt writer." How profound, and how clear! It was Greek to most people, even to those completely untainted by "intellectual decay." "It is strongly recommended that all city, central and reference libraries keep one copy of every book, however dangerous, in its 'poison chest,' so that these volumes may be available for the coming reckoning with writers of asphalt literature. The books to be eliminated are best divided into three groups:

Group 1. To be destroyed.
Group 2. To be kept in locked poison chests.
Group 3. To be laid aside as doubtful and subjected to careful
        examination for later classification under Group 1 or
        Group 2."

Works by the following authors were to be unconditionally destroyed:

Lion Feuchtwanger	Alfred Kerr
Ernst Gläser	Egon Erwin Kisch
Artur Holitscher	Emil Ludwig
Heinrich Mann	Ernst Ottwald
Plivier	Erich Maria Remarque
Kurt Tucholsky	Arnold Zweig

* See Translator's Note, page 32.

Reserved for the "poison chest" were the following, according to the temporary list, which was to be later amplified (as in fact, it was):

Henri Barbusse	Iwan Goll
Waldemar Bonsels	Maxim Gorki
Bertold Brecht	Walter Hasenclever
Max Brod	Bernhard Kellermann
Alfred Döblin	Joachim Ringelnatz
Kasimir Edschmid	Arthur Schnitzler
Kurt Pinthus	Upton Sinclair
Ludwig Renn	Fritz von Unruh
Adrienne Thomas	Franz Werfel
Jacob Wassermann	Bertha von Suttner (awarded
Stefan Zweig	the Nobel Prize for *Die*
Ilya Ehrenburg	*Waffen Nieder!*, Lay Down
Leonard Frank	Your Arms!)

I have set down only a tenth of the names of our "undesirables" in the field of greatness. The list also, by the way, included the names of Albert Einstein and the German-born Franz Boas, America's greatest anthropologist.

The Paris *Matin* published a photograph of a burning book with the caption: "They have burned thirty thousand books in Germany. Will they also burn *La Condition Humaine?*"

Hans Heinz Ewers had also been branded an asphalt writer. He found a neat way of saving his royalties by writing a novel around Horst Wessel. He was gladly forgiven his pornographic predilections.

The reorganization of the Prussian Academy of Letters followed on the heels of the book burning. Heinrich Mann renounced his presidency and others resigned permanently: Alfred Döblin, Bruno Frank, Ludwig Fulda, Georg Kaiser, Rudolf Pennwitz, René Schickele, Fritz von Unruh, Thomas Mann and Franz Werfel. These "un-German asphalt writers" had to give way to unknown "poets of the proper stamp," such as Beumelburg, Blunck, Dierfel, Griese and

[83]

Villfester, who formed their own exclusive little group, a group of slaves—in the words of Thomas Mann—to "those impermanent, though potent, figures that rule over Germany today."

Following the suppression of authors who had once made Germany famous throughout the world, the literary destiny of our country came to hinge on the personal preferences of the Führer. His favorite author was Karl May, whose works our ten-year-olds slyly lap up under cover of their school desks. Karl May died in 1912 at Radebeul, near Dresden, leaving to the world a series of tales of adventure in which he played the solo rôle of the virtuous, moralizing hero among savage Indians and swarthy Asiatics. Much blood flows in his books, scalps fall to the tomahawk, men die on the rack. Yet his name is not to be found in any history of literature. However, he has been officially admitted among the immortals of the Third Reich, witness the *Frankfurter Zeitung*, once Germany's leading literary newspaper, which after its co-ordination reported the celebration of Hitler's birthday in part as follows:

"Perhaps one of the most original of all birthday gifts presented to the Führer and Chancellor was that offered by the town of Radebeul, near Dresden, when on the evening of the twentieth of April an oak tree was planted in the Karl May Park, established in memory of the beloved author, of that name."

An original gift indeed, and how spontaneous! And what a tribute to that rare connoisseur of literature, the Führer!

Thus step by step German culture declined, and Minister Göbbels summarized its course for us on the first of May, 1935: "The National Socialists were the first to set art free."

Were there, then, no able men left in the Third Reich? Oh, yes, and that is the saddest chapter in the story. How bitter for us all that a man of the musical attainments of Furtwängler accepted the political title of "Counselor of

State" at Hitler's hands. Considerably later he did timorously raise his voice in the cause of freedom in behalf of the composer, Hindemith, but after intimidation from above he made a public retraction saying that he had been wrong, that of course all decisions concerning music rested with the Führer. The Nazis have set art free, and Furtwängler may conduct again; he may even travel outside of Germany, seeking friends for the Third Reich abroad.

Now began the defamation of the dead, the voiceless dead, who cannot contradict. It began with Frederick the Great. At the grave of the greatest of German democrats the sanctification of the spirit of evil was celebrated. Where would the famous mill of Sans Souci be today, if the hearty miller had to make his plea for justice before Herr Göring, instead of going to old Fritz with it?

Nietzsche was for a time the hero of the storm troopers, for he had prophesied the Superman. When by accident Nietzsche's views on anti-Semitism were discovered, he lost his prophet's crown, and not even "the Lama," his sister Elizabeth, could save it for him, despite the fact that she married the arch anti-Semite, Förster, in defiance of the author of Zarathustra. In no time at all the energetic lady, now completely co-ordinated, had the Nietzsche Memorial converted into a temple devoted to Hitler and his henchmen. In 1921 she had accepted an honorary doctorate from the liberal Weimar Republic. On November 12, 1935, she was buried with full Third Reich honors, and the highest members of the Party assembled to do her homage. Superman Hitler himself attended the obsequies. She lies at rest near that monumental slab of porphyry in the cemetery of the village of Röcken, to which I have so often made my pilgrimage. The "Lama's" nearly nonagenarian spirit was still flexible enough for co-ordination. With what sort of greeting will her Olympian brother have received her among the clouds on high?

The loud appeal to "return to our classics" died off into silence when it was discovered that the man who had dared to write: "Sire, grant us freedom of thought," was a starving good-for-nothing named Schiller. For a hundred and thirty years the last books read by the poet had lain on his desk in the Schiller House at Weimar. Plutarch, Shakespeare and the political essays of Moses Mendelssohn. Herr Sauckel, National Socialist Party leader for the Gau of Thüringen, saw to it in December of 1936 that the volume by that despicable Jew, Mendelssohn, was destroyed. But then, Herr Sauckel thinks along more German lines than did Friedrich Schiller. Whether the name of Sauckel will outlive that of the contaminated poet remains to be seen. Even Goethe is not highly regarded in the Third Reich. His poems contain too many un-German, not to say un-Aryan, elements. Also, the man might have supported home industry by drinking his wine at home instead of in Italy. Was he not a government official? Lessing, of course, was a mean slave of the Jewish spirit, yet a play of his entitled Nathan the Wise is known to every German.

But there remained music. Beethoven—in anticipation of his Führer, no doubt—wrote the Eroica. Once, in answer to a letter from a prosperous man who signed himself "Proprietor of a mill," Beethoven followed his signature with "Proprietor of a brain." Such insolence toward a bulging purse has not yet come to the notice of the Ministry of Propaganda; otherwise the popularity of his music would be over. It would become "asphalt—offensive to the backbone of the nation." The composer of the Third Reich is Richard Wagner, who not only wrote resounding music to Germanic themes, but left behind him a plump daughter-in-law. Besides, there is the Badenweiler March, the favorite of the Führer.

Still, musicians are scarce. Owing to the universality of their art, which knows no national limits, they easily amalgamate with Roman and un-Aryan elements. They are apt to yield to that contrary virtuosity that only too often shows "Eastern" racial characteristics, doomed thereby to destruction. Hindemith, in defense of whom Furtwängler almost lost his baton, was in spite of his pronounced blondness, condemned as a leading exponent of asphalt music. Not even his *Matthis, the Painter* counted in his favor. A simple method has been found of producing favored musicians by command. The Reich's Department of Culture runs a series of frequent compulsory broadcasts of contemporary music, which rates as "popular" from the day it is first heard. To the *Frankfurter Zeitung* with its old cultural tradition is assigned the unpleasant task of criticizing these broadcasts. The unfortunate critic twists and squirms like a snake in the fire, trying as discreetly as possible to bury the unfortunate composers. It is apparent that it isn't altogether easy to turn out genius to order.

How much easier it is with writers! These are cheap in the Third Reich. Blunck, Kalbfuss, Rossmann, Seidenfaden, Edgar Kahn, Gottfried Kölwel, Götz Otto Stoffregen, Giselher Wirsing are the new crop in the neat rows of the Third Reich literary garden.

Such was the transformation effected in the genius of our land—far more terrible to us than the ever-swelling sound of marching feet. To us a book was of greater importance than a new silent airplane motor; four bars of music more telling than any amount of political clamor. We tried to live as quietly as possible. But more and more was taken away, and nothing given in return.

Our hopes that our connection with Scheller was a thing of the past were not to be fulfilled. One day Jules received an odd letter from Oslo, from Dr. S., an old friend with whom he corresponded regularly. Since the publication of Jules' exhaustive monograph on the development of animal traps and the methods of capture of primitive tribes, this Northern scholar had formed a lasting attachment to him, and scarcely a month went by without a letter teeming with penetrating questions, often adorned with charming sketches. Up to now, like many of Jules' colleagues, he had used the Museum address. Suddenly one came to us in the Siebengebirgsallee, telling us that after much effort he had finally succeeded in discovering where we lived. Weeks ago he had sent Jules several reprints, but had never received any acknowledgment. His last letter had gone unanswered for a long time, and when the reply came, he could not believe his eyes as he read the utterly childish comments on the scientific queries he had put to Jules. He was further surprised at the request that he continue the correspondence with the "Administrative Office" of the Rautenstrauch-Joest Museum. The signature, "Acting Director Scheller," was totally unknown to him. Dr. S. had at once written the high-handed correspondent for Jules' private address, and in reply Scheller wrote that he did not know where former Director Lips lived. Really alarmed, Dr. S. had written to the University and thus finally learned our whereabouts. He was most anxious and quite in the dark about what had happened to his colleague. Was Jules a Jew or a Communist? Were these events connected with the political changes in Germany? He begged Jules to write and reassure him at once.

Scientific works by colleagues were to be stolen. Scheller had opened letters addressed to his teacher and answered them himself!

Jules wrote to Scheller, demanding an explanation. He wrote to Commissioner Ebel demanding satisfaction. He wrote to the Minister of the Interior, enclosing Dr. S.'s letter and demanding a prompt investigation. He wrote to Dr. S., explaining the situation and asking for further details.

When all these letters had been sent off, we packed our African basket, put the non-Aryan Tapir on a lead and went to Buchensee.

A few years previously Jules had bought this little piece of wild, weed-grown land for the price of a broadcast. With the help of a couple of unemployed boys he had burned the underbrush, cut down the dead trees and cleared the ground about the magnificent old beech trees which could now be seen to advantage. A little rock garden leaned against the raised plateau. Tables and benches made of our own timber stood about, and Jules had built a tiny look-out, from which one could look deep down into the valley. Then our cottage was put up. It consisted merely of a bed-room and a living-room-kitchen, harmoniously done in green, white and orange. On a beam was painted *Petit Eze*, for Eze, which lies midway between Nice and Monte Carlo, was paradise on earth to us.

In a country community of this kind the county sheriff is master and it was to our friend, Peter Wiesel, who occu-pied this office, that we owed our discovery of Buchensee. On this visit, seeking refuge from the confusion of Cologne, we discovered to our dismay a changed Buchensee.

The kindly fat sheriff had been "removed." He had at one time permitted a lecture by Minister Hilferding in his district and had thereby come to grief under Paragraph Two of the law governing the re-creation of the civil serv-ice. That libelous paragraph, which made "lack of training for office" a valid ground for dismissal, could be applied at will. Without a moment's notice, Wiesel, friend of the peasant, hero of the county races and cattle fairs, had been driven from his sheriff's residence. He and his family moved into a Cologne garret. He spent his days hurrying from one employment bureau to another. He, too, had held a life-long job, had been unable to save out of his scanty earnings and no agency would even consider his application. He was too old. He now lived dully from day to day doing what oc-casional work he could get. We often visited him in his trouble. He would sit in an old wicker chair beside his despairing wife, his little terrier in his lap, tears rolling down his cheeks as he mechanically petted his dog.

So the sheriff had been removed and replaced by an "old campaigner," a worn-out officer, who was doubtless excellent at directing a battle in his study, but had certainly never learned what "blood and soil" looked like from actual experience. That the disappearance of the sheriff would result in any awkwardness at Buchensee for us, as friends of his, had never occurred to us. We were, however, soon to find out the nature of the devotion which the villagers had previously avowed.

Even the little station of Waldau was altered. Above the entrance to the inn, where formerly the sign of a horse's head and a horseshoe had hung, the face of Adolf Hitler, of Bohemia, beamed down upon us. On the door there was a sign: "The German greeting is: Heil Hitler!" The host, whose long lectures on crops and statecraft we had so enjoyed, was nowhere to be seen. His son, a little boy in a brown shirt, served us. Three days ago he had become a Hitlerite. We bought our customary two bottles of Rhine wine from him and fled from the heroic roar issuing from the radio.

At the usual corner Tapir was let off the lead and galloped down hill in wild spirits. "Are there any mushrooms out?" Jules asked the milkman, who came toward us with his basket turned down over his head. The old fellow walked on as though he had not seen us.

Farther along the road at the entrance to the valley we ran into day laborer Jacobs. He was a poor workman and a poor Communist. He had helped cut down the trees in our place. Now he called out: "Heil Hitler, Professor Lips." He probably meant it as a joke, we thought, hearing his coarse laughter behind us. We climbed the last bit of the way, a steep uphill rise. At the white gate sat Tapir, puffing like a steam engine, one foot caught in a raspberry twig. Jules opened up the house, stopping to drive a nail into a flapping shingle. The rock garden was bright with buds.

He changed his clothes and set to work in the flower beds, but today I heard no song. I missed the call of his sentimental chanty—"Blue as the skies are thy waters, O lovely Venice." Even when the smoke rose from our little chimney, there was still silence in the garden. Tapir gazed angrily up at the branches of the beech tree, where the squirrel, Karasek, showed off in impertinent acrobatic leaps, defying the pompous, panting creature below.

In the evening we roasted potatoes in the open fire and ate them with butter and salt, enjoying a view of the valley through our wine glasses. Tapir sat hunched on the bench between us in a Rodinesque pose. Beneath us, where the pine trees stood wrapped in their cloaks of mist, their faint shadows falling on the water, there was peace.

We heard a heavy tread in the neighboring garden, a sound we knew only too well. It was too late to fly. We would have to listen to the deaf peasant woman's shouted tale. Would it be of the thirty-six needles in her abdomen, or of the thieving gypsies that roamed the fields by night? There she was, at the fence, her heavy breasts bulging against the railing, leaning over as far as she could.

"So you have been kicked out," she shrilled, her voice echoing through the valley. "I read about it in the papers. The storm troopers have taken possession of your house in Cologne and the sheriff is imprisoned for fraud. Not so nice here any more, is it? My man has been co-ordinating for a week now. Tomorrow your place is to be attacked. We all know that here!"

"All know that here," sang the echo from the valley. I held on to Tapir, who hated loud noises as much as we did.

We heard her shuffling tread as she moved away. She had said her say and was now going to sleep.

Jules refilled our glasses. Slowly we lifted them and in silence drank to someone far away. A few steaming potatoes

[91]

lay before us on the table. It was still fairly light. Among the pine trees beneath us on the side of the hill stood a small house. The door opened and a man with a package came out and busied himself about the flag pole. And suddenly before our eyes a flag went up, swelling in the evening breeze. A huge brand-new flag, blood red in color. In the center on a white circle was the sign of the swastika. It fluttered there beneath us, cutting off the clear view into the valley.

"I'll put away my tools," said Jules. "We won't spend the night in Buchensee. We'll take the last train back to Cologne."

A little while later we locked up. Darkness overtook us as we walked down the country road, Tapir leading the way, a weary and disillusioned guide.

When we turned into the Siebengebirgsallee, welcomed by the sweet-smelling acacias and the contours of our house agleam in the moonlight, we yielded for the first time to a feeling of profound desolation. These hours were worse than anything that came later—when we had to be calm in the face of hatred and danger—for they taught us that there could be no more happiness for us in the Third Reich. No home, of any sort, was left for us.

V

Anthropology is international in scope. It deals with all cultures of the world, and therefore the representatives of this science are to be found in all the universities of the world, in Oxford and Tucuman, in San Francisco and Madrid, in Brussels and in Rome, in Shanghai, in Constantinople, in Vienna and Tokyo, in New York and in Paris. Letters are exchanged between Stockholm and Teheran, Basle and the Gran Chaco, between the home of the Eskimo and the Australian bushman. Research reports are published, expeditions sent to observe dying civilizations. The scientific brotherhood concerns itself with the fate of all its members. Every anthropologist is known for his particular sphere of activity; all the great museums and their directors are in contact with one another, for they share the task of tracing the history of humanity. Each has his own important contribution to make, each places his own bit of mosaic in the composition of a vast picture, more ancient than Greece or Rome, than Peru or Egypt, than India or China— the picture of the rise and development of all the material and spiritual attributes of the race of man.

The anthropologists of Germany at the outbreak of the Third Reich hastened to destroy what they had previously revered: truth in research and freedom in teaching. No science was as well fitted as anthropology to protest against the madness of classifying races according to a scale of values. No one knew better than the ethnologist that such a thing does not exist. But then, no one knew better than he that a stand for truth and honor meant the sacrifice of security and position, and to no one was the process of coordination so dishonorable as to these men of science whose sphere of activity was the world. They hurriedly wrote their pernicious pamphlets, driveling of a "nation in need of space," and played safe by clinging to the middle course of compromise in their scientific findings. Not one of them, unless he was a Jew and was forced out, not a single man rose up when the Third Reich broke over Germany, to lift his voice for truth and freedom in science, content to face the uncertainty of want and persecution if he could but retain his honor.

This was a bitter thing for the reputation of German science throughout the world. For the world was waiting for at least one man to rise up and say "No," one single representative of the old German culture, one who could be loyal to the standards of German scholarship, regardless of consequences.

Elsewhere in the world, devotion to the ideal of scholarship was cherished. One afternoon in May a letter reached us by a circuitous route telling us that a sanctuary dedicated to independent research was being planned. They would be proud to receive Jules, to offer him a post in a splendidly equipped international college on the outskirts of Paris. There he could continue his work in peace and safety. Would Jules come to France as soon as possible to talk things over? They were already arranging the purchase of a big house in Versailles in which we were to live, together with other members of the staff.

Paris! A wave of happiness came over me! Was France to become our haven of rest? The rose gardens of Versailles, peace and freedom—all that the heart could desire!

"We must start at once," I said. "We will live in Versailles. Evenings we will go in to the Étoile, walk along the boulevards, eat a brioche with our black coffee, and watch the world go by."

But Jules was not so enchanted. He did not see the rose gardens of Versailles; he saw his duty, and his duty as a German and a man bade him persevere.

"But they won't give you any books," I exclaimed, "they will take your salary. They will dismiss you and we shall be beggars. They are already stealing your letters; soon they will steal other things."

He, however, thought that no one in Berlin knew how far Scheller's delusions of grandeur were carrying him. Of course, they would shake off fellows of this sort. Just because he was an "Aryan," and not a Nazi, it was his duty to remain.

"How long will you stay? Until they lock you up?" I asked sadly.

Jules replied: "Until they make scientific work impossible for me, until they steal my country from me. Then it will be time to go, not before."

My heart cried "Paris," and Jules replied "Germany."

So the matter was set aside and the interregnum went on.

Letters remained our only tie with the outside world. One came from my parents, saying they intended to visit us soon. I dreaded their coming. No one was human any more. There were only two fronts of battle—for Hitler against Germany, or for Germany against Hitler. We belonged to the latter. And we knew that our parents were ready to turn from us. What should we say to them? We knew what they would attempt to do and what bitterness our refusal would bring.

Another letter came from the "Society for the Advancement of the Rautenstrauch-Joest Museum," signed by Scheller. It informed Jules that he was dismissed from his post as editor-in-chief of the Society's publications, that Scheller would take over the management of *Ethnologica*, that in the future his signature alone was binding and that Professor Lips must secure his approval of all arrangements previously entered into in connection with the publication. Jules ignored it.

On the eighteenth of May a gray car drove up to our door. Tapir, a wreath of flowers around his neck, barked a loud

[95]

welcome, and Ziska, dainty as a kitten, flirted with the chauffeur. My parents got out. We led them to their rooms and later through the whole house, took them to inspect the peach trees in the garden and offered them home-grown asparagus, Rhine wine and Westphalian ham at our table. We chatted late into the night, avoiding all mention of the burden that weighed so heavily on all our hearts. I watched my father carefully and never gave him an opportunity to offer us the advice which we felt obliged to refuse. We knew everything that he would say. Alas, he would not understand us, and our hearts ached for him. However, we said good night cheerfully. We woke up the next morning to enjoy the sun in the garden. I got into the gray car with my mother and we drove through the streets of Cologne. Ziska hurried out to fill her basket with delicacies for a festive dinner. My father, Jules and Tapir were alone in the house.

They sat in the garden. My father put his hand on my husband's hand and begged him to join the new Germany, to recognize the good intentions hidden behind the initial confusion. He must think of his students; his sincere teachings had left their trace. For the sake of what he could impart to them he should yield in those matters which appeared strange to him, because of their devotion, because in spite of everything they were really splendid fellows.

There was a ring at the door bell. As Jules had sunk into a troubled silence, my father said he would answer it. He walked through the garden to the front door and opened it.

My father was an old officer. Dignity and decision were his essential characteristics. At that time he was in his sixty-third year. He opened the door and saw a young man whom he knew. It was the same student who had gone with Jules and me to Leipzig to an ethnological congress held in the city of books and had there enjoyed the hospitality of my parents.

"Herr Fröhlich," said my father. "How nice! I have just arrived for a visit."

An extraordinary thing happened. In the doorway of our house, student Willy Fröhlich pushed aside the hand my father stretched out to him in greeting, forced his way into the hall and muttered: "Don't know you!"

A fat man appeared behind the student, following close on his heels. They had both come in and closed the door. The fat man wore a Museum attendant's uniform.

"Professor Lips here?" said a raucous voice. At that moment the inner door opened. There stood the master of the house, holding his dog by the collar.

"Fröhlich? Weiss?" said Jules. "You are not welcome in my house at present."

Weiss held his head down. Jules saw the veins in his heavy neck throb. Student Fröhlich thrust his lips up toward his nose in an effort to push his glasses upward—an unpleasant gesture, peculiar to him. He said nothing.

Jules offered my father his arm and led him back to the garden, ordering Tapir to stay with my father. Tapir at once lay down by the bench.

The two embarrassed figures were still standing in the doorway when Ziska returned from her marketing. She uttered a cry on seeing them, but her common sense at once returned and she noticed that Fröhlich was wearing one of those suits which we were in the habit of giving to needy students. She burst into speech.

"So you come in here with a swastika on our clothing?" The situation had lost its drama. By then Jules was back.

"Well?" said he, looking Fröhlich squarely in the eye. He made the same awkward gesture with his nose and glasses. Then he recited his carefully rehearsed speech.

"I am here by order of the Society for the Advancement of the Rautenstrauch-Joest Museum to take over property belonging to that institution which you have illegally appropriated."

"And you, Weiss?" asked Jules.

"I was obliged to come along, to carry it," said the old man in indescribable embarrassment.

By the word "obliged" he seemed to wish to imply that he would rather have walked into hell than follow this creature. But what was he to do? He lived in the Third Reich. He had a family.

"My wife has already returned all the Museum property," said Jules, "but perhaps we have overlooked a book or two. I asked to have Weiss sent in the first place. Have you any authorization?"

"Here," said Fröhlich, producing a document signed by Scheller. "It is not so much a question of books," he added in a tone of impertinence. "It is primarily a question of the manuscripts for the new issue of *Ethnologica* and the photographs belonging to the Society."

"Photographs?"

"You published some in the *Kölner Illustrierte*."

Jules burst into a laugh. "So you mean my manuscripts. You know very well that I have written half my book on the backs of those pictures."

"Well, Professor Lips, I'll talk plainly. I have come to make an official search of your house."

"I take it, then, you're a member of the police force?"

"No, but I have the authority of the police behind me."

"Very well," said Jules. He led the two men upstairs to his study and closed the door.

Ziska had remained in the hall all the while. Professor Lips would need a witness against that riff-raff, she explained later. The reference to the police—that word so frightening to simple people—had made her suspicious. She ran through the garden and looked up and down the street. She saw nothing unusual. Suddenly at the street corner near the mail box she saw a head bob up. She walked over. There stood a man, not in uniform, but a plain-clothes detective. His eyes were riveted on our front door.

"We won't hurt your Fröhlich," she said over her shoulder, and the man replied, "Get along home!" That was enough. When she got back, our gray motor had just stopped at the door.

My mother and I had just returned from town, our arms full of packages, elated over our shopping tour, as only women can be. Ziska told us quickly what had happened.

"Are they still upstairs?"

"Yes, Frau Professor."

"And the man at the corner?"

"There he is."

I did not turn around. I took my mother to her room and hurried to my father in the garden.

"I am so sorry, Father, that you . . ."

"I don't understand at all! What's the matter? What does the lad want?"

"Ah, Father, that's how things are at present. Excuse me, I must go to Jules. Down, Tapir, down."

As I opened the door of the study I saw Weiss with a few little paper-bound books in his hand. They were the reprints of scientific publications. I went to the table and handed Weiss a cigar, as I was in the habit of doing. He thanked me timidly and I gave him a light. Fröhlich, who was crouched in front of the lowest shelves, shot up.

"You show great delicacy of feeling, Herr Fröhlich," I observed, "in daring to enter our house for such a purpose as this."

He did not reply, but bent over the desk on which a slip of paper lay. His face was scarlet.

"I can do what is necessary, with Ziska's help," I said to Jules. "Don't you want to go into the garden?" But Jules wanted to stay. His conventional bearing, so different from his usual cheerful manner affected the intruders unpleasantly.

"And the manuscripts for *Ethnologica*?" asked Fröhlich.

"I believe you came to search my house? Go right ahead," said Jules.

"Would you not like to give them to me?"

"I regret that I am unable to give to any student, Fröhlich, information regarding manuscripts confided to me by my colleagues. I am still the editor of *Ethnologica*. But you have threatened me with police authority. Please do what you are empowered to do. You are, of course, prepared to take the consequences."

Fröhlich hesitated. Weiss in the background sought to hide his distress behind clouds of smoke. The situation was ridiculous. How shoddy and mean the whole thing was!

Fröhlich decided to let the matter drop. He went on to the next part of his task.

"Now, please give me all your photographs."

"Which ones?"

"The pictures for your book, *How the Black Man Looks at the White Man*."

"Would you not also like my doctor's diploma, my professor's certificate, my towel and my tooth brush?"

"The pictures belong to the Society."

"I see now why Scheller has suddenly assumed the rôle of editor of the Society."

"The Society paid for the mats on which the photographs are mounted."

"Then the Society can send me a bill."

"No, it's the pictures we want."

"You?"

"The Society."

"Herr Fröhlich, when you were still my pupil, you begged for the privilege of sorting these pictures. Do you remember? True, several weeks have gone by since then. Is it possible that since your promotion to the post of inquisitor you have forgotten that these photographs are my private property, the fruit of five years of scientific work?"

"The European is ridiculed in these pictures—the Aryan . . ."

"I see. Surely you don't regard the Aryan as a tragic figure, my dear Fröhlich? As a matter of fact the type you represent is, though not in the way you think."

"The white race . . ."

"Is astonishingly well portrayed in these pictures. However, our discussion is now at an end. Go back to your superior, to Scheller—let Weiss carry these little books—and tell him that my scientific property will remain where I see fit." And Jules glanced at the tables, the boxes and shelves which held his photographs, his work and his future.

"But I have the order . . ."

"You have the order to leave my house at once."

The old influence still held. The coward bowed his head and left; Weiss followed, a pathetic figure.

When we were alone, Jules leaned against the heavy column of the bookcase, white and tense.

"How degrading!" said he. "A student of mine!"

We went into the garden to join my parents.

"Please excuse the interruption, Father; they merely wanted to steal my manuscripts."

"But that's intolerable! You must do something about that! I am positive no one in Berlin knows anything about it!"

"The Führer principle, Father. Every man is a Hitler on his own."

"Don't say that. Berlin will certainly see to it that a World War veteran receives justice."

"Don't worry about it, Father. I will take action. Forget it, it wasn't anything important. However, it disturbed our conversation. Let me see—where were we?"

"Jules, Eva, I can't advise you any longer. I don't understand what is going on. Act as you see fit."

"Thank you, Father."

That afternoon my parents left, depressed and perplexed. My mother wept. She had brought me an evening gown—so little perturbed had she been—and now everything was sad. We had always tried to keep the serious things in our life from them. Sometimes we felt as though they were our children, instead of we theirs. We protected them against the bitterness of reality. Now they had accidentally been forced to witness an incident of our life in the Third Reich, quite unvarnished and against our will. We were glad when the gray car drove off into a pleasanter world.

When we returned to Jules' room we saw that Ziska had brought down a whole collection of empty trunks. We were astonished.

"We are going to put our pictures in here and send them away," said Ziska. "Those men will be back. On one of my former jobs we once pawned the piano and didn't let the collector in."

We laughed at so much worldly wisdom, but we realized what a good idea it was. So we packed the manuscripts of Jules' lectures and all the important documents of our lives in the rough old African trunks, putting the photographs on top: Benin, the South Seas, Asia, Australia, and all the other places neatly labeled. There lay our possessions, secure from attack by Swastika-wearing students. The three of us dragged our heavy burden down the steps. Tapir howled when he saw the trunks; he thought we were going away.

When all the trunks had been put in a taxi I drove off. Where to? That's something I cannot tell, for our friends still live in Cologne. The friend to whom I went wears the official insignia of the National Socialist German Labor Party, known to the world as the Nazis.

On my return, we ignored Tapir's barks of welcome and sat down to write to Berlin. Perhaps it was as my father said. It was wrong to confound a clique of hysterical students with the German government. So we wrote to one of the highest officials in Berlin, described what had occurred—

quoting the Nazis' own grandiose promises of academic freedom—and asked the Minister to take action at once.

Jules bade good-bye in writing to Herr Rautenstrauch as the representative of the "Society for the Advancement of the Rautenstrauch-Joest Museum" and told him briefly a few details about Scheller's letters and the searching of his house by Fröhlich.

We had a prompt reply.

"I feel that I should tell you that your attitude strikes me as neither practical nor wise. I would avoid everything that might irritate those now in power. I am afraid any opposition on your part must end to your disadvantage. Open or secret opposition of any kind would only place obstacles in the way of mutual understanding, whereas, if you will now wholeheartedly agree to all reasonable requests, I am confident that you can continue your scientific activities indefinitely at the Museum."

Such effusions and their authors were known as "March violets," for they had bloomed in the spring, two months after the National Socialists had seized power. So Rautenstrauch, like Scheller, like Fröhlich, Fluss, like several million others, debased the German language in the composition of their spring bouquets.

VI

Events piled up. A notice appeared in the *Frankfurter Zeitung* reporting that at a meeting at the Sorbonne, Professor Rivet, the anthropologist, had urged the foundation of an international college, where scientists who were forced to leave their country because of their convictions could carry on their work.

A reminder and an invitation reached us, again by a circuitous route, signed by men of world-wide renown, offering Jules the opportunity to live, as they did, for his work alone.

He was still holding the letter in his hand when Ziska announced Frau Venn. She was a neighbor of ours, the wife of a prominent Judge with whom she was on very bad terms. While she was living with a lover in Marseilles, her husband —whose special subject was divorce—was engaged in issuing final decrees to others. We met him occasionally in society or on walks in the park, and only recently he had told us that the criminal Communist faces which he had been accustomed to see in the prisoners' box in court had all bobbed up again, this time as brown-shirts. When Frau Venn turned up again in Cologne, our house was one of the few that were open to her. She was a reader of good literature and talked rather well on what she had read. In spite of her failings she was cultivated—and we were sorry for her husband. Whenever she entered a house she caused a sensation. But that was in her nature. There was always a new story in the air about her; she had a wide circle of masculine acquaintances, and there were plenty of facts behind these stories.

Inge Venn appeared in a very pretty knitted frock, which

accentuated her generous curves a shade too freely, but somehow added to her self-assurance. She smoked incessantly and her voice was hoarse and of a peculiar timbre. She immediately began to tell us about a scene that had just taken place in her house. She was just finishing Upton Sinclair's *Love's Pilgrimage*—"*a perfectly mad book . . . Fancy, there's a description of a childbirth in it! Absolutely marvelous! What a man, that author! Women after him by the dozen!*" That was Inge Venn—when her husband entered the room. "What! Another of those anarchistic books!" And he flung the door open violently and threw his wife down the stairs. She had fallen against the door of the apartment on the floor below, occupied by the recently discovered poet, Steguweit. He had come out, had heard the whole business, and—"*Just think, Steguweit, who had received a prize in the rose-room of the Wartburg, from the hand of Herr Göbbels, half made eyes at me, half died of embarrassment.*" Well, she hadn't stayed to provide any further amusement for the "little squirt," but had dashed off straight to us. We had a vision of poor anemic Venn "throwing his wife downstairs," the robust Inge, who would have made two of him. But we were used to her.

She had not come to tell us this story, she went on, but to warn us.

"Warn us?"

"Good heavens! Do you mean to say you don't know who has become president of the Rhineland government-board? My own fat cousin! He discovered that his heart was with the Nazis at just the right moment! I went straight to Olga, his wife (she's just had the grippe; a scrawny cow, but she has oodles of money), and said: 'Now you'll be able to afford a new dress. You have been running around dressed like the daughter of a deacon! And your first official act must be to get Lips reinstated.'

"Olga—you know, she hasn't the shadow of a brain!— brings the matter up at supper. An hour ago she rang up.

My maid gabbled out: 'The president's lady wishes to speak to the District Supreme Court Judge's lady.' How those damned bourgeois love their titles! Finally Olga rustled over to the phone and said: 'Are you crazy, Inge? Reinstate Lips! Out of the question! Why, the day after tomorrow the secret police are going to raid his house!'—'Are you mad?' I ask. 'Whom are you going to put in his place if you throw Lips out? A man with a beard eighteen yards long? You won't find another fellow as good-looking as he is in a hurry! Thank God he took to anthropology! Do you want to make a mummy house out of the Museum?'

" 'There are two students back of all this,' said Olga; 'they want some sort of pictures. Then, Lips kicked some man out of the house who came to him with a good offer. He should have handled that fellow with kid gloves!'

" 'You made overtures to Lips?' I asked.

" 'Well, yes, the Party did—everybody else accepted. And now an article is coming out against him—one of the students is doing the thing for the *Westdeutscher Beobachter!*'

" 'And you are permitting this?' I shrieked at her. 'Why, you're just as crazy as you are mean!' Olga only laughed and asked me to supper."

Thus Inge Venn ran on in her hoarse soldier's voice. But there was no doubt about it; what she said was true. To her it was a trifle. She babbled on about California—she intended to go there next year. She raved about her dressmaker, offered to knit me a cap of bright wool. "I'll put a feather on it—just the thing!" She lighted her seventh cigarette, borrowed a book of Erich Kästner's, pulled a pigeon bone out of her bag for Tapir, told how she had received the court attendant, who had called to deliver some papers for her husband, in her bath—"My land! you should have seen his face! Ha! Ha!"—and departed.

She had left heavy words behind her. The house was to be raided by the secret police—we should have handled that

[106]

fellow with kid gloves—there are two students back of all this—an article in the *Westdeutscher Beobachter*.

Jules had long since ceased to be able to work. He sat at home with me and the dog. A letter had come from Paris in a roundabout way. He still held it in his hand. "They shall live here for their work until it is possible for them to return home."

"We've reached our limit," he said suddenly. "Yes, we've reached our limit."

The train leaving the main depot in Cologne stopped at a small station: South Cologne. It was an insignificant little place. There were no photographers waiting to snap departing passengers, as there were at the main station. For the train went to Saarbrücken, and this city in the year 1933 was an El Dorado for certain visitors from the Third Reich. Many who were persecuted and had not enough money or knowledge of languages to attempt to go farther, went there. The League of Nations still ruled in the Saar, and one could easily cross the French frontier.

The man who left that afternoon in May had no need to fear that he would be regarded as an "emigrant" at the border, for he was a native of Saarbrücken and wanted to see his old mother who lived there. At the station, near his trunks, stood his family—his wife, his housemaid and a German Boxer. It was raining. The train came to a stop, the baggage was handed in through the window, the engine puffed and the train moved on. The man leaned out of the window. His wife took a little red rose—it may have come from their own garden—and put it into his disappearing hand.

When the train was out of sight, the lady, the maid and the dog went out of the station into the rain. On their way home Ziska dropped a letter into the mail box. In it Museum Director Lips, in accordance with the terms of his contract, informed the city of Cologne of his departure. He was forced to have recourse to the libraries of other museums, he wrote, since the student Scheller had forbidden him either to enter the institution or to make use of his private collection of data in the building. He mentioned no return address.

In Saarbrücken Jules took the little local train which went to the town where his mother, sister and brother-in-law lived. The hills of his boyhood moved past the window, the green meadows, the blast furnaces and shafts, the streams, and the remembered sites of many a school picnic, warm with childhood memories and the tenderness of home.

Unannounced he walked into the garden and opened the door of the house. In a chair near the radio sat his aged mother. As she stood up to greet him, smiling happily, the radio burst into the Horst Wessel song, broadcast from Berlin.

Jules had been due in Paris some time ago, and I was anxiously awaiting my first news of him. It was to pass through several hands and therefore would be delayed. In the meantime I had been greatly cheered by a communication from the office of the Prussian Minister of Science, Art and Public Education in Berlin. It carried the assurance that the house search conducted by student Fröhlich would be investigated by the Minister. It was signed "Yours very sincerely, Gerullis."

This at a time when every village grocer-mayor was obliged to sign his butter-and-eggs receipts with a Heil Hitler! Someone in official Berlin still signed himself "Yours very sincerely." It had a friendly ring, like an echo of old times, when Germans still exchanged the usual social courtesies. What did the mean little intrigues of Cologne matter, if there were still Germans in Berlin?

Shortly afterward we read in the papers that Executive Secretary Gerullis had been removed from office, and we received a letter from his successor, informing us that the

[108]

Minister "saw no occasion and no possibility" of intervening in the matter of the search of our house, the interception of mail or the interdiction of the use of books by students Scheller and Fröhlich.

A terse message came from Jules: He needed me; I was to come at once, perhaps for several weeks. With the house, the dog, Ziska, I was to do as I thought best. Our future lay before us. It was of the utmost importance. We were to go to Paris together, see what was offered us and decide. I was to come on Whit-Sunday. That was four days off. "Make a good job of it, Panther! I am relying on you."

I wired immediately that I was coming. Ziska stood in front of me, smoothing her little apron. "I'll have to give you notice again, Ziska," I remarked sadly, and she replied, "Oh, if it's only that, Frau Professor."

When she found that I was closing the house and that I thought it was dangerous to leave her in it alone, she merely said:

"What about Tapir?"

On hearing his name the dog came trotting up to me and pressed his head against my knee, looking up at me. I stroked the deep little line that ran between his short nose and his forehead, and his tail moved up and down; it was too short to wag.

"Tapir will go to Seiler," said I. Seiler was an old circus clown who had fallen from a trapeze and since then devoted his life to animals. Before Ziska came to us Tapir had often stayed with Seiler. He loved the man.

"Have we enough money for the trip?" asked Ziska, as always concerned for my welfare.

"Certainly. Professor Lips' salary is due on Whit-Satur-day."

"And when will the Frau Professor be coming back?"

"Ah, Ziska, if I knew that."

"I shall not take any position. I shall go to my aunt. I

have saved some money; it will last a few months . . . If only I get word from you . . ."

We made our arrangements so that even a long absence would not upset things. We went to Buchensee and oiled the tools and put up locks. Six edelweiss were blooming in the rock garden. I picked these for Jules. The radishes were already fat and red. Ziska took a heart-shaped beech leaf with her.

In Cologne my furs were sent to storage, the locks on the trunks were repaired. Mail was to be forwarded to Ziska's aunt. At the post office I met Mrs. Beyer, the wife of a former Supreme Court Judge. Her husband had been denounced in the papers and prosecuted for fraud; the accusation had been made by a former employee who had been discharged—one of the March violets. She was running up and down the town looking for a lawyer, but no one dared to represent the Judge, for the Third Reich was against him. She fell on my neck in the post office and wept. I shrank from her. I was beginning to forget the meaning of emotion, of tears and confidences, of despair and the craving for help.

"And what about you?" she asked. "What is happening to you?"

I shrugged my shoulders, shook hands with her to show my good will and left the building.

We sprinkled pepper and camphor on our rugs, rolled them up and piled them on top of one another, a heap of fallen columns. Our footsteps resounded on the bare floors. Tapir sneezed. I went into my altered room and picked up a volume of Hoffmansthal.

The door bell rang. It was the hunchback clown, come to call for Tapir. Ziska put the dog's collar on him and walked with him and Seiler to the street car.

The whole house smelled unbearably of camphor and pepper; I fled to the bathroom and washed my hair. Ziska returned with reddened eyes. She had a letter for me. We had been so busy that we had forgotten to look in the mail box. It was from the Rathaus and stated that since Jules had left Cologne without the Mayor's permission his salary was stopped and would not be paid unless he returned. It was signed by Ludwig, Acting Deputy Mayor.

No money, and I was leaving for Paris the following morning. With my hair still wet, I ran to the telephone and called the Rathaus, but it was too late. They had all left. The homes of the new officials were not yet in the telephone book. I could not reach anyone.

I called up the president of the government-board and asked to speak to Olga. I told her what had happened, but she declined to intervene.

"Now the Frau Professor can't go," said Ziska.

She did not realize what it meant when I said to Jules: I am coming.

"Go to sleep, Ziska, and don't worry. The train leaves at ten. Wake me at seven. Good night and, mind you, no tears."

Then I went to my bedroom, unlocked my little jewel box and took out the most beautiful thing I owned, the diamond, Trembal. It lay on white silk in a green leather case; it was set in platinum and shone in my hand, a cool drop of splendor and hope.

At nine the next morning Ziska and I got into a taxi. We had found an address in the telephone book, but we did not drive the whole way. We stopped at a street corner and Ziska got out. She carried my passport, a green leather box and a signed authorization from me. I waited and looked out of the window. A woman walked by with a yellow Boxer on a leash. Three storm troopers were marching—not walking. A street car bound for Klettenberg passed by. The meter ticked on. A door opened and Ziska was back. She had a receipt and money in her hand, but no green leather case. I gave a deep sigh of relief.

"To the main station!"

We drove through the dear old streets of Cologne and I took Ziska's hand in mine and stroked it all the way. I boarded the train. The house was closed and all bills were paid.

VII

On the sixth of June I arrived at the Gare de l'Est. We drove at once to our usual quarters, Hôtel de l'Univers et du Portugal, in the Rue Croix des Petits Champs, not far from the Louvre.

The red haze of many lights hung over the Champs Élysées. We walked slowly past the marble nudes, the fauns and legendary beasts, the illuminated fountains, the seductive women. On one of the big boulevards there was an aquarium in a shop window with fishes of rubies and aquamarines afloat among water-plants of beryl. A cinema flashed a lighted sign, "Tovarich." Burma's displayed brilliant clips, the newest thing in earrings. In the Rôtisserie du Cardinal they still served their wonderful lobster à l'américaine. We drank apéritifs, although after dinner is not the time for them, and watched the perfumed cocottes with their charming glances and alluring silk legs. "*Comme vous êtes gentil,*" the whisper carried from the next table.

The next day there were many important calls to be made. I waited in front of offices, rang concièrge bells, looked up our friends. There were letters with official seals, telephone calls, appointments, cautious questions. Men with gray beards, men with white beards, immensely important men. Buildings supported by caryatids. Taxis descended from vehicles of the day of Master Rabelais. Timid side glances at the shops in the Rue de la Paix. One long wait after another. Jules white with headache. Conferences —the Salle Blumenthal in the Sorbonne. Sometimes the name "Itlère." Crowded, exhausting days.

One evening a party was given for us which began at Jarraud's, where the iced melon is spiced with a dash of curaçao. People had met to welcome us, to assure us of their eagerness to help. Toasts were drunk: *L'humanité! L'honneur! La liberté de la science!* Our cheeks were flushed with happiness as we listened to the graceful speeches, uttered in the most graceful of all languages. There around the table sat the great men whose names illumine the encyclopedias of the world, the heroic brotherhood of scientists. Next to me sat a famous novelist, who owned vast stretches of land in Abyssinia and wrote fanciful books about this least fanciful of lands. His German wife, a niece of Hindenburg, who bore a high title, shed tears of sympathy. The lights of Paris gleamed on the red rosettes in the men's buttonholes and on the red lips and fingernails of the women. In the "Coupole" our gaiety infected the painters, and one of them set us all down in brilliant caricature.

The crisis came the next morning. Jules was asked to come to the Rue de Grenelle, the Minister of Culture would receive him. The Collège Internationale gleamed like a Fata Morgana in the sky of our future. We drove off side by side in the rickety taxi.

My wait outside the Ministry netted me a delightful hour. After issuing the usual snubs to the usual gallants of Paris, I yielded to the importunities of a cavalier. He wore a proud uniform; he had a wooden leg, a slender, tapping peg, pathetic in the extreme. It was the concièrge, come to offer me a chair in his home. His little room gave me a clear view of the entrance, and I gratefully accepted. On the wall hung a key fully twenty centimeters long, and the kind soul in charge of it seemed to me another St. Peter who could unlock the door to the heaven in which at that very moment the Collège Internationale was being sanctified. I insisted on photographing my host. St. Peter put on an even more elegant coat and with a final twist to his cap he took his pose, key in hand, at the door. It is a charming picture, even though it was my old camera that I had to use and not the new one I never earned, and St. Peter was delighted when I sent it to him.

Afterward we fell into talk about the War, which had cost the poor fellow his leg. Madame Peter came in and poured us a Pernod, and we sat together until I caught sight of Jules crossing the court in the sun, when I hastily said my thanks and hurried away.

The Minister knew Jules well. Their acquaintance dated back to the time when, as director of the Rautenstrauch-Joest Museum, he had come to attend the opening of a great exhibition at the Trocadéro, to address the assembly in the name of the anthropologists of Germany. Anatole de Monzie was an admirer of the old German culture and a warm supporter of the Collège Internationale. He had welcomed Jules cordially. He intended to take up the details of the plan with his colleagues, and that evening Jules was to hear the decision.

That evening's interview brought a shock. The idea of an international college had, unfortunately, to be given up. The Ministry of Culture had done its utmost, but had foundered against the opposition of the Minister of the Exterior. The latter feared that the founding of such an institution would too greatly antagonize the Hitler government.

Our friends were inconsolable. A few hours later they came to us with another brilliant idea: a professorship in Indo-China. A fine modern university was being founded, the salary was princely, the wines ambrosian. Perfect! We shook their faithful hands. We thanked them. We took another long slow walk through the streets of our beloved Paris. Then we got into the train and returned to Cologne.

The smell of camphor greeted us in the garden. We went into the house, flung the windows wide open, unrolled the rugs and made up the beds. In the evening two dark figures stood in front of the door: Ziska and Tapir.

Jules informed the Rathaus of his return. After two weeks of struggle with Burgomaster Ludwig, after a succession of humiliations at the hands of insignificant subordinates in the government offices, after days of cold lunches, frantic letters, telephone messages and petitions, we finally were paid a part of the confiscated salary. Ziska fetched the diamond from the pawnbroker's.

Then began again those oppressive days, which some time, somehow must end. Jules scarcely went to Buchensee any more. He hated to leave the house; he hated to have "friends" call after nightfall to assure us of their "loyalty." He was more cheerful and poised than I had ever known him in our days of good fortune, but one day when he bent down to throw a stone for Tapir I saw that the hair at his temples was streaked with gray. In the evening he sat and smoked; he no longer worked.

As we had long ago given up attempting to get access to our own or any other scientific books in Cologne, we were greatly surprised at a letter which reached us on the twenty-second of June. It came from the Department of Culture and was signed by a Dr. Zülsch. It assured Professor Lips emphatically that the city of Cologne would in no way interfere with his scientific work. He was free, as every other scholar was free, to use all the libraries of Cologne.

Who was this? The name was new to us. Upon inquiry we learned that the plump gentleman named Ebel was no longer Commissioner of Culture at the Rathaus. He had been suddenly ousted. His successor was one Dr. Zülsch, a university man. Were the Nazis getting wiser? Were they learning that the theatres, schools and museums could not be directed by the same hand that had filled out bills of consignment at a railroad station? Dr. Zülsch was an art historian and had published several works on Grünewald. That explained the tone of his letter.

Jules took his hat and went off to the Rathaus; he wanted to see this man. In the ante-chamber of the office of the

Commissioner of Culture there sat a rotund little man who got up in embarrassment when Jules came in. It was Trimborn—Dr. Hermann Trimborn. Jules had been instrumental in getting him his position at the University of Bonn and had since helped him professionally.

"Hello, Trimborn. A long time since I've seen you."

"I am glad to see you, Professor Lips!"

"What are you doing in Cologne?"

The secretary who had disappeared with Jules' card came back saying that Commissioner Zülsch wished to see Professor Lips.

As Jules entered, a faultlessly dressed gentleman arose. He had the narrow face of an artist, betraying intellectual refinement of the highest degree. Heaven knows what sort of person they had led him to expect in the director of the Rautenstrauch-Joest Museum. He showed his surprise. The two men shook hands and were silent a moment. Then Zülsch courteously offered Jules a chair and a cigarette. Finally he began to speak.

"I am a hundred per cent National Socialist," he began, pointedly. A superfluous remark, since he occupied this chair in the Rathaus of Cologne. It sounded a little like a justification, almost like an apology. Jules, like himself, had instantly felt that they would have gotten on admirably if they had happened to meet at some neutral dinner table.

"At one time my wife and I came near starving because we were National Socialists," he continued. "Now it's the others' turn . . ."

What a curious introduction! Was this a Nazi talking to his political enemy, or was it one intellectual to another, impelled by the urge to explain his stand?

"I know all about you," said Zülsch, and it was impossible to tell whether he meant Jules' work or his difficulties. "Scheller—a crude creature—has been filling my ears with some clap-trap story about mats, some nonsense about non-Aryan photographs which you are said to possess."

"These mats have pictures mounted on them which I have been collecting for the past five years for a book I am doing," said Jules. In no time they were deep in a discussion of the valuation of the art of primitive peoples. Zülsch showed himself eager to learn more.

"It's odd," said he. "Once upon a time I should have been glad to go into the subject myself . . ." He broke off, somewhat confused. However, he assured Jules that he might take whatever scientific material he needed from any of the Cologne libraries, particularly, of course, from the Rautenstrauch-Joest Museum. Naturally, too, he could travel in Germany, if that were necessary; he was on leave and a free man. The necessary instructions would be given to the municipal personnel office and to Scheller.

"Just look, Professor," he said, rummaging around in his desk for a bundle of papers, "I am already being pressed to name your successor. There is a man named Trimborn, of Bonn, who won't give me any peace. He deluges me with denunciations—about your so-called private life. Seventeen pages! The man would do anything to get the directorship of the Rautenstrauch Museum. Do you know him?"

"Certainly. He is in your waiting room at present. Yes, I got him his chair at the University of Bonn. . . ."

"A filthy business! At the Wallraf-Richartz Museum, with all those wonderful paintings, there's that Otto Förster in the directorship. I know the whole story. A man who broke into his chief's desk in order to collect 'material' against him. Dirty pack! What on earth has struck the museums of Cologne? It's disgusting!"

"Too bad, Commissioner. We have met a little too late. I don't envy you. Commissioner of Culture at a time like this . . . Culture!"

"Don't forget that I am a hundred per cent National Socialist!"

"Yes, I heard you, Commissioner. Thank you for the pleasant half hour. *Auf Wiedersehen.*"

[118]

"Auf Wiedersehen."

In the waiting room Trimborn got up. He had his loud "Heil Hitler!" ready before the door opened.

Suddenly another group of students began to act—not all of them were like Scheller and Fröhlich. At first they had been intimidated and were silent, but now they emerged from the shadows with proofs of their fidelity. These young people informed us that they had framed a petition addressed to both the Minister of Culture in Berlin and to the Commissioner at Cologne, asking to have their teacher reinstated. It had traveled all over the country and carried a large number of signatures. It was rather halting in style, but it touched us deeply. The petition to the Minister had already been sent, that to the Commissioner was to be presented at the Rathaus by a special committee, headed by our golden-haired Renate. It cited Jules' "national merit" as former adviser to the Ministry of Colonies, as well as his "untiring efforts to develop his students into personalities capable of independent thinking and creative work."

Obviously it was futile to recite such qualities as these, and naturally it was unavailing, with a government given to the burning of books and the building of concentration camps, where Germans were put to torture for their convictions. We learned that the students' committee had even gone to Herr von Rautenstrauch's bank and had been received by the founder of the Museum. Renate had suggested that he use his name to intercede with the city and the Minister for Professor Lips' reinstatement, and he had shaken hands with her and consented to do so.

"Ah, what times those were under Lips' direction!" Eugen von Rautenstrauch had murmured, and when Renate had urged him in consideration of those times to stand by Lips, he had answered: "But he won't turn Nazi! And the others are in power. . . ."

The others were in power, and now things took a serious

turn. On July the twenty-second a registered letter was brought to us again, signed by Burgomaster Ludwig, informing Jules that by seriously offending student Scheller he was sabotaging the work of the city of Cologne. He was required to give Scheller "full satisfaction." The time, form and degree were to be determined by Scheller, with whom Professor Lips was to communicate through an intermediary—but not a lawyer—within forty-eight hours. Communication by word of mouth, continued Herr Ludwig, would be vain, nor would communications by letter be accepted.

A professor was to apologize to his student for an offense which was not named. The student—who owed his position to this professor—was to determine the form and the degree of the apology. In normal times a healthy man who received such a letter would not hesitate a second. He would go straight to the Museum and either give the student a stiff rebuke or a thrashing. A phlegmatic man would simply throw it into the waste-paper basket.

Jules, however, was not phlegmatic; he jumped up and seized his hat.

"Jules," I implored, "don't go; we'll send an intermediary."

"I haven't lost my wits," he exclaimed. "How dare they write me, a doctor of law, such a letter? An intermediary but not an attorney! Do you think that I'll apologize to Scheller? Apologize for something I haven't the faintest notion of? They want to get me to box his ears. All right, let them have their fun!"

It took me two hours to make Jules understand that we were not living in normal times, and another hour and a half before he agreed to send an intermediary. At least we must hear what it was all about. We soon agreed on Venn as just the right person. He was "not an attorney," but a prominent Judge.

The robust Inge was not at home. Venn received us very warmly and listened to us with great interest. He was silent for a long time. From the legal angle Burgomaster Ludwig's letter seemed incomprehensible to him. Even the murderer, he said, is told of what he is accused. To demand satisfaction for an unnamed offense was new even to a Judge in the Third Reich. He advised us under no circumstances to send an intermediary, but to write, declining to take any stand before we were informed of what the "serious personal insults and intrigues against Herr Scheller" consisted.

"But, dear Judge," said I, "the Burgomaster expressly writes that no written communications will be heeded!"

"That's utterly ridiculous," he replied; "it's impossible."

"We must send an intermediary," I insisted.

"I absolutely advise against it," he replied.

Then followed a desperate search for a human being who would help us. Not one of those who had assured us of their devotion in former times were we able to persuade to come to our aid.

Before the expiration of our time of grace, "forty-eight hours after the receipt of this letter," I stood once again at half past eight in the morning in front of the gates of the Museum. As it was still closed to the public at that early hour, I rang the bell. Through the big glass panel I saw Weiss coming down the steps. He unlocked the door in silence. I walked past the two bronze lions to the administrative offices. The big door of the director's room was wide open and remained open, so that listeners had no difficulty whatsoever in hearing what went on. I asked Weiss to announce me to Scheller, and the "acting director" received me at once.

I took the few steps to Jules' room and the few more from the door to Jules' desk from which Scheller now got up. Everything was the same as usual; the blue and gold rug, the carved Javanese framework over the library door, the mask over the niche. Only the golden god had disappeared. His place was taken by Herr Scheller's Führer. My husband's chair too was now occupied by a caricature.

Scheller did not appear in the least embarrassed, although he certainly could not have expected to see "the intermediary" embodied in my person.

"I have come in the name of Professor Lips," I began. "I have come within the appointed time. Do you admit this?"

"Yes."

"As his representative I should like to ask whether you are familiar with the contents of the letter of July the twenty-first from the city of Cologne?"

"Yes."

"Does Commissioner of Culture Zülsch know of this letter?"

"No, I fixed matters with Burgomaster Ludwig."

So Ludwig was the unknown enemy. It was he that had thought up the plan of stopping the salary payments, the whole string of tricks, and finally this letter. And Zülsch was on the other side.

"What is the nature of these undefined complaints that you see fit to raise against your teacher, the man who has placed you in your present position?" I spoke very softly, but very clearly, as though I were reading the words from a script on the wall before me.

"Insults!" screamed Scheller into the echoing room. His wooden leg knocked against the edge of the desk; his lips became repulsively moist and the veins of his bloodshot eyes swelled red behind his glasses. "Insults! But now I am an official—and the Party is behind me! I won't put up with anything, not with anything!"

"How could the gentleman I represent have insulted you?" I asked calmly.

"You know, don't pretend! Two weeks ago in a bar in the Budengasse! Don't come play-acting here."

"In the Budengasse, Herr Scheller?"

"*The Lantern* is the name of the place. There your husband met . . ."

"You mean the gentleman I represent, Professor Lips?"

"There he met Rodens, the editor—in the men's toilet.. "

"What?" I interrupted him, completely confused. "What are you talking about?"

"There he met our party member Rodens and said to him: 'Scheller is an utter idiot.' "

I fought down a burst of laughter. Was *this* the source of an official threat from the city of Cologne? The men's toilet in *The Lantern*? Little Rodens with his quick-change political convictions? Rodens, the divorced husband of our charming friend Anita? Scheller: an utter idiot? An official? Threats? Was there a place called *The Lantern*? I had never heard of it.

"Is that all?" I inquired in measured tones.

"All? Let me tell you this: now it's my turn! Now we'll see who's master!"

"But you weren't there that night at all?"

"I am sure of my witnesses."

How had he hit on Rodens? I considered a moment, then I replied:

"Do you know that Rodens is divorced? We have continued our friendship with his wife, who has broken with him. We looked into the divorce proceedings and they seemed rather shabby. Do you know that Rodens cannot stand alcohol—that he cannot take two glasses of wine . . ."

"That's all one to me! I have my witnesses, I tell you, witnesses!"

"And Rodens rushed to you with this statement?"

"No! My assistant Fröhlich—and you need not smile—it's quite unnecessary! I am the master in this Museum now. My assistant delivered something to Rodens. Then he was told about the insult. And I took action. You may be sure that I won't put up with this!"

"Accusations at third hand! Rodens, Fröhlich—insult of an official! Oh, Herr Scheller, it seems beneath our dignity—grubby tale-bearing . . ."

"Don't think you can get round us!"

"I consider it impossible that the remark was made!"

"Why?"

"You have reason to be familiar with Professor Lips' manner of speaking. His style is more literary than that, you know. He simply doesn't express himself in that way. It's vulgar."

"You deny that the remark was made?"

"How could I 'deny'? I do not know whether Professor Lips was in the Budengasse two weeks ago; I do not know a place called The Lantern. Moreover, I can assure you that I was not in the gentlemen's toilet at the time. So how could I deny it?"

"Stop splitting hairs."

"Very well. Let me ask you quite plainly. What do you really want of Professor Lips?"

"I want an apology!"

"I shall tell him how matters stand. He might possibly write you a letter . . ."

"No! I demand a personal apology!"

"What do you demand?" I asked, dumbfounded.

"That he shall come into this room and apologize!"

Lightning is more likely to strike this very instant, or Hitler to resign of his own free will, I thought to myself! Jules apologize!

"And you make such a demand, on the basis of a vicious tale brought by a third party from such a place?"

He opened his desk, took out two pages of manuscript, handed them to me across the table and said: "He is to read this aloud, here in this room, and sign it!" Scheller wiped the tip of his nose with the back of his hand.

I cast a quick glance at the memorandum: "I, Julius Lips, former director of the Rautenstrauch-Joest Museum and Professor at the University of Cologne do hereby admit . . ."

"I am going," said I. "I am afraid your nerves are troubling you. You really should do something about it."

"Be careful, I tell you! I can promise you reprisals!"

"You are determined to make an official matter of this absurdity?"

"I am a National Socialist—and you'll soon know what that means! Let me know by telephone whether Professor Lips admits the remark or not!"

"No. I do not want any written link missing in the chain that begins with Burgomaster Ludwig's letter. I will write you a letter, telling you what attitude Professor Lips wishes to take toward your charges."

Scheller sprang from his chair with surprising nimbleness.

"I know why Lips is doing this! I know why he feels himself so strong. Since Zülsch got in, things are not coming my way. Those fellows at the Rathaus are behind the whole business. They are making things hard for me. I'm supposed to be director! And what am I—what am I, after all?"

I left the director's room with measured steps, walked slowly through the empty waiting room, through the hall, down the stairs and out into the street, where the sun was shining. Not till I was around the corner did I begin to run.

To Jules I said: "You must leave Cologne. And as soon as possible. Flight is your only resource."

He had me tell him everything that had occurred. At first he could not recall any place called *The Lantern*, or any occasion of this sort. He laughed heartily at the whole matter. "And a Burgomaster of the city of Cologne writes a letter of this kind about a farce like that?"

"Try to remember. Have you seen Rodens at all, anywhere, of late?"

"Wait a moment. Yes, now I remember. I did, one night not long ago."

Jules had been delayed in town and had dropped in at a little bar where there was dancing. At a table he had seen Frau Schober, Rodens' lady love. Later in the men's room he had noticed Rodens, white as wax; he had had too much to drink. Jules had tossed off a casual greeting: "How's the divorce going?" We were interested in the fate of our charming Anita.

"Getting on," said Rodens, "I'll be glad to be rid of that creature," and with that he staggered out. Frau Schober was waiting for him, to help him back to their table.

"Was that all?" I asked, disappointed. "Didn't you talk about Scheller or the Museum?"

"Oh, the man was too drunk for that!"

Jules immediately wrote a short note to Scheller, telling him that the alleged remark was pure invention and untrue. On the evening in question not a word had been said about Scheller or the Museum. Then we telephoned Anita and asked her to come to see us.

Anita was the handsomest woman of our acquaintance. She was a perfect Creole type, and her Southern coloring and features fully justified her adopting the Spanish version of her name. Instead of Anna, she was known as Anita. I was glad that she had come. I told her everything that had happened. At the end of the story she remarked: "You'll never have a moment's peace. Rodens can't live without his false and filthy tales."

When we examined the date of the incident in The Lantern more closely, it turned out to be the very day that Anita's divorce had been granted. Rodens had lost the suit; he had been declared the guilty party. And Jules had asked him how the case was going! Had Rodens thought that Jules knew of his defeat and wanted to make fun of him? Had he planned a revenge—a revenge characteristic of his intellect— with the place of action the men's lavatory of The Lantern? Anita told us the three goals of Rodens' life: to be a cardinal, to have a diplomatic passport and to be waited upon by a servant in white gloves. Here was material for a psycho-analyst.

Anita went on with the depressing story of her unfortunate marriage. The only daughter of a well-to-do family, she had married the unknown journalist, "a penniless poet," and had discovered too late that he loved nothing about her except her money. As she sat there talking, nibbling at chocolate almonds, absently scratching Tapir's back with the heel of her dainty slipper, we heard a sharp ring at the bell, a confused noise and the banging of a door. Ziska opened and suddenly Renate burst in, our fair-haired Renate in her prettiest blue frock. Her appearance caused us all to jump up in alarm. Her hat was awry, her eyes red with weeping and her manner uncontrolled and hysterical. She rushed up to me, fell into my arms and burst into sobs. Anita, Ziska, Jules, Tapir and I surrounded her and tried to calm her. We led her to the nearest chair and gave her a sip of cognac and dabbed her burning cheeks with eau de Cologne. It was a long time before she could collect herself and talk.

Renate and another student had selected this morning to go to the Rathaus to give Commissioner Zülsch the petition asking for the reinstatement of Professor Lips in the name of his students.

Zülsch had declared himself ready to receive the committee, but hardly was the door of the room closed before he pounced on the two trembling petitioners "like a beast." When he heard why they had come he refused even to read the petition. "Your efforts are absolutely futile!" he had shouted. "The whole matter was settled long ago." He had ridiculed them with cold irony, referring to the Museum as a "pig-sty." He would have nothing more to do with the place. It was all repugnant to him. Lips should either join the ranks of the National Socialists or go to the devil! As for them, they could go to hell with their petition. He forbade anyone to mention the name of Lips in his room: he would have nothing to do with traitors! Any swine of a Jew was better. Lips belonged either in a madhouse or in a concentration camp!

With his furious voice ringing in their ears, the students had rushed from the Rathaus. Renate herself had jumped into a taxi and hurried to us. Everything was over, everything was lost!

Jules was not surprised at the outcome of the undertaking. From the beginning he had considered the petition a hopeless effort in a hopeless cause. Zülsch's unrestrained fury indicated that there was tension at the Rathaus. Later this was corroborated. Burgomaster Ludwig, who had written the letter on *The Lantern* incident, had had a sharp clash with Zülsch. As a University man, he objected to the application of gutter tactics in the city's leading hall of science. Infuriated by his discussion with Ludwig, he had returned to his office to find the two unfortunate petitioners waiting, and had vented on them the full force of the anger aroused by the Museum intrigue.

Our talk turned from him to Scheller and Rodens, and how the matter would end. We had pictured our quiet leave of absence rather differently. It was clear to me that Jules must not under any circumstances meet his slanderer face to face. Somehow the matter had to be settled—somehow.

We heard the door bell ring again, but we paid no heed to it. A moment later Ziska came in very red in the face and whispered something to me. I was calm. I did not care what else might happen on this day.

The maid opened the door. Before us stood two policemen in uniform. Renate uttered a cry; Anita gazed at them, fascinated, Jules sat in his chair unmoved. Tapir growled and crept toward the two figures with his head down. Ziska behind them made desperate gestures, indicating that she was not to blame for the intrusion of the uniformed State police. Tapir sniffed at them disapprovingly.

"We wanted to speak to Professor Lips alone," the more stalwart of the policemen, a thick-set fellow with the face of a peasant, finally said. "We must search your house. Don't you want to send your guests away?"

"These are friends," said Jules. "Why do you wish to deny

[128]

the two ladies the thrill of witnessing a search? Does one see a thing like that every day? What are you looking for?"

"Give us your license to carry arms."

"I no longer have one. To be more accurate, I tore it up. A friend of mine was suspected of murder because there was shooting in his street and he had such a license . . ."

"Did you use the license to buy a gun?"

"No. I only got it as a precaution, because I often worked late at the Museum and attempts at robbery had occurred there. But I did not buy a weapon. I went to Africa shortly afterward."

"So you have no revolver in the house?"

"No."

"Be careful. You have been reported."

"Please proceed with your search . . ."

No one was allowed to leave the room. One policeman was stationed in the corridor. The other began to turn over the chairs in the living room and to feel the upholstery. He pushed all my books untidily back against the wall. He opened the piano and looked into it. He rummaged through my music. He took the masks off the walls and peered into them. He unlocked my glass case and took the little animal figures from Monte Carlo in his heavy hand. He felt the stove, opened the big clock, pulled the rugs back and groped around in the waste basket. He got up on a stepladder to examine the chandelier. He shook the curtains; he opened the drawers of my desk; he fingered our field-glass cases and my box of water-colors.

At every move he was followed by four women and a dog. Jules sat in a corner and smoked.

Then came the dining room—to the last little fork. The flower pot on the windowsill. Next, the terrace. The kitchen. He went through the hall quickly. He was about to go upstairs, when Jules remarked:

"As a lawyer I must draw your attention to the fact that it is your duty to search the cellar also."

It was eleven o'clock. The policeman called his colleague and we all went down to the cellar. We had just had a fresh supply of coal put in and a goodly pile of coke.

"Your duty," began Jules, but the man knew his job and picked up a shovel to shift the pile of coal. Only Ziska and Tapir watched them at their sweating toil. The rest of us picked up a bite in the provision cellar.

At twenty minutes past eleven they were through with the coal bin and ready to clear the large boxes of empty wine bottles. At eleven forty-five they were through with the water basins in the toilets, the slop buckets and the fuse boxes. At noon they examined Tapir's straw bed. The bells of the nearby baroque church sounded melodiously.

"Don't you want to try the garden?" asked Jules politely. "Your duty requires at least a few spadefuls."

"Not necessary," said the man in uniform. Then slyly to Ziska, "Have you any stove pipes?" It was lucky for him that we had none, as his duty would have required him to dismantle them.

At a quarter past twelve we went upstairs: Renate, Anita, Ziska, Tapir, Jules and I—the policemen, of course, preceding us.

Into my bedroom. "Wait a minute," I exclaimed, "you've just come from the cellar. May I ask you to wash your hands before you touch my bed?" They followed Ziska obediently to the bathroom and were given a pink towel, on which they dried their hands in embarrassment.

Off with the chintz covers, out with the bedding, flop went my frocks shoved back and forth in the closet. My dressing table yanked open. The contents of my jewel case littered about. Suspicious glances at the electric vibrator.

"What is that?"

"A patter for cold cream—not a weapon—or perhaps, after all, it is one."

As they left my room Ziska politely told them that my

bed would have to be remade. "The Frau Professor hates untidy beds." They made it up. Twelve forty-seven.

Jules' study. Here I suddenly lost my exuberance. I remembered a little yellow box that stood among the books in the niche at the window. It was left from Jules' army days. Did it contain . . . ? I hurried to the window and stood in front of it. My heart beat fast. By the grace of God, Tapir trotted after me, hiding the box with his body. There were too many books about. Only a few, at eye-level, were pushed back. No time to unlock the desk. No time to prod the upholstery, to turn over the pillows on the chairs. Shoveling coal is hard work, and makes men hungry. In this, our largest room, the search went most rapidly. At twenty-five minutes of one they were through.

Next came Jules' bedroom. They left the bed untouched. Their haste increased. The opera-hat box. The shoe closet. A gymnastic apparatus.

Then the floor above. Ziska's room. In the closet there was a package wrapped in tissue paper. "Open it!" It contained six tiny, tinted egg-cups, treasures secured by Ziska on coupons. They did not look at all like weapons.

After that they went into the guest room. Then into the storeroom, where I kept my "archives"—all our correspondence, newspaper clippings, posters announcing Jules' lectures, trophies from Africa, two huge desks, cupboards crammed full of material. Two armchairs. The whole thing was examined in four minutes.

In the hall stood the sewing machine. In spite of Ziska's urging, the men showed no desire to look under its domed lid.

The attic. Here Jules showed slight signs of nervousness. Did he think that here . . . He pointed to big chests and trunks.

"Still unpacked. From my last expedition. Do you wish to begin?"

No, they did not wish to begin. They wished to stop.

They began to perspire so violently that Tapir took to following them with keen animal interest, wagging his tail in excitement.

"Are there any weapons here?" asked the man automatically.

"Yes," said Jules. He drew a *kukhri* from the trunk, a horrible sickle-shaped weapon in use among the Gurkhas of Nepal, with which the British equip their native troops in that district.

"Be careful!" said Jules, as the policeman ran his finger along the blade. "It is poisoned."

"That's not a weapon," declared the policeman; "that's an antique."

Jules did not laugh. He looked around anxiously.

"Oh, please show it to me," said Anita; "it's so interesting."

But she received no answer. A deep-toned sound from the Tower. Four clear strokes. One o'clock. The policemen exchanged a glance of manly decision.

"The search is at an end," said the fat one. "There is no weapon in the house. Excuse the intrusion."

No one said "*Auf Wiedersehen!*" That would have been unsuitable in the presence of the uniformed men. No one said "Heil Hitler!" for that was not the custom in our house. Not even Hitler's civil servants said it. They departed in silence, depressed. In all probability, they were tired.

We were gathered in the hall. Ziska let the two policemen out of the garden gate and locked it. Then she closed the house door carefully, and before any of us could say a word she came up to me and said impishly: "And do tell me, Frau Professor, where *have* we put the thing?"

VIII

In the evening, when the moon was high over the acacias, Ziska led the way into the garden. Against the back wall, overgrown with yellow and red roses, we saw a remarkable arrangement, a big empty chest resembling a platform. On this stood a ladder propped against the garden wall so that one could easily climb over it. Our neighbor's large grounds opened onto two streets, the Klettenberggürtel and the Ölbergstrasse. One had only to climb the ladder and drop into the adjoining garden—a convenient exit from our premises—without going through the Siebengebirgsallee.

Ziska looked at us earnestly while explaining all this, and I marveled at her ingenuity and practical foresight. Her theory was two-sided: "The policemen will return" and "they shan't get our professor." She strictly forbade Jules ever to show himself at the window or door when there was a ring. "In case of a crisis" she would wave her handkerchief three times, and he was to slip into the garden.

I pulled a new key from my pocket and gave it to Jules. He looked at me, bewildered. I mentioned a name, a street and a house number.

"That's where you are going to sleep tonight."

"But you're mad, my dear! Is there . . ."

"We arranged it all this afternoon. They expect you. Your night clothes are already there. Tomorrow morning I'll come to see you."

We argued for half an hour.

Jules owned a house, had his own bedroom and bath and many things which made life pleasant. And here he was, stealing through the night like a shadow under the acacias, to sleep on a strange bed.

One gets up, bathes and dresses. The morning room is flooded with sunlight. The cacti throw bizarre shadows on the wall. The furniture is as red as poppies and the covers are the color of the Mediterranean, green and milky, cool and beautiful. A single cup stands on the breakfast table. Tapir comes bounding in from the garden. A ladder leans against the rose-grown wall.

A ring at the door. Ziska draws me to the window. Ah, our friends, the police, are here again. Yesterday they were searching for weapons. What would they want today? We exchanged a glance of anger and delight, anger that they actually dare to come again and delight that the house is empty and its master in security.

It is the same fat policeman that came yesterday, but to-day he has a different companion, who looks like a shabby student. But he wears a uniform like the other and is there-fore a policeman. Today I am alone. There will be no jest-ing today, no fine-spun sarcasms. The Hausfrau's peace is threatened—no small matter!

"Have you come for the Indian knife?" I asked. "I have also a pair of poultry scissors and a sharp spade or two."

"Today we're after the books."

"The books? What do you mean?"

"Marxist and asphalt literature."

"Certainly, please come in. Begin in the living room. You know your way around. You can sort them. And what is the purpose of all this?"

"We are to take all dangerous books away."

"Where to?"

"To police headquarters."

"You will pay me their cost?"

"No."

"So, it's stealing! That's what the police come to the house for, to steal! Safe times, these."

"We must speak to Professor Lips at once!"

"He is not here. You may search the house for him, too."

"Let's begin."

"Who is your chief?"

"The president of the police."

"Just be careful; I am warning you!"

I went to the telephone and called up the president. I got through to him and made a complaint.

"There is nothing I can do, Frau Professor. You have been denounced by a municipal institution."

"Ah, something new!"

"Let the men do their duty."

"My husband is not at home. The police have broken in! I want a signed receipt for our property. Our books are the most important things we own."

"Let the policemen give you a receipt."

"Thank you, Mr. President!"

"Heil Hitler!"

"Good morning."

They were kneeling in front of my red bookcase holding my parchment-bound Baudelaire in their hands—Arno Holz's *Riesenbusssträne*, Oscar Bie's *Music on the Volga*, Erich Mühsam's rare little autobiography, a gift edition presented to the bibliophiles of Leipzig. Kakutso Okakura, *Das Buch vom Tee*, and Heinrich Mann's *Flöten und Dolche*— published in Wilhelm's days of censorship. *C'était le Soir des Dieux*, the wonderful hand-colored work, awarded first prize at the Brussels bibliophile exposition. This bookcase contained the choicest treasures, almost all of them numbered copies. Many were inscribed to us by their authors. Also there was our Goethe, the Grossherzog-Wilhelm-Ernst edition in soft leather, and Molière and an old edition of Shakespeare and the original Ex Libris that Max Klinger had made for my parents. Into such company the Third Reich thrust its black finger-nails.

"*Music on the Volga*—is that Communistic?"

"Don't you know that the Volga is in Italy? Give me that book at once!"

A loud commotion at the dining-room window. There is Tapir on the terrace, panting, his tongue showing red. Ziska has unchained him. He barks furiously and rushes to and fro.

"What language is this?" the policeman asked, puzzled.

"It doesn't matter. It stays here!" said I, putting back Maurois' volume, *Le cercle de la famille*.

Tapir has disappeared. Ziska comes in.

"Those are valuable books," she remarks, "every spot you make will cost you ten marks."

The knowledge that Jules was away elated us; the presence of the two oafs in uniform enraged us. The combination sharpened our wits.

"Hölderlin—is he dangerous to the State?"

"The man was insane," said I significantly; "but don't worry, it was before 1933."

They are through in the living room. They tramp up to Jules' study. The telephone rings. I answer it.

"Dear Frau Doktor," I say, in a carrying tone, "we haven't heard from you in ages!"

"Have you gone mad?" asks Jules at the other end of the wire.

"Yes, really," I reply. "But will you excuse me, please? I am busy with company at the moment."

"The police! Are they threatening you? I'll be home at once, darling."

"You are mistaken. My husband is unfortunately not here and won't be home all day. He's at our week-end house in the country." The policemen exchange glances.

"What do they want? Arms again?" asks Jules anxiously.

"Only book collectors, dear Frau Doktor!"

"Don't let them steal our books!"

"You are too kind. I am of the same opinion."

"Let me know as soon as they have gone!"

The man with the dirty hands stands helpless before the

bookshelves with their thousands of volumes, of every shape, size and description.

"Have you any Marxist literature?"

"We have nothing of the sort," declares Ziska.

The policeman mutters a list of memorized names: "Kerr, Remarque, Heinrich Mann, Polgar, Magnus Hirschfeld, Wassermann, Emil Ludwig, Gorki, Freud, Tucholsky . . ."

"Numbers one, two, four, five, eight and ten are right under your hand," I am tempted to say. But it is really wiser to stand by innocently smiling.

Thick volumes are brought out and added to the pile brought from downstairs. Right at the policeman's elbow stands Remarque, but he wears a protective coloring—gray—and how are the police to know "corrupting books" by their binding? They have not come to read. Now they are rummaging among Jules' own works. I can stand it no longer.

"That's the dangerous corner, over there," I say, pointing to the political section. There Trotzky stands—but next to him is Hitler's *Mein Kampf*. There stands Lassalle, but next to him Bismarck. There is a lot to be taken away here. *Der Bonze* is confiscated, a Nazi attack on the Socialists, but the title sounds as though it were against fat-bellies in brown shirts. Add it to the pile! Leopold von Wiese, *The Village from the Sociological Angle*. Sociological? Probably the same as Socialistic! Confiscated! Two unworldly Viennese priests had conducted a technical dispute on methods of approach in ethnological problems, known as the *Schmidt-Koppers Controversy*. Controversy? It sounds dangerous. Add it to the pile!

The pile becomes quite high. Then the policemen ask for wrapping paper. They are ready to go. Great gaps show in the shelves. Not so fast, gentlemen. We must make an inventory. Ziska fetches the little white typewriter. The man on the left has to read out all the titles, with the authors' names and the dates of publication. Each book is listed and numbered, and the man on the right has to stack the volumes in tidy piles. It is a long list—seven hundred and ninety-three books. Then it is signed by both men. I write, "The following books were removed on July 25, 1933, from Professor Lips' house by police agents, in violation of the law." They object to "in violation of the law" and I substitute "without authorization," which they like better. A little crowd gathers to watch the uniformed men staggering through the garden with our books. They cram their booty into a taxi and squeeze into the back seat.

It was high time that they left. There was a weapon in the house, a sharp, poisoned Indian dagger.

I rang the door bell of our friends' house and handed Jules the list. We immediately wrote a complaint to the president of the police.

Jules decided for the time being to yield to the urging of his host, and to mine, and to sleep where no one would look for him. For the master of that house wore a swastika.

That afternoon we called on our lawyer, an old friend. He was tremendously Aryan and fully acquainted with Third Reich threats. We told him about Scheller and Fröhlich. For their affair, though on the surface far more harmless an incident than the descent of the police upon us, seemed to us far more serious. How right we were in this assumption we found out later. The lawyer, who was surprised by nothing, simply said one word: "Danger." He wondered that the "insult" extended only to Scheller. He knew of very different cases where a simple oath, sworn in support of an invented comment on Hitler, Göbbels or Göring, had sent reputable men, guiltless victims of denunciation, to prison. A friend of our lawyer, Counselor von Coellen, specialized in defending such cases of slander. He telephoned Herr von Coellen that we were coming and sent us away with the advice to bring an action against Rodens for slander.

Von Coellen was an old man. He received us in an office ornate with pilasters, plush and photographs—the stuffy eighties to the nth degree. He read Burgomaster Ludwig's letter and the record that I had made of my visit to Scheller. With delightful candor he spoke about the practice of law under the Third Reich. "I would rather chop wood than be a lawyer in a State where there is no justice!" When he heard that Jules was completely Aryan, a veteran and a former officer, he declared himself ready to represent us in the suit against Rodens, naming a retainer of fifty marks. Then he wrote to the magistrate of the district in which Rodens lived, for this worthy citizen must first make an attempt at settlement before the charge could be brought in proper form. Comforted, we shook his honest right hand.

In the evening we stole home together for an hour. I searched the road for signs of ambush before I could allow Jules to approach his own house. Tapir gave us a concert of joyful barks, licked Jules' shoes and rubbed his head contentedly against his master's knee.

Suddenly there was a ring. We started in alarm. I pulled Jules through the open terrace door into the garden. Ziska did not budge until we had disappeared. Then she opened the door, her handkerchief ready for waving. Outside she saw a pair of lovers leaning against our hedge. In their embrace they had brushed against the bell. We came back from the garden, laughing. But there was nervousness and uncertainty in the air. We could not relax. I was not calm until Jules had left. We had all been seized by a psychosis—a longing for the "peace and security" which the National Socialist State never tired of proclaiming to its citizens.

IX

The next post brought another registered letter from Scheller, addressed to Frau Eva Lips. We learned that Herr Scheller could not take cognizance of Jules' letter. Professor Lips must present himself at the Museum the following day, Wednesday, at twelve noon, to apologize in person. The new director did not fail to give warning of consequences, "if the matter were not adjusted by tomorrow night."

The situation became more and more clear. It was no longer a case of a difference of opinion. The denouncer was now commanding. Behind him was the administration of the city, and back of that—the police. As a screen, the authority of the Rathaus. The choice lay between compromising one's honor and the road toward—nothing. It was simple blackmail. They had taken care to demonstrate how agreeably the police conducted themselves in our house. Matters had been excellently arranged. The first pretext was the search for weapons, the next was the confiscation of books. The two poor devils in policemen's uniforms were intended only as evidence that they had us in their power. At the same time Burgomaster Ludwig encouraged Scheller to further excesses. The threats were now scarcely veiled. One single gesture would have withdrawn them, a gesture which they still seemed to expect, the raising of the right arm. But the arm would rather wither.

Before noon Jules "must" appear at the Museum. At eleven o'clock a letter from him was at the Rathaus, one copy for Herr Ludwig, the other for Dr. Zülsch. Jules briefly stated the situation and refused to sign the admission of guilt which Scheller had prepared. The offense of which he was accused was untrue, and his honor forbade him—even under threat—to put his name to anything of this sort.

When I came to the Museum at eleven o'clock, I found Scheller in an ugly mood.

"You here again," he growled at me. "Where is Professor Lips?"

"He has gone swimming," I answered calmly.

"During Museum hours he must stay at home. In the future I demand that he remain in his house from eight until four-thirty!"

"You demand?" I said. Since I was not offered a chair I got myself one and sat down.

"Swimming? Where?" asked Scheller.

"In the Rhine."

"Then I presume he did not see my letter requiring him to come here?"

"Your letters really do not interest him, my dear Scheller. You overestimate yourself."

"You lied. He really did make that remark. Why don't you say something?"

"You are making your statements without waiting for my answer. I am merely telling you officially that the gentleman I represent wishes to inform you for the second time through me that Rodens' statement is a false calumny. Professor Lips herewith distinctly declines to sign the document you have drawn up. He will not sign anything you may submit, since your implications are based on lies."

Scheller's head bulged like a puffed balloon. Good heavens, I thought, he's really physically dangerous. I moved my chair a little farther away.

"But we believe Rodens," cried the man in a frenzy, "and you had better be careful." And quick as lightning, in spite of his wooden leg, he ran to the door of the library, pulled it open and produced his chief witness, Rodens in person. He had him in readiness for Jules.

Rodens, a man of humble origin and more stupid than

bad, was frightened when he saw me. He approached and seated himself without speaking, staring at the floor like a schoolboy who is preparing to deny a misdemeanor. He looked white and ill at ease.

"Really, Herr Rodens," I remarked, "up to now I thought that this was some dream of Herr Scheller's. What is your rôle in this affair? Are you looking for a little job in the National Socialist Party? Are you really this tale-bearer, or did the idea originate with the jaunty Herr Scheller? May I ask you to tell me what you have said about Professor Lips?"

"I must look it up first," was the astonishing answer, and Rodens reached for the document which Scheller had prepared for Jules' signature.

"Don't you even know it by memory? How awkward for you!"

"I know it absolutely by heart!" he burst out, wiping the perspiration from his forehead. His voice rose to a squeak. "Lips walked up to me and bawled out: 'You are a scamp not to have mentioned me in your article on the Museum, in place of that numskull Scheller, whom even his superiors brand an utter idiot.'"

"Do they really?" I asked curiously.

"That's what Lips said!"

"And did he bawl?" I asked.

"'Utter idiot,' is what he said of Scheller," repeated Rodens like a somnambulist. "I was there with some gentlemen from the *Westdeutscher Beobachter*."

"Gentlemen from the *Westdeutscher Beobachter*?" I saw which way the wind blew. I had a vision of them standing up to take the oath, the editors of the *Westdeutscher Beobachter*.

"I regard you as untrustworthy, my good man," said I.

"Me?"

"Do you remember the stranger whom you named as your wife's lover in your own divorce case? Your wife made his acquaintance for the first time at the conclusion of the trial. Oh, I have a number of proofs of your devotion to the truth, Rodens, well-established proofs, supported by facts."

"The city stands behind him," screamed Scheller; "the Party believes him! He is my witness."

"You were formally charged with libel yesterday by Professor Lips," said I. "When the case comes up, by way of illustrating your trustworthiness, the history of your divorce proceedings will be publicly reviewed, if you support the lying statements of these others."

"You will regret this!"

"I hope that the denouncers will regret . . ."

"Before tomorrow noon Professor Lips is to appear here and read this document aloud in our presence, after which he will put his name to it. That's all we want."

"Nothing more than that?" I asked with a laugh.

"We can retaliate; we are dangerous!" shrieked Scheller.

"Have you our books, too?" I asked. "They were taken away from us yesterday on the grounds of a denunciation by one of the institutions of the city."

"If your husband is not here by tomorrow to apologize, he may come to know the new State!"

"*L'état, c'est vous?* So you are the State?" I asked, impressed. "Yes, that's true, the Führer stands back of all his agents; they only carry out his will."

"He will apologize here, you'll see!"

I got up. I looked into Rodens' cowardly eyes. I looked once more around the room. It was no longer the impressive sanctum of a scholar who had explored the cultures of mankind. It had become a barbarian camp. How could I get out fast enough?

I have often marveled that those two did not utilize that moment to invent dreadful things which I was supposed to have said about Hitler or the government. For they could easily have supported each other as witnesses, as they later did against Jules. Why did they not think up something? I would at once have been arrested and put into a concentration camp. It would have been a magnificent revenge, worthy of that pair. My only explanation is that their imaginations were too feeble and could get no farther than an insult to Scheller!

Jules was standing in his friend's room. A little Russian icon hung on the wall. Somewhere a holy candle was burning. The tortoise Li Tai Po sprawled across the rug. I opened the door and fell into Jules' arms. How often we had laughed at such gestures in our mutual dislike of emotional display. But at this moment nothing counted but his presence. We sat down on the couch. Jules opened the wings of his coat and I put my head close to his heart.

"You must get away," I said after a while; "you cannot stay here. It would be suicide. The consequences are clear." We did not even mention the possibility of Jules going to see Scheller, or signing the confession.

Suddenly I exclaimed: "Why, my parents! We have forgotten our parents. They must help us. We are not alone. We will go to Leipzig, to human beings who will stand by us."

I ran to the telephone, put in a long-distance call, and five minutes later was connected with Leipzig. I heard my father's voice.

It must have been an alarming outburst, of narrative, of entreaty, fear, childishness and despair. My father had no idea what I was talking about. "Help us!" I exclaimed. "The students are threatening and persecuting us! You saw it when you were here. They have the power. They will make us unhappy forever. They are lying, Father. May we come home? We must leave Cologne—forever!"—"Your house," I heard my father say, and: "You misunderstand the new State. If you are in the right, you will win out." "Why, they are lying, don't you know that they are lying?"—"Don't be precipitate. Think matters over calmly. You are exaggerating the situation."—"Mayn't we come home, Father, may

[144]

we not come to you?"—"Your duty is to see this thing through, your duty is to fight for the truth."—"The truth, ha ha! The truth, Father, what do you know about . . ." "Be careful, calm yourselves."—"All right, Father, I understand," I said very softly. "Thank you very much. Forgive my nonsense. We'll stick it out. My love to Mother. All right, I am laughing again. Of course it's all nonsense. You're quite right. Good-bye." Slowly I put down the receiver.

"We are quite alone," said I. "Do you see how far away they are? Quite alone. We will go along alone."

"It is well to be clear about things, my dear," said Jules.

The next day there came another letter from Scheller, repeating his demands. Ziska brought it to us in our friend's house. Then she went home, and we took the train to Buchensee.

We picked some green little sugar-peas in our garden, and then we went down to the valley, where there was a fine modern bathing establishment, for a swim. We blinked in the sun. Suddenly an attendant came up to us. We only saw his white trousers and his naked brown feet, not his face. He whispered:

"An official has come and wishes to speak to you." A cold wave of fear ran through me like an electric shock. Too late, I thought, too late. I began to tremble. Something must be done instantly, instantly.

"Where is he?" I asked hoarsely.

"Behind the house," said the man, and returned to his swimming lesson.

Jules jumped up. I said: "Swim across to the other side and wait at the pheasant's bush. I'll go."

I got up. On shaking legs I made my way to the rear of the house. There stood the local forester. I knew him from former times as a subordinate of our poor old sheriff. I was indebted to him for a bird house and many hints for my vegetable garden.

"How goes it?" I said with an effort. "A good season, isn't it? We're having such lovely roses . . ."

"Professor Lips not here?" he inquired, playing with his belt.

"Not—here," I faltered.

"Then I can tell you. Wasn't there a spade stolen from your place a bit back? I am on the track of the thief. We'll find him. Don't worry, you'll get your spade back. The inquiry has begun."

"The inquiry!" I exclaimed, breathing a deep sigh of relief. I wanted to fall on the man's neck.

"Wait a minute, perhaps I can find my husband," I cried, and hurried away. Throwing my bath cape off as I ran, I dived from the springboard into the water.

"*Huuaaúuuu!*" I called across the water in breathless excitement. "*Huuaaúuuu!*" It was our old African cry, which meant that all was well. And across the river a bronzed figure hurled himself into the water and swam toward me. As our arms touched I sang out:

"The spade! He says that he's looking for the thief who stole our spade!"

"Grrrr!" snorted the seal at my side. We came out dripping, flung on our togas and ordered some beer for the forester, and soon we were absorbed in discussing the lack of lime in the soil.

"And how is our sheriff getting on?" he asked, lowering his voice suddenly. "We won't get another like him in a hurry. Our country fairs, our horse races, all the friendly fun —all over with."

"Things are going badly with him, Forester."

"Tell him that we haven't forgotten him. No one here can. *Auf Wiedersehen*, Herr Professor, and good luck to you." Then in a loud voice—"Heil Hitler!"

"*Auf Wiedersehen*, Forester."

When we returned to Cologne that night, I rang up Ziska

from the station as usual, to find out whether everything was quiet, and learned that Frau Venn had called during our absence. She had heard from Olga, the wife of the President of the Government-Board, that Jules was in a concentration camp. She had not believed Ziska's emphatic denials. So we decided to go straight from the station to the Venns', to contradict by our actual presence a rumor bound to be believed if it emanated from a Nazi Judge. When they saw us they thought a pair of ghosts had descended upon them. Then, dog tired, we crawled away to our separate lodgings.

When two days more had passed and nothing had happened, no word from Scheller and none from the city, I fetched Jules home again. We made a real party of it. Ziska baked a Rhenish cake and we all sat up late into the night, grateful for the stillness in the house that we loved.

It is said that the Third Reich has only torn down. But it has also constructed—monuments to culture. We read in the *Westdeutscher Beobachter* that the lottery, which had been forbidden in Germany since the days of Homburg and Baden-Baden, had been reopened, that the State was taking on the task of developing this important branch of German culture. And one fine day an announcement blossomed forth.

CASINO ON THE RHINE

GRAND OPENING

SPIRALO ROULETTE

THE LUCKY GAME

GIVES EVERYONE A CHANCE

Just the thing for two old habitués of the Côte d'Azur! We dismissed the Third Reich from our minds and drove out for a look at the place.

We walked through the beautiful gardens of the Casino

on the Rhine and entered the lobby. There was only one gaming table. People were staking fifty pfennig. A mark attracted attention, and three was plunging. The machine itself had twelve figures; numbers five, six, seven, ten, eleven, twelve were black, the others red. When a zero turned up, the even-money chances also lost—so the thing was unfair. I sat down next to the shabby croupier and Jules next to me. I pushed my money to the middle of the table.

"Sept-douze," my favorite transversal.

If a player won unexpectedly often, the game was stopped. Suddenly a fat man in a brown shirt came in—the chief. It was his task to see that matters were conducted satisfactorily, for the license had probably not been granted with the idea that the bank should lose. He stationed himself at the back of my chair and began a gallant conversation in exceedingly bad French.

Jules shook with laughter. When we left they were all sorry and asked us to come again. We had won sixteen marks of Nazi money.

The managers of the Casino on the Rhine had assumed that we were French. These devout Nazis inspired us with an idea. It was easy to wave aside the collection boxes thrust at us at every street corner with a "Non, merci!" It proved to be an excellent idea, for bitter experience had taught the brown-shirts to respect everything foreign. We remained faithful to the roulette table when it moved from the pavilion on the Rhine to the "Charlott" bar in the center of the town. It was our only distraction—until it crashed. Our pursuers had more endurance than the struggling Spiralo-Roulette, so during our last weeks in Cologne we were obliged to give up this absurd relaxation. We really missed it.

X

These days of apparent calm were interrupted by a fresh call from the police. Jules was in the house; Ziska's signal had been overlooked. Suddenly the man stood in the room. We were no longer frightened. We merely asked ourselves, "What can it be now?"

It was good news, a message wisely told by word of mouth instead of by letter. The president of the police had heard our complaint, and our books were released. We could get them when we wished. We thanked the man for the news and told him we would attend to the matter ourselves.

In the evening when it was dark, Goswin Rath, a young poet, came to see us. He had studied ethnology under Jules and came to offer us his help if we needed him. He himself was trying to keep his stand-in with the West German Broadcasting Company by adapting his writing to the "Blubo" (Blut und Boden) style and was succeeding for the time being. He was affiliated with S.S. and that safeguarded him. Had not Commissioner Zülsch told Jules that he could take his books out of the Museum at any time and use them? Would it not be nice to send for a few books with a letter to this effect? Would it not be delightful, if the messenger happened to be a friend of Herr Rath in the black uniform of the steel helmets? Rath promised to send his storm-trooper friend to us for instructions the next day.

An hour later came a sharply worded summons from the police; Professor Lips was to appear at headquarters the coming Saturday. There was no statement of the reason, no hint of what this was about. On Saturday we would know what was wrong. The police cared nothing about how we spent the intervening days.

[149]

Our wits had been sharpened by the experiences of some of our friends. We decided to go on Friday. In case the president of the police had made preparations in the way of summoning certain persons, or taken other precautions, we could always say that we had made a mistake. Furthermore, this diminished the interval of waiting.

Tapir remained to guard the house. Ziska, Jules and I left on Friday morning. The maid took up her position near the gate of the building. If we did not come out in two hours, she was to telephone certain friends who had promised to take action. Everything was well prepared. I went in with Jules.

First we went to see the man who had charge of the confiscated books. The booty was piled up on the floor of his office.

"You are a scholar," said the official; "excuse us. We were obliged to act since you were denounced; the regulations require that. You may take the books with you."

"I presume that I may expect the books to be returned in the same way that they were taken? Am I to carry seven hundred and ninety-three volumes under my arm or call a taxi? You will be so good, sir, as to have your office attend to this matter."

"Certainly, Professor, if you wish me to."

"Thank you. *Auf Wiedersehen.*"

"*Auf Wiedersehen,* Professor Lips."

Here no one "Heiled Hitler!" Here courtesy prevailed. We looked at the summons: the top floor, the president's office, Room Ten. We climbed up. A policeman stopped us. "Where do you want to go?" Jules showed the card. We were allowed to pass. We now seemed to be in the holy of holies. On the door was printed: "All visitors must be announced. Knocking forbidden." The hall was paved with flagstones. Our steps reechoed. There were lots of little doors and passages. A person could easily be whisked away and disappear. My heart was heavy with anxiety. I clutched Jules' hand. We came to Room Ten.

In spite of the inscription we knocked, and someone called: "Come in."

It was a big room in which there were perhaps ten desks, where the policemen were working. I disappeared at once behind the high top of an empty writing table, and Jules walked alone up to the man in charge and produced his summons, which was marked: "Penalty for non-appearance, two days' imprisonment." Jules said he happened to be passing by today and wondered whether his hearing could take place at once instead of tomorrow. The fat policeman replied in the affirmative, and everyone in the room stopped working to listen and stare as Jules sat down on a chair near the man's desk, and began to give an account of himself. No one noticed me.

At the end of Jules' deposition as to the dates of birth, confirmation, marriage and the listing of all titles and offices, the recording police officer suddenly shouted at him:

"And how long have you been a Communist?"

Jules smiled. "I never was a Communist. I am not one now—whether I shall ever become one, I don't know."

"So! You are not a Communist? How does this book happen to be in your library? The officers found it in your house."

He pulled out a fiery red little book, on which there was a picture of a working-man, his shoulder in the rough clutch of a policeman. The booklet began with the words: "There is a ring. Your heart knocks. Outside are the police. What is to be done?" The title was: "How Does the Proletarian Behave before the Law?"

"This is the first time I have seen that," said Jules. "I am a doctor of law and have passed the State's bar examinations. Do you think that I need to read how the proletarian behaves before the law?"

"It's not so simple as that," growled the man. "You see,

[151]

on the outside there is printed: 'price ten pfennig.' By buying this book you have made yourself guilty of supporting Communist propaganda. That is high treason."

My heart grew sick at the word "treason."

While Jules and the man continued to argue, the line of listeners began to grow uneasy. One after the other got up, took his luncheon box and left the room. The clock in the church tower struck twelve. Noon. Once again the hour of twelve checked the eagerness of the police. Order at any price. Gradually the room emptied until there was no one left except Jules, the investigating policeman and myself, hidden behind the back of the desk.

There was a pause. The uniformed officer at the desk looked around and suddenly said to Jules in an altered voice: "Well, let's make an end of this enmity-to-the-state business. I know where this book comes from. We take them away from the Communists—and . . . I am sorry, but I have to act as I did. I have heard many of your Sunday lectures at the Museum, Professor Lips. Never thought I'd have a run-in with you. I must do all this, but you can be sure of one thing—this just goes into the general pile. It won't come up again. You're not the only one. This is happening to hundreds and," he lowered his voice still further, "they are all as innocent as you."

At the first words I had come out cautiously from my hiding. Suddenly there were two of us. The man was astonished. I pushed my chair up to his desk and the three of us put our heads together to compose the report on Jules' deposition. The policeman typed it and Jules signed it.

"Thank you!" we both said simultaneously, when it was finished.

"Our times are like this," began the representative of the secret state police. "One must keep everything to oneself, and say nothing. Keep as quiet as possible; keep your thoughts to yourself. We have to follow up every case of denunciation. We are even supposed to urge anyone who comes near us to make denunciations. Have you any dismissed servants who have a grudge against you? Have you neglected to pay a bill? You can't imagine what *that* leads to! If anything happens to you again, I am almost your neighbor: Ölbergstrasse 33. Aren't those your cactus plants in the front window? If anything else happens, just give me a ring. My name is Brachvogel."

He laughed uneasily. We shook his hand. "Many, many thanks, Officer. *Auf Wiedersehen! Auf Wiedersehen!*"

This was our first encounter with the secret police. More astonishing ones were to take place.

Upon this followed an amusing afternoon. Several police cars drove up. The officers got out. Each had a pile of books in his arms. They stole through the garden and brought the plunder back.

That was something for Ziska to enjoy! Jules and I remained invisible. But when she recognized the men who brought the books as those who had taken them, she demanded that every volume be put back in its proper place. She took her time, separating the living-room books from those that belonged in Jules' library. She insisted on their being arranged in sets and rows. She had the policemen first creeping about on the floor, then running up and down the ladder. "The French books go there," she commanded, "back of our books. That gray book belongs here; that purple one goes in the living room. Take it down—on the top shelf." She hugely enjoyed her revenge.

"They won't return," she said, when her slaves had disappeared. It took me hours to get the volumes—arranged according to her capricious notions—back in their original order.

I joined Jules in the living room. We had just lighted a cigarette when there was a ring. Ziska, who was certainly a shade too high-spirited today, stuck her head in the door and said: "Now there will be fun. It is the S.S. man from Herr Rath," and she hurried to let him in. She admitted

[*153*]

him at the garden gate, closed it tightly and ushered the man into the hall.

"You have come from Herr Rath?" she asked, just to be on the safe side. The stranger replied brusquely.

"Rath? Who's that? I am from headquarters of the N.S.D.A.P." *

Ziska's gaiety was abruptly extinguished. She had admitted the wrong man! He could hear us talking in the adjoining room. It was too late to say that we were out.

When the door opened we beheld a strange storm trooper with a swastika badge on his arm, a revolver on his hip, the death's head on his cap, the complete Nazi paraphernalia. The stranger carried a little suitcase in his hand. He had a sunburned brigand's face. He might have been thirty. He said, audibly, "Heil Hitler!" No one replied. At the door stood Ziska, white with terror. Jules motioned to her, and she vanished. Now we three were alone. The man smelled of leather and perspiration. He was embarrassed.

Finally he opened the little bag, took out an object wrapped in tissue paper and unpacked it slowly. Our eyes followed his every movement, but our lips said nothing. The contents were revealed—a dark plaster cast of the profile of Hitler.

"A handsome plaque of our Führer," said the storm trooper. "There should be one in every German house. The price is only eight marks." He handed it to Jules, who took it up with the tips of his fingers. We both looked at it a moment, and Jules smiled.

"You have made a mistake in the number of the house. We don't buy anything of that sort. It's rubbish. There's a verse of Kästner's that is very apt. 'Whatever may happen, never let yourself sink so low as to eat of the mud through which you are dragged,' and if I bought this I should be eating mud, my dear man."

* *National Sozialistische Deutsche Arbeiter Partei* (National Socialist German Workers Party).

I was trembling again. I watched the stranger anxiously. He calmly packed the cast up again and put it in the little bag, which he closed with a click. Yes, he even smiled, and a most peculiar smile it was. Had he already framed the wording of his denunciation?

"Forgive the intrusion," he murmured, but he remained standing near the threshold and let his eyes wander over the entire room. From the crimson silk throw on the piano and the porcelain figure of Lo Hesse, the dancer, his eyes traveled past the bookshelves and the ornamental glass animals to the masks on the walls. They rested on a rust-brown mask with a pained, bitter mouth. It was from New Guinea. The one next to it we had brought from Algiers. The eyes of the N.S.D.A.P. man clung to the sardonic, henna-tinted face on the wall.

"Is that from Africa?" he asked timidly.

"Yes," replied Jules.

Then the stranger noticed the amber chain in its gazelle-hide case.

"Women and children wear that on their bare skins," said he; "it protects them against illness and the evil eye."

"How do you happen to know such things?" asked Jules, amused.

"I was in Africa a long time. I was once in the Foreign Legion."

Jules threw me a glance: Spy! Watch out!

"How long it is since I have seen anything like that," said our visitor. "Do you know Africa?"

"I happen to be an anthropologist," said Jules. "But now let us see whether you really know Africa. Where were you over there?"

"In Algiers and Marakesh."

"What's the name of the governor? Where are the barracks located? What does the uniform of the Legion look like? What money do they use in Morocco? What is a policeman called in Arabic? How does the Muezzin sing, and when?" Jules' questions rained upon the man. He answered them all. Spy or no spy, he knew his Africa—and well at that. He had put down his little bag, and had seated himself close to Jules, chatting cordially and puffing away at his cigarette. We rang for Ziska. She came in looking like Lady Macbeth, and Jules whispered an order in her ear. The conversation went on.

"I know something that's good to ward off mosquitoes. . . . When the women stain the palms of their hands with henna, they first mix a green powder that looks like spinach into their cous-cous, that infernal paprika-flavored mutton stew of theirs. Filthy muck those fellows eat. . . . We couldn't go into the mosques except in our stockinged feet."

Ziska came in with the wine, the good, red wine.

"À votre santé," exclaimed the S.S. man. "Let's drink to the pleasant land of France."

We touched glasses and drank. It was a Burgundy, bittersweet like homesickness.

Tapir came galloping in, sniffed at the man's riding boots and lay down contentedly at his feet. The stranger had passed his second examination successfully.

"And how do you come to be a National Socialist?" asked Jules.

"I am a mercenary," replied the man with the white teeth, "and I must be ready to fight for anyone. I returned from Africa a sergeant after seven years. Not many in the Legion get that far. I had my own orderly. But in Germany there was nothing doing. The Nazis were in power, fighting the Communists and talking about a better Germany. I at once put myself at their disposal. I am an old war horse! But now they have forgotten us—they merely make use of us. In the government bureaus we are overlooked because we speak the truth and know too much! We did the fighting so that they could get the power. It was we that got the bloody heads, not those who are so busy placing rush orders with their tailors for brown uniforms. And now the slogan is: Out with the old fighters and in with the March violets! One pins one's hopes on an ideal"—pointing to the bag containing the Hitler bas-relief—"and one fine day the scales fall from one's eyes. We have been working for a lot of crooks and fat-bellied profiteers! And people are scared into buying the Hitler stuff by the sight of the black uniform. I paid for this black thing myself and I don't own a civilian suit. The Jews give me ten marks and more for that plaster trash. Out of five hundred houses you are the first that has refused me. The cowardly rascals! What do you think of it? You're a professor!"

As Jules did not reply, the man looked him earnestly in the face and asked again: "What do you think?"

"We will answer you some time when we meet in Africa," said I. "My husband is on leave because he is politically untrustworthy. You had better go; this is no place for you!"

"We'll see about that! I never met a professor before. I never knew they were anything like this. Those intellectual acrobats were painted to us in quite other colors. Oh, yes, just another example of their everlasting damned lying. Please allow me to come again. Aren't you planning another expedition? I know my way about down there. I can pack a donkey so the saddle won't slip. I can make those black men toe the line. Won't you take me with you? I'm free. This nonsense won't last much longer. I am known in the Casbah of Algiers and in Blida. Mayn't I at least come again?"

"In that uniform?" asked Jules thoughtfully.

"Don't you need a 'house Nazi'? They are a protection today."

"We have no money. Furthermore, I am not in the habit of buying people."

"You don't know me—I'm talking too much. I don't want any money. Africa! I want to talk about Africa! You're

[157]

a professor! Isn't there something I can do for you, just to show you how happy that would make me?"

"All right. You can go to the Rautenstrauch-Joest Museum tomorrow morning and get some books for me. Here is the list. After that we'll see."

"We'll attend to it, Herr Professor. The Hitler salute will take care of everything. And if some time you should want someone put out of the way . . ."

"Not so fast, not so furious! We are still in Europe. In your S.S. barracks things seem to be even cruder than among the Tuareg."

"My name is Zange, August Zange. I was born in Flensburg."

"You are a Zombi," said I, "a real, wretched Zombi."

He had never heard of the practice prevalent in Haiti, of drugging perfectly healthy persons so that they take on the semblance of death. They are actually buried; then secretly dug up and brought back to life by means of antidotes. But they have lost their wits; their self-confidence is shattered and their will broken. They have become machines—Zombis—who obey whatever orders are yelled at them, slaves who perform inhuman feats of labor without protest until they fade away into death, destroyed by their exploiters. The statute books of Haiti expressly forbid the making of Zombis. But the Party program of the N.S.D.A.P. does not forbid it.

August Zange sat spellbound. From that day on we called him the Zombi. His head and his heart were certainly not yet dead, but he loved this name because it reminded him of his extraordinary introduction into our house.

"Forget the uniform when you come," said Jules; "we will try to bring the Zombi back to life. And one thing remember: no 'Heil Hitler!' in this house."

"And what's the dog's name?"

"His name is Tapir."

It was a Third Reich scarecrow squawking "Heil Hitler!"

that had invaded our house. It was a friend who left it, a friend as fierce and unchanging as the African sun. In trusting him so readily we followed our intuition, not our reason. And we were proven right.

The Zombi picked up the bag containing his Führer in painted plaster and waved it in farewell. Then he walked out —smart in his black uniform, revolver on hip, swastika on sleeve. The soldier of the Foreign Legion, the blond boy from Flensburg, became not our house Nazi, but our guardian angel of the Third Reich, as lively and astonishing in his behavior as any of Aladdin's genii.

The maids in the house next door saw him and whispered up and down the Siebengebirgsallee: "There's trouble again at the Lips'! This time it is the S.S. Göring personally has it in for the professor. They'll soon be in the concentration camp." And they scuttled away in alarm when I walked through the garden with that non-Aryan, Tapir.

Imagine the faces in the Museum at the sudden entry of a storm trooper. Those brown-shirted March violets shook in their shoes before the old soldier. How came such a one to ask for Professor Lips' books?

"Don't you know that Professor Lips is in disgrace with the Party?" Scheller asked the messenger. "How can you have anything to do with him? Where do you come from anyway?"

"Don't talk bilge, man," answered the Zombi. "Will you give me the books or not?"

"Next week, not today."

"I'll deliver the message. Heil Hitler."

And Scheller, louder and more firmly, "Heil Hitler!"

XI

The reprisals threatened by Scheller had not yet taken place. Immediately after Jules' request for leave of absence, the city authorities had requisitioned a number of his credentials, his military pass, the muniments of his World War decorations, his officer's papers, his doctor's diplomas from Leipzig and his birth and marriage certificates. These were important documents and we felt that the time had come to ask for their return. An hour after our inquiry we were informed by telephone that Jules' papers had been lost. Where? If anyone were now to state that Jules was not a doctor of philosophy, a professor, or a war veteran, there would be no way of refuting the statement. The documents were "lost." That was an old trick, but we were not inclined to have it played on us.

The documents did not turn up, but we were informed on the third of August by the president of the Rhine Province—Olga's husband—that the Mayor of Cologne had requested Jules' dismissal. Since the Mayor does what the head of the personnel department recommends, Ludwig's hand could be recognized here, too. He made it a point not to receive Jules. Jules had often tried to see him, but never had he, the chief of the personnel division, thought it worth while to see the director of the Rautenstrauch-Joest Museum—though Ludwig had bombarded him with offensive letters. To this day he does not know what Jules looks like, for throughout the whole affair he relied upon his intermediary, student Scheller, whose decisions he accepted without question. This was in accordance with the principle that there is only one person who stands higher than the Führer himself, and that is the denouncer.

When we inquired again as to the whereabouts of our documents, we were told that they had not yet been found. The Zombi had gone to the Museum a second time in vain, and the moment had arrived for writing two more letters.

The first was addressed to Commissioner of Culture Zülsch. It charged that to refuse to deliver Jules' scientific books, as Scheller had done when Jules had sent the storm trooper after them, was sabotage of Professor Lips' scientific work.

The second went to Burgomaster Ludwig. It stated that if the "lost" documents were not in the hands of their owner within forty-eight hours, a complaint would be made to General Göring.

We had learned the Nazi style and method of procedure. The very words with which we had been threatened we used to frighten our opponents.

It was child's play. Simply copy the lingo of the day, spice it with threats of reprisal, and you have a letter that gets results in the Third Reich.

Ziska delivered both letters to the Rathaus, demanding a receipt for them. Nine hours later a handsome limousine drove into the Siebengebirgsallee and a man in gray livery got out. He returned all the lost documents. They had miraculously turned up. That is how things were done in the Third Reich.

Meanwhile our libel suit against Rodens had progressed. We were kept busy incessantly. Many precious hours and much precious money was spent. But it was all necessary. We had been forced into an offensive defense.

We were obliged to see the district justice of the peace in Cologne-Mülheim. He was a tailor by occupation. While Jules went up to see him, the Zombi and I stood before the entrance of the house.

We waited a long time. The Zombi entertained me with the wildest of tales. He was the best story-teller I ever met, and even Tomo Kak'wa, whose favorite yarn concerned the invasion of their tent by a wolverine, the animal most feared by the Indian trappers of the Algonquin tribe in Labrador, did not surpass the Zombi in fire or fantasy. He wanted to get out—out of this hell. Cheating, lying, stealing; this was the new Germany for whose success he had fought. He told me about the concentration camps in which he had been a guard, of Cologne-Poll where people were yanked about by cords attached to their throats, and freed just before choking to death in order to force them to confess. And always his thoughts kept traveling toward Africa. He asked me whether I could not do something for him in Paris that would get him back into the Foreign Legion—this time as an officer. Poor Zombi, I thought, if you knew how things go in Paris; beginnings are so splendid, and endings so bitter. Besides, it was rather doubtful whether they would appreciate having a former soldier of Hitler's. "I wonder whether I shall ever see the Casbah again?" Meantime he went about distributing his resounding "Heil Hitlers" among the women and children he met and among his fellows in uniform.

As the door of the district justice's house opened, Rodens came out. He stared at the Zombi and me as though we were ghosts, and stumbled away.

"That's the fellow that started the toilet-room tale," said I, and Zombi took note of him. Jules came out shortly afterward. The earnest efforts of the district justice had not succeeded in persuading Rodens to take back his story. "I have taken an oath," was his argument. In Jules' presence, he had not dared to repeat the words. Instead he asked anxiously what Jules was going to do with him. "You will find out in court," Jules had replied.

When we came home we found that Commissioner Zülsch had called up, and when Jules telephoned him he learned that Scheller had been instructed to give Professor Lips or his messenger any book that he asked for at once.

When the Zombi called at the Museum again, Jules' property was promptly delivered to him. When he appeared

[162]

at our house for the hour's chat which had become a daily institution, he told us about his best friend: "He is a man who does not talk; he listens and acts. He is a stone breaker. May I bring him along some time?" Yes, the Zombi might bring him.

In the evening Rath burst in breathless. He had been unable to send his friend the storm trooper, and had been forbidden to enter our house. Something dreadful was threatening us; he had heard this from a superior officer of the storm troopers. We had better clear out right away. There was still time. And now he must go. Good luck, and goodbye for a long time!

We went to dine in the *Prinzenhof*, a restaurant near the Cologne Opera House, a meeting place for men in judicial, artistic and professional circles. We had just raised our wine glasses when a man at an adjoining table greeted us, got up and joined us. It was Paul Baumgartner, the pianist, who had played on our Museum programs with such subtlety and virtuosity. He was delighted to see us. We asked him whether he was still playing in concerts. Yes, he could play; no one interfered with him; he was Aryan and a Swiss. Did he still play Milhaud? No, he no longer played Milhaud. He played Bach, Beethoven, Schumann and Hindemith—occasionally. We enjoyed seeing him. He was a lively talker and overwhelmed us with his cordiality.

Suddenly the pianist broke off, glancing timidly toward a table near ours, where a gentleman had just seated himself. He got up hastily.

"That is Dr. Zülsch," he whispered, "the new Commissioner of Culture. He is head of the music division, too. It will be better for me to go. You will understand . . . I should not be seen with Professor Lips just now." He slipped away, a pitiful and shabby soul. We never saw him again.

Zülsch however, seeing that Jules had a lady with him,

[163]

came up and greeted us. The fact of his being a "hundred per cent" National Socialist did not interfere with his sense of etiquette. He seemed to have forgotten how he had treated the committee of students headed by Renate. He sat at our table for a few minutes. I was glad to meet him, and I liked him. How had he come to be a Nazi? Was he one of the few ideologists of the Party, one of those advocates of change and revival whose faith in Germany made them overlook the new political vulgarity? We talked about Stephan Lochner and his paintings in the cathedral, and the "Last Judgment" in the Wallraf-Richartz Museum. We got on excellently, while at a table near by our unfortunate pianist friend sat dumb and puzzled, watching the unexpected turn of events. He had backed the wrong horse.

Within a week Dr. Zülsch lost his position. He was removed from office because of "academic presumption" in his capacity of Commissioner of Culture and his post was given to an elementary-school teacher, who held no doctor's degree, but was doubtless a two hundred per cent National Socialist.

Autumn was creeping toward us, soon winter would come and this eventful year would end. There was no escape from the poisoned morass where no one could get a foothold, where one could only sink deeper and deeper, where one might easily disappear forever. It was too late to withdraw. The only thing left for us to do was to wait—and to pay. For Herr von Coellen knew how to get money out of us. Since the district justice had made his futile effort at settlement, we had paid Herr von Coellen a hundred and seventy marks—and nothing had happened.

Let us forget all this and take Tapir on the lead, have Ziska pack the baskets with provisions, invite a few cheerful friends and go where one is now happiest: to Buchensee.

The Zombi had brought his friend along, the fellow who does not talk, but acts. He was a lively chap, that stone

[164]

breaker, with hands like steam shovels. Tapir peered about for Karasek, the squirrel. The sight of our two escorts in uniform had caused a sensation. Hedwig, our sharp-tongued neighbor, had stayed away entirely.

We sat by a log fire over which a roast hung, African style, a red-gold drop hissing now and then into the flames. A name was whispered: Gregor Strasser. Was he working for the "second revolution"? Was he getting ready to rout the job-hunters and denouncers? Had he really his swarming thousands willing to die for Germany rather than leave her in the hands of the upstart adventurers flocking in from Riga, Cairo, the Argentine, and Braunau? Gregor Strasser . . . ? On June 30, 1934, he was shot, without a trial of any sort, at the order of the man who calls himself the highest legal authority of the German people.

Let us leave politics. We are sitting by a camp fire and the Zombi is beginning to talk as he learned to do in the Legion and among the inhabitants of the land of the Arabian Nights. The sky is above us and the warm earth beneath. The fog weaves its veil over the tops of the pine trees. The little brook gurgles in the grass.

". . . We are wrapped in burnooses, legionnaires who have taken the field against Abd-el-Krim, the mighty. We talk of the chieftain's night ride, followed by his harem of two hundred and eighty-six women, of how our colonel saw him pass, of how he raised his revolver—yet did not shoot. Abd-el-Krim is an impressive enemy, with a native majesty that forbids the ambushed bullet. He rides unharmed. No one dares move. He is Africa.

"Zombi stands watch over the sleeping camp. The bush holds hidden danger. The glitter of a knife or of a throwing spear stabs the darkness. Once caught, life may well be over for a legionnaire. He is thrown to the women of the tribe, who have their secret, horrible technique of mutilation. Many a victim has been found, left to bleed to death after their barbaric surgery.

[165]

"Careful, Tapir! You breathe too loudly. . . . There below us comes a gliding figure, white in the shadowy night—a burnoose. In a moment the spear will flash. Nearer it comes. It rises. My gun! Two shots, four shots, six shots—the figure falls with a thud. The camp look-out may rest. We shall have no more visitors tonight. The wall of the watch tower is warm, the heat of the sun still simmers in the stone. The following day a proud Zombi reports in answer to a summons from his colonel, eyes shining, chest out, ready for the reward that comes to one who has saved the sleeping camp from night attack.

"Reward? Kicks and curses are more like it. You dog! You damned hound! You shot my milch cow last night!" A fine end to heroic adventure! The nights of Africa are deceptive.

"Behind us rides a train of carts filled with women, bumping along over the rocks and over the plains of sand. They are brought along for our benefit. There is something disgusting about it, even to a tough crew such as we. In the Casbah, things are better. In the Étoile, where the slim, brown-skinned girls dance, there things are better. Page to the Major's favorite, soap her back in the bath, pedicure her little feet—yes, take a look at these hands. They can do anything. But it's no good, no life for a man.

"It's fine to ride in the advance guard. It's fine to bully the recruits, as brutally as you were bullied once upon a time. It's fine to make secret deals over paprika, nut oil or grain. It's fine to have an orderly of one's own. What wild chaps there were in our ranks! One fellow thought he was Napoleon the First and stalked around wearing a paper tricorne on his head. He was allowed to eat in the officers' mess—they couldn't do a thing with him otherwise. Another was a Danish prince, who found it bliss to be free from the buzz of court chamberlains in their buckled shoes. One day they went through our lines in search of a man wanted for murder. Not one of us batted an eye, though we knew he had long since escaped to the Ural Mountains and was swanking around in a general's uniform. Ha, ha! And at night we sang. *Olé, olé, Jacquita!* Then we filled up on that damned cous-cous again. I managed to get the bits of mutton down, but I never could go the olives in it. . . ."

We are out of beer. I walk down to the restaurant at the mouth of the valley, taking the Zombi with me. Are there not spears and wild tribesmen and jackals abroad in the night? As we enter the bar, the idlers look up from their games of skat and stare at us in silence. The innkeeper fills our jugs. His hand trembles, the beer runs over; he refills the jugs. What is the matter? Oh, yes, I have come with a storm trooper. Heil Hitler! Who is this Hitler now? Oh, yes! The Third Reich—we had forgotten it. Above gleams our fire. We walk up the hill carrying the beer. Jules carves the roast. *Olé, olé, Jacquita!* Tapir begs for a bite.

Blood and soil, says Adolf Hitler, are what shape human beings. I know better; it is our aspirations and environment that form us. So with Jules. His longing for the cradle of mankind has constantly driven him among strange races, and he has been formed by the rivers on which we lived, by lakes and by the salt sea. And deep within him there was love for but one patch of soil, and that was the soil of Buchensee. For Buchensee was more his than any dozen books he might write; it was his creation, his garden, his little house. What has the Saarland—in which he chanced to come into the world—to do with this? And this Zombi; he happened to be born in the calm town of Flensburg, but his tongue waxes hot with tales of the East.

The following week we came to Buchensee again. We were out trout fishing one morning and were getting a nice catch, when a child came running down the hill with a telephone message: Professor Lips was to go back to town at once; he was to be at the Rathaus within an hour.

[167]

Jules jumped into his clothes and I took him to the station. He promised to rush back in time to eat our trout. That was at ten o'clock in the morning. At nine o'clock that evening I was still seated on the bench overlooking the road, waiting. Late at night Jules arrived, exhausted, hungry and angry through and through. There had been another "hearing." Herr Schoppe, the secretary of the town council, had been hauled over the coals by the Minister of Culture. Why, in the name of heaven, did the Mayor of Cologne want to fire Lips anyway? The worried secretary had sent for Jules expressly to try to make him lose his temper, to irritate him to the point of an impulsive outburst against the government, or, failing that, to draw from him some comment that might be considered "dangerous to the State." He had not succeeded, even with the help of a stenographer taking notes, in finding anything that would serve his purpose, and finally the inquisitor had collapsed with exhaustion, and had let his cool-headed enemy go. Jules had managed while he was in the Rathaus hall to control the tension of his nerves completely, but Secretary Schoppe would have felt it a good day's work if he could have seen Jules' condition as he sat near me, trying to eat the trout that he had caught in the morning. We could not endure much more.

XII

Jules' birthday was in September. On the morning of the day, the city of Cologne sent him a little present for the occasion in the form of a notice summoning him to appear in court on the thirteenth to answer a charge of insult. It looked like a criminal case. But how could this be?

Herr von Coellen found out the meaning of the summons for us. The State, that is, the Germany of the Third Reich, had made the "question of honor" of the student Scheller its own. It interpreted the remark "Scheller is an utter idiot"—reported by Fröhlich—as an attack on its authority and had brought a criminal charge against Jules as a defamer of the State. For it was the State that had made Scheller acting director of the Rautenstrauch-Joest Museum. There were three advantages to this. First, our private slander suit could be brushed aside, and delayed for an indefinite time. Second, Scheller would not have to spend a penny; the State would pay all costs. Third, Rodens could appear as a witness, under oath. This last was a strong point, for if our suit had gone on, he would never have been allowed to testify under oath.

On the thirteenth, Jules went to what proved to be merely a preliminary hearing. I did not have to wait long on the little wooden bench outside of the court room. Jules came back soon. He had merely answered a few formal questions and declared his stand in the case.

Did Scheller sit in the director's office at the Rautenstrauch-Joest Museum with nothing to do but occupy himself with threatening his teacher? All those who were concerned with the reputation of the great Museum since Scheller had taken over its direction could now be satisfied.

Herr Scheller had accomplished something. The *Westdeutscher Beobachter* did itself proud with a solid page in large type headed: *A new Acquisition of the Rautenstrauch-Joest Museum—the Peill Collection*. The author of the article was Rodens. It was a song of songs celebrating the "scientific acumen of Party-member Scheller, who has secured the wonderful, valuable Peill Collection of incomparably precious possessions for his institution. Thus the new contemporary spirit has penetrated into the Rautenstrauch-Joest Museum!" A "spread" of enlarged photographs of outstanding items in the collection gave further credit to the master mind that had acquired the hoard for the Museum. So Scheller, in the midst of his many-sided efforts to destroy that menace to the Party, Professor Lips, had found the time to acquire this magnificent collection for the Museum. It was astonishing—and incredible.

There were three people in Cologne who smiled as they read their newspapers that day: an aged housekeeper, a Museum attendant named Weiss and an anthropologist by the name of Lips.

As to the Peill Collection: Some time ago, in 1930, when Jules was assembling his data on the European as depicted in the art of primitive peoples, he heard of a valuable collection from the South Seas in the possession of a lady in the Rhineland. She was the widow of a rich manufacturer. Before her husband's death they had taken long trips around the world together. In the South Seas she had found the paradise of her dreams and had returned there repeatedly, particularly to New Guinea. At the time the natives had not yet begun to turn out souvenirs by the carload for tourist consumption. The mementos she acquired were the exquisite and delicate images of their gods and ancestors, colored with chalk, soot and ocher, many of them decorated with cobalt extracted from the soil.

Jules went up to the third story of the Museum, where the South Sea collections were housed, the beautiful art of

[170]

the most beautiful beings on earth. He looked at the totem poles, the carved ravens, the iridescent nautilus shells, the hornbills, the ancestral portraits with the curiously inserted pupils of the eye. Only the collection in the British Museum could be compared with it. And there in the Rhineland lived an old lady, Frau Geheimrat Peill, who had a collection of the same sort. Jules intended the Museum to get possession of these treasures.

A week later the struggle for the Peill Collection began. A letter addressed to the little town on the Rhine announced that the director of the Cologne Museum would do himself the honor of calling. Jules passed under a high, arched gateway. Behind a wall of plane trees stood a palace. Its mistress was a grande dame, in the style of those elderly aristocrats to be met in the white cabins of ocean yachts or at the head of some foreign diplomat's table. She knew a great deal, but betrayed it only in passing. Her charm was greater than her wealth. Together they walked through the hall into the park. Frau Peill unlocked the doors of the cabins where the collection was stored. It was incomparable, said Jules. It must not be allowed to spoil here, to be exposed to robbery or the ignorance of unappreciative heirs.

Jules and the old lady had a delightful chat. He left at a late hour, and his hostess asked him to come again. On his next visit Jules brought Weiss with him; they were already discussing the means of transportation. Frau Peill was willing to leave the choicest pieces to the Museum upon her death. Jules wanted everything. He lured her with the promise of immortality, with visions of a handsome hall filled with the sceptres of jade, with ceremonial paddles, with symbols inlaid in tortoise shell, the words "Peill Collection" engraved on the door. After seven months of persuasion on Jules' part they went to a lawyer, and the Rautenstrauch-Joest Museum was named the legatee of the entire Peill Collection. Mayor Adenauer accepted the pledge with enthusiasm, expressing the gratitude of the city of Cologne to Frau Peill in a document stamped with the municipal seal. Tremendous preparations for the housing of the collection were made at the Museum; everyone was proud, everyone looked forward with tense anticipation to its coming.

There was one condition attached to the gift. As long as the founder of the collection lived, the director of the Museum was to come once a month to chat with her about the various countries of the globe. Jules kept his word. He took Weiss with him and Weiss ate cake with the housekeeper, while two world travelers sat in the magnificent drawing room talking about Bangkok and the Tuareg, about Australian deities, about the theories held by brown-skinned men concerning the flood and immortality.

Then came the Third Reich, and there was no longer time to think about the pleasant things of life. Frau Peill died in May, 1933. The will came to probate, and Scheller and the Museum could take over the collection. Now they saw the long-awaited treasures, the treasures secured for the Museum by Jules, as is fully recorded in the Rautenstrauch-Joest archives. But they were unashamed of such evidence.

"Thus the new contemporary spirit has penetrated into the Rautenstrauch-Joest Museum ... incomparably precious possessions," wrote Rodens in praise of Party-member Scheller in the *Westdeutscher Beobachter*.

Jules merely smiled and waved the whole matter off into the limbo of the negligible, but I, a weak human being, subject to the human impulses of anger, revenge, curiosity and mischief, determined to play a trick on the conquering hero of the Peill Collection.

One fine September day I had Zombi and his friend, the stone breaker, call for me. Both of them were in their handsome black uniforms with all their paraphernalia. To walk between them was like walking on velvet in the Third Reich. Exclamations of "Heil Hitler!" boomed in our ears, for every passer-by was eager to assure our trio of his loyalty.

We rode to the Ubierring. My two escorts were strikingly fine specimens of the genus storm trooper—muscular, brown, resplendent with vigor, blue-eyed and white-toothed; in a word, exactly as Herr Hitler would have liked to look. Not one of the anemic crop at the Museum could compete with them. And my Zombis were S.S. men. Not one among the opportunist students had got beyond the brown-shirt uniform; not one of them had, like the Zombi, "1927" embroidered on his sleeve, the badge of merit of the "old campaigner."

The stone breaker jerked the Museum door open and we marched in with a clatter. To the left of the ticket table stood Fluss. He broke out in a sweat. The Zombi showed my membership card in the Society for the Advancement of the Rautenstrauch-Joest Museum, which gave me free admission to all the museums of Cologne.

"That is for the lady," said the Zombi. He paid the entrance fee for himself and the stone breaker. "When does the tour of the Museum announced in the newspaper take place?" he inquired. "I should not like to miss it."

"At eleven o'clock," stuttered Fluss, and rushed up the steps to the administrative office. He might as well have sounded the fire alarm.

It was half past ten. I led my bodyguard to the South American Hall, to show them one of the greatest treasures of the Museum, the little smoke-darkened human heads which the Ivaro Indians preserve as portraits, first filling them with sand and then holding them over the fire. These trophies were the size of oranges. A thick shock of human hair hung from each head. We went on. How often I had guided guests of honor through the Museum! We reached the exhibit of Peruvian pottery, all shaped in the forms of men or beasts, at eleven. From there we passed to the Peill Collection.

At the spot where once our masks had glimmered in the greenish light of the virgin forest, a crude latticed column

[173]

had been set up and hung with a wrinkled rope. There, on a cord as thick as a telephone wire, hung the masterpieces of island art. I saw it in a flash: a clear case of sabotage. Weiss was a master at hanging an exhibit without a trace of its support. Jules had spent years in training him. Weiss knew that wetting the panel before attaching it prevents its wrinkling. This was deliberate and intentional ill will. I could not help being grateful. It was a protest, if merely an aesthetic one, but all the more telling to anyone who understood. Photographs were roughly pasted on the walls. Thrust into a box of sand, like a discarded bunch of dried flowers on a rubbish heap, was the jewel of the collection, an ancestral image, tinted in faint island pastels. On the top of the cases lay the sacred skulls in confused disorder, looking for all the world like a heap of sponges at a sale.

As we entered the room, a little man in a new brown uniform came up to us. "Heil Hitler!" he exclaimed, clicking his heels. The Zombi and the stone breaker had raised two fingers in the "German greeting." The brown uniform was student Baumgarten. He looked as though he had seen a ghost. So he too had joined the Scheller and Fröhlich combine! It must have been painful to him to see me, for night after night I had sat at his sick bed, when he lay hovering between life and death. After a short struggle he came up to speak to me. But before he could say a word I pointed to his uniform and said: "Where did you get that? Since when are you a member of the National Socialist German Workers Party?"

"Since June," he stammered.

"Then for once in your life you can have a look at the real thing," said I, pointing to the two death's heads at my side. "Real National Socialists!"

"How is Professor Lips?" Baumgarten seemed to think himself bound to ask.

"Why this sudden interest?" said I. "But I think the tour is starting."

[174]

He talked of the islanders' skill in the art of sepia and of their spirit houses, not saying much about the culture of the South Sea Islands, but a great deal about the difficulties of Herr Scheller in acquiring the collection for the Museum.

The crowd hid him from sight, but another figure took his place near me, a roundish man with a bald head and brown eyes. I could not repress a thrill of emotion. It was Weiss, the man who had slept on boards next to Jules and me when we had arranged the exhibitions in the State Capitol, the man who had held the ladder for me as I tried new effects, the man who had worked with me at coloring the programs, the man whom we had promised to take to Africa with us on our next expedition. He came close to me.

"They are quarreling already," he whispered in my ear; "it's hell broke loose. Scheller, Fröhlich and Baumgarten, each wants to be the head. Letters go unanswered. There's nothing but fear, all over the place. Please tell Professor Lips . . ." and he was gone, as though blotted out. The student had turned around. "And here we have a tapa . . ." But I understood nevertheless what I was to tell Jules. Poor Weiss!

I gave the exit cue. The Zombis departed with a flourish. We left the Museum amidst the clatter of spurs and the click of heels.

Our Führer liked—as is well known—at critical moments to convince himself by a vote of the people that the nation was solidly behind him. Before he hit upon the idea of having the Germans return election blanks with the word "yes" stamped upon them in advance, experience had consistently shown him that the city of Cologne produced the relatively largest negative vote in all Germany. That was not surprising, for the many devout Catholics and Protestants and impious asphalt intellectuals in our city had worked out a system which guaranteed security to all who voted "no."

On November the twelfth, 1933, for example, Hitler

wished to find out whether his sudden withdrawal from the League of Nations had the approval of his subjects. "Yes" or "No" was to be checked off on the election blanks, but "No" of course was treason. The trick was to get hold of one of the election blanks issued to travelers, permitting them to vote at the polls set up in the railroad station, thereby achieving a fair degree of anonymity. The office distributing these blanks was jammed with applicants. It seemed that the entire population of Cologne had chosen that particular Sunday to bury their aunts, see their kinsmen in the neighborhood married or visit a distant, much-missed comrade of the trenches. One had to give the reason for leaving town, or the blank was not issued. Every statement that the trip was urgent was subject to strict investigation. The travelers all looked honest; they were all inconsolable at the necessity of voting at the station instead of in their home precincts. Nevertheless, there were suspicious side glances. A little peasant girl ahead of us, very likely the only genuine traveler in the place, almost failed to get her blank, for, aware of her easy conscience, she rebelled against the inquisitorial questioning. Like Little Red Riding Hood, she was on her way to see her grandmother. The intervention of a couple of brown-shirted knights protected her from the wolf. She got her blank, for everyone had to have one. Not to vote was synonymous with "No."

We had made up the shrewdest pretexts, but we got our blanks without having to use them. For the officious clerk was a typical subordinate; he loved titles. Jules had enough of these, and a fur coat besides.

The blanks secured, the next thing was to buy the "Yes-pin." This decoration was sold by the S.A. men on the streets. The desired word was printed on it in silver curlicues. Since not one of our acquaintances wanted to spend as much as ten pfennigs in support of the "Movement," ten of us banded together at a pfennig apiece and bought one pin, which passed from hand to hand as we cast our votes.

It was wiser actually to leave the city; so we went to Buchensee. Dressed like tourists, with the dog on a lead and the pin conspicuously displayed on Jules' coat, we moved slowly forward, following the long queue of people. Ahead of us was an elegant couple. Although the man wore the required pin—at the station almost everyone wore it; on the streets they were much less in evidence—the woman was the more confident of the two. "For heaven's sake, don't put your voting slip in the envelope," I heard her whisper to her husband. She was evidently afraid that her husband would put the blank with the "No" on it into the official envelope which bore his name and address, and then hand it to the brown-shirted attendant, a possible mistake which filled me too with panic.

While I went into the booth to put my cross against the word "No," the Nazi inspector took charge of Tapir. What confidence I must have inspired in him!

The "Yes-pin" was the only slight concession that we ever made. Even if our lives were at stake, no one could have forced us to wear a swastika, just as no one could have compelled us to raise our right arm, or any official or anonymous threat send the new flag flying from our balcony.

In spite of everything we were glad to have come away and to be on the train bound for Buchensee. A gentleman with a bull dog had seated himself opposite to us, for we sat in the compartment where dogs were allowed. He introduced himself to us as Captain Kerr and showed us some magnificent pictures of horses. He was a circus man. Tapir ignored the bull dog, which looked like the apotheosis of doghood. It no doubt irritated Tapir to see himself outclassed.

One evening a week there met at our house a group of brown-and-black-shirted men. The Zombi had brought a number of them; a few others were former students, lads with glowing ideas and suffering hearts. The house in the

Siebengebirgsallee had come to be secretly famous as a place where one might dare "to speak," where people had a tongue and ears but no memory, where after one's departure the words one had uttered sank into silken silence. We were far from desiring to influence such desperate and willing hearts in any strategic way. Jules accepted their trust, their rebellious outbursts, their confessions and even their tears. For, once their army belts and revolvers had been laid off in the hall, they dropped their reserve completely. Reacting like an emotional barometer to their talk, he recorded the astonishing fact that the Third Reich of the newspapers and radio speeches did not exist. A few adventurers had used the economic crisis and the despair of the helpless as a springboard to power. The only Nazis, as the outside world pictures them, are those men who have pushed their way up through the new regime. Former lobbyists, men who could never hold a job, men who shunned work, and, above all, criminals; men who accepted a new code of life with their new uniforms, both handed to them ready-made by the Party; a fist-driving, brute-muzzled, heel-clicking, pedlar-minded crew, hawkers of terroristic slogans and, first and last, of lies, lies, lies!

The others who darkened our streets with their black and brown uniforms were German lads with hearts aglow with imagination and romanticism, hopes of "recovery" and a burning love of their Fatherland. They were too young, and perhaps too healthy, to see that the Moloch whom they served wanted only their blood, their young bones, their courage and their readiness for death; that he had long ago begun to stamp out the essence of all that is German, more German than the tramp of millions of boots—the heart, the mind. It is easier to march than to kneel. It is easier to obey than to think. It is easier to swallow bitterness than to create sweetness. It is easier to shoot than to be shot.

And with their hearts emptied of everything that is decent, with the blaze of their petty, childish passions con-

[178]

sumed in talk during those evenings at our home, maturer impulses took their place, a hundred times more vicious and a hundred times more potent.

Their love of humanity and of flowers and of God was quenched, their ears became deafened to the music of poetry and to the gentle words of love, their lips estranged from song and laughter, their eyes blind to the glory of the sun and to all beauty. Worst of all was the transmutation of sacred concepts into false coin: Germany came to mean Herr Hitler, of Austria; the Fatherland—an armed camp; heroism—hatred of the arch-enemy, France ("victorious over France in battle" sang the seven-year-old children in the schools); honor—slaughter, in the name of a few phrases echoing from the studio of a foreign "painter"; manliness— the rattle of swords; God, synonymous with the nonentity out of Bohemia. To the most intelligent and the most upright, the most sincere, the most German, the mystery had long been clear. They saw the truth. They shuddered at it. They damned it. They tried to repudiate this false coin. But they were afraid. They could do nothing. Power lay in other hands.

They found relief in talk, in words and tears. If only for once, they must bare their hearts freely to some one man who was not an agitator, to a man who loved the sorrowful for the sake of the help he could give them, to a man who himself knew suffering, whose smile was balm to pain—a man who asked nothing of them, but waited only to hear their woes. His silent sympathy was a message from the realm of love and thought, a greeting from the land once known for its poets and philosophers. Here was a man who lived by the spirit and for the spirit. There was nothing one need withhold from him, because he had the grace of forgetting. Above all, he was a man who was a stranger to that specter in their ranks—treachery.

On these occasions we heard unvarnished talk, frightful and grotesque. All these stories had one thing in common;

they were true. We were told of the fate of that "old soldier" who had mounted his bicycle one day and ridden off into the woods to put a bullet through his brain. He had starved and fought for Hitler and for the promise of a "better Germany." Victory came, and he knew it for what it was. He could not desert; he had pledged himself to Hitler. Nothing was left but death and a slip of paper: "All in vain. I can't begin over again. It was all a lie. I am dying for Germany." What man is there that will dare to stand before the throne of God, with a conscience burdened by the fate of the youth of his nation? For the flower of Germany's youth, perceiving that their idol had feet of clay, there was no choice but death or a dishonored oath. Standing broken-hearted at the grave, under the shadow of the swastika flag, the young widow had to hear herself reviled by the Party leader of the district, reproached with having driven her husband to his death by her "un-German and uncomprehending" conduct.

"When I shoot myself," concluded the lad who told this story with a sob of rage, "others too will go out with me." Many ended their accounts: "I say this because it's true—let them put me in a concentration camp, if they will."—"This is the truth, though I die for telling it."—"I saw it with my own eyes—I declare it, even though I risk being 'shot while escaping'." What hideous testimony to the despair of youth! They were strong, young men who spoke thus—men wearing the black uniform.

There was another whose party number was 683. He was one of Hitler's oldest adherents and had been with him under fire in front of the Feldherrn Halle in the Munich Putsch. Others who were present had become ministers and presidents. But this lad had no connections, only an honest heart. One day he was told that his number was now 943277. A new racket had developed, the sale of old party numbers to March violets. "No," he protested, "I want my own number; old fighters are given preference. My number

[180]

is my future. I was with the Party in Munich. How am I to prove it with this new number?" He was immediately accused of "underhanded dealings," sentenced to five weeks' hard labor. When he got out he was grateful for permission to keep the number 943277.

Out on the lonely meadows thousands of men were being fitted with black steel helmets at a time when it was still being denied that the S.S. even knew what a gun looked like. Hand grenades and machine guns, too. It was given out that it was all in defense against Communism, but it just so happened that the walls were hung with maps showing the French fortifications on the border.

When their words became too wild, their cheeks too flushed, their eyes too desperate, Jules knew how to give the talk a lighter turn, how to open their hearts to laughter again, their ears to amusing tales. That was Zombi's great hour. When he began, they clustered around him like Arabs around the camp story-teller in the desert.

"Buckets of cous-cous before us, day in, day out. Food, they call it; but it's hardly even fodder. You roll up a lump of boiled millet with your right hand (mind you, you have to watch your table manners!) and dip it into the mutton stew, then toss the whole thing into your mouth—like this! There's a trick to getting just the right curve to the gesture. For dessert we had huge bowls of wild honey, with blobs of rancid butter swimming around on top. It was worth your life to let them see that the sight of it made you want to vomit. . . .

"At Sidi-bel-Abès, it was, bow-legged Loulou came to me with a problem. During the occupation of the Rhineland he had picked up a blonde girl from Coblenz. He had just received a passionate letter from her and wanted me to compose an answer, a hot love letter. I wrote a hot one, all right; had she no shame, a tow-headed German girl getting mixed up with a bow-legged black? Loulou signed his name to it with a flourish, delighted with the rigmarole I read out to him. He never heard from her again. . . .

"There was one of them—came from Persia. Had little blue dots on her forehead, 'oriental buttons' they called 'em. . . ."

Their heads full of dreams, a last echoing laugh sounding behind them, our guests departed from the oasis of light-heartedness in their weary journey.

When the garden gate closed behind them, they had to readjust themselves, for they had walked out into the Third Reich and they wore the uniform which called forth "Heil Hitler!" from every nervous passer-by.

XIII

Of what was going on in Cologne my parents had not the slightest idea. In their opinion Jules, as an Aryan and a war veteran, belonged in the ranks of the storm troopers. How would he get on in the Third Reich otherwise? The news of my only brother's having joined the S.S. was hardly a surprise. Our belief in the liberty of the individual gave him the right, in our eyes, to do as he saw fit.

The attitude which I had hoped for from my parents I could not, of course, expect to see realized. What I wanted was respect for the one individual who had the courage of his convictions. But life is not like that, and that fateful thirtieth of January separated many families as clearly as the fall of an ax. Yes, my parents were interested in our future; they liked to hear about our rugs and our books, our maid and our dog; they cared about Jules' pension and the state of my cactus plants. They were honestly concerned about our welfare. But they were waving to us from a valley which we had already left.

On November the eighth, we received a thick letter. Sender: the president of the Government-Board of Cologne. Contents: a communication from the Minister of the Interior in Berlin. In accordance with Paragraph Four of the law for the re-creation of the civil service, Jules was formally dismissed from his city post and expressly forbidden to enter his former offices or to appear in person before any member of his Supervisory Board.

So this was the dismissal of the director of the Rautenstrauch-Joest Museum! How did Paragraph Four run: "Civil servants whose political activity up to the present has not offered the guarantee that they are prepared at any time to stand unconditionally by the National Socialistic State may

[183]

be dismissed." At any time and unconditionally? They were right. Paragraph Four really did apply to us.

We called Ziska and Tapir and showed them the document. Then we got out another. It was a large sheet of parchment, handsomely lettered in black and red, Jules' appointment as the director of the Rautenstrauch-Joest Museum. It expressly stated that the appointment was for life, specifying his right to a pension with full pay and his claim to life and accident insurance, and it was stamped with the seal of the city of Cologne.

"What are we going to do now?" asked Ziska anxiously.

"We will see what they do about money," replied Jules.

Although Jules' life appointment as director of the Rautenstrauch-Joest Museum lay at our feet, a torn scrap of paper, his dismissal from the staff of the University of Cologne was never effected. This is due to the peculiarity of the position of professor at a German university. It is not merely a title, but a permanent distinction, comparable to consecration to the priesthood. It follows, therefore, that technically Jules is still a member of the faculty of the University of Cologne. It was not until December the twenty-seventh, 1933, that he received a written notification from the Minister of Culture revoking his right to teach in the University of Cologne, according to this same Paragraph Four. The right to teach was revoked, but not the position of professor, for this was taboo even to a Nazi Minister. A professorship is attained only after years of teaching, when the faculty suggests a name to the Minister on the basis of scientific achievement and scholarship. It is not an appointment which expires with the loss of a position but a life-long and irrevocable title.

I felt it my duty to bring my parents the news of Jules' dismissal in person. We could look forward to three more months on full salary; then the pension would begin. It would be three-quarters of his pay, as prescribed in Paragraph Four. It was a tight squeeze, but we could continue to live in our house, and above all begin to work again. For matters were clearly settled, and this brought calm.

The gray motor stood at the station; the chauffeur opened the door; my mother had brought me a sheaf of carnations.

A childhood passed in Leipzig means an association with books, with music, or with furs, for these are the city's chief occupations. I knew nothing of the fur trade. I grew up in a world of books, and as for music, just around the corner of our house was the Gewandhaus, with its inscription: *Res Severa Verum Gaudium*. "True joy lies in serious purpose." In front of it stood the statue of Mendelssohn. I was really surprised to see it still there. They seemed to have forgotten to remove it. This was not done until the winter of 1936, and the Mayor of Leipzig, Herr Gördeler, lost his post in the process. Under political pressure, he was willing enough to see the monument to the non-Aryan Mendelssohn removed, but he refused to have it destroyed. His Nazi opponent, Haake, succeeded in destroying both the Mayor and the non-Aryan composer. They both went—Gördeler and Mendelssohn—never to return. The monument was a sentimental group in bronze by Werner Stein; it had been placed in front of the main entrance to the Gewandhaus in 1892, and as a child, when I accompanied my lovely mother to a concert, I had often stopped to look up at its many little cherubs, clustered round the master, their chubby fingers clasping scrolls of music and tiny lyres. They looked as though they loved him dearly. A few steps farther on was the Supreme Court of Germany.

While I was enjoying the luxury of my parents' home, the Reichstag fire trial had aroused the city. While I walked on Persian rugs, reliving the carefree days of my childhood, under the patina of the copper dome five men were fighting for their lives: van der Lubbe, Torgler, Popoff, Taneff and Dimitroff.

[185]

I strolled about my native city; I visited the scenes of my happy girlhood, but I could no longer capture the melody they had once sung to me. All my being was centered in Cologne, in the little house that held my happiness. Here in Leipzig I saw again the countless books; I passed among them and my heart contracted with pleasure at their familiar smell—of dust, of glue and of the secrets they contained, a back-stage smell. But the old volumes breathed of vision, of nobility and of eternity. They stood behind the glass doors of their cases; they lay about on tables, and over them hovered the spirits of those whom the stake had dared to burn. They cried aloud for vengeance.

In a great room of book-lined walls and alcoves that invite communion with a volume, I saw the old gentleman again. He was fine, kindly and enigmatic. He held a very high post. It was he whom the constitutional government had intended to place in the Presidency after Hindenburg's death, if the gentleman from Bohemia had not interfered. He was a holder of many honors; he loved books. His only fault was that he had remained silent when he should have spoken. He stood before a table piled with rare volumes such as bibliophiles dream of, numbered editions, incunabula. It happened that we both reached for a parchment Casanova at the same moment, and as we turned to apologize, we recognized each other.

He still remembered me. We talked of Nikisch, for we had had adjoining seats in the Gewandhaus for years. We talked of the facsimile of the "Passion of St. Matthew" which lay before us on the table. We talked of Axel Munthe, the wizard of Capri, and of his book. We talked of everything—except the present. Nor could I conceive of anyone so fine and subtle as he having anything to do with the present. Nevertheless, at the end, quite casually I made a request, and it was concerned with the present. My old friend smiled; he was surprised and amused, but he was glad to be able to gratify me.

Two hours later I had in my hand a card of admission to the Reichstag trial. I could go when I liked; there were two seats. My parents were shocked when they heard that this card meant more to me than all the pleasures of my native city and that some of the precious hours of my stay at home were to be spent in this hall—on which the eyes of the world were fixed.

"Politics?" they asked in dismay. "Are you so changed?" They did not realize that it was my Fatherland that had changed.

Oh, what did I care about politics? I wanted to see with my own eyes the dragon that brooded over Germany raise his hungry claws. I wanted to behold that formless monster that lay over Germany—at the spot where he must come out from his lair. The field of our libel suit was only the men's lavatory of a small beer hall, but here it was the German Reichstag. It was only our peace that was in danger; here, lives were at stake. But the germs of all unrest were the same: lies and denunciation.

I could not say this in my parents' house, for no one would have understood me. I merely laughed and replied: "Politics? No. Excitement." A young relative, hearing this remark, hurried up, an elegant little person with pretty curls over her birdlike forehead.

"May I not have your second place?" she begged. "I should love to go with you." And I agreed.

It was a rather cold day; men in the Square of Justice, with Christmas trees for sale, called up memories of my childhood. The path to the great round ramp was slippery with ice. There rise the massive columns which I had climbed as a child, to watch General Merker's * men at

* This refers to General Merker shooting down on revolutionaries gathered on the Reichgerichtsplatz in 1918. Mrs. Lips remembers siding with the general, whereas Professor Lips' sympathies were with the republicans. —Translator's Note.

[187]

their guns. But today there was no shooting; inside this building there were three men whose names filled the headlines of the newspapers of the world. Against them the Third Reich had invoked the paraphernalia of the law, of massed witnesses and sworn oaths. I shuddered, for I knew what such an accusation from such a source must mean. And there was a man who dared to speak recklessly, even wittily, in words that combined grace and danger, whose utterances were hungrily awaited by all those in our country who suffered for the sake of the spirit. What would be the revenge of the Third Reich on such a mind? How would it end, this struggle between honesty and baiting? Could the man escape from the bog on which he had already stepped? Would he be sucked under, this Savonarola who loved an idea more than his own life? Would Dimitroff be defeated?

Wrapped in furs, two inquisitive geese in their soft down, my pretty companion and I stood in front of the gates at half-past nine in the morning of December 1, 1933. As yet no one was allowed in. We were obliged to wait; there were many waiting, although we all had our cards of admission. No suspicious person was allowed to enter; every ticket bore a name. Ladies tripped about in the cold on their high heels. In planning their day this sensation had triumphed over the pleasures of the country club. Gentlemen stood about in groups, their untroubled heads crowned with stiff derbies, their double chins folded smugly in collars of virgin otter, chatting with well-tailored journalists. Ladies in silver foxes, mink coats and capes of Persian lamb had assembled to stare at the Communists who, according to Minister President Göring, had set the Reichstag on fire. They had come to gaze at these wild animals with the same delight as at a rare leopard in the zoo, at a stage idol, at a horse that has fallen on the street, or at a fashion show. Here there was no one "dangerous to the State." All were well-fed, warmly dressed and—bloodthirsty. Such was the German nation, in whose name judgment was to be pronounced.

Among the crowd my companion caught sight of the patroness of the cavalry division of the storm troopers. She was bent on getting her husband into this crack outfit, and she was just about to dash up to the influential lady, when the wall of people began to stir. We were pushed forward and soon found ourselves in the lobby of the Hall of Justice. Here quarters with temporary telephone booths had been set up for the press. To the right and left were tables with several men at each.

"Ladies to the right." We were obliged to show our cards of admission and our passports as well. The photographs and signatures were examined. The transfer of a card of admission to someone else would have been impossible. A small side door opened. We streamed through—still separated from the men—and up the stone steps. It was cold. At last, the corridor. Solid walls of waiting women. A glass door that opened and closed. No one spoke. Indignation at the lack of courtesy in the Hall of Justice was mirrored on those spoiled faces. The minks and silver foxes and Persian lambs formed a queue, as obedient as the lines that waited for potato rations during the War. From time to time, two figures were admitted. They disappeared up a winding staircase. We moved forward slowly, the lady of the cavalry division murmuring "Unheard of!"

When our turn came and the glass door closed behind us, a silent young man joined us, leading the way up the steep spiral staircase and through a labyrinth of corridors and passage-ways. We stopped before a blank door. The young man left us to fetch the next pair. A woman opened the door, and we entered.

We found ourselves in a kind of cloak room. The woman locked the door. "Coats off," commanded the Saxon Megaera, and my companion retorted: "Are we the accused?" The probing hands of a wanton stroked our dresses, felt the curves of our bodies—the police matron searching for hidden weapons. "Hats off!" We might be concealing a bomb.

[189]

"Handbags open!" I had a box of pralines and an opera glass in mine. "That stays here!" We protested, and as our coats looked rather good, we were allowed to have our way. We were permitted to keep our shoes on. "That's all. Next!"

A murmur of voices in the corridor. This time we needed no guide. The men came out through a door at the left and joined us to form a new queue. "Show your cards!" One by one we passed through the line of guards into the court room. The room was fairly full. We were ushered to our places by policemen. We eluded them and succeeded in obtaining two seats, at the front, far to the left, directly behind the reserved rows and on the same side as the prisoners' bench, which I recognized easily from the newspaper illustrations.

"Your charming little daughter," I heard behind me. And the reply: "It was her first ball. She had such a good time!"

Such a good time! I was excited. My breath came short.

The room was enormous. The high windows on the right looked down upon the court-house square. Around the wooden ledge of the balcony ran a brightly painted frieze of the coats of arms of the German States. High up in the center of the balcony sat the sound recorders, ready to catch every word that was uttered on their wax discs for the radio, for the Minister of Justice—and for posterity. Below and directly opposite us was the Judges' table, covered with green baize, a high-backed chair behind it. Round, black-mouthed loud-speakers were stationed throughout the room. In front of the rows of reserved seats were the tables for the press. A buzz of talk came from them. The correspondents could easily be recognized by the papers they were reading. In front of me sat a suave, white-haired gentleman from Le Temps, and next him, two slender men conversing in English. Court-house attendants hurried busily about, placing documents on the Judges' table. Ladies in the audience waved at one another from remote corners, exclaiming:

"You here, too! How's everybody at home?" and were hushed by the police.

Far back to the left a door opened. Policemen appeared. Instantly the prisoners' bench was flanked by moving guards. Then, unhandcuffed, a slender man came in and sat down in the second row between two guards: Torgler. Two new figures took their places in the third row, the one thick-set, the other wiry: Taneff and Popoff. And then, supported by two policemen, came something pallid and green, a bundle, almost lost in the thick folds of a badly fitting overcoat—van der Lubbe! Could a human being look like that? A living human being? Could a face be green?

"Are those the Communists?" inquired my neighbor. I did not answer. Dimitroff was coming in.

He walked with the light, easy step of a guest. His dark pin-stripe suit fitted to perfection. Everything about him was clean and trim. A hundred necks craned, a hundred silly voices whispered, "Dimitroff." Now they had seen him. They could go home. It was not the trial these whispering women had come to see. It was the villain of whom Göring had said: "I would like to strangle you with my own hands." The jester whose *bons mots* were quoted throughout the press.

Dimitroff walked to his place in the front row of the prisoners' bench. He was a middle-aged man, smaller than we had supposed. He was the farthest from us, and the closest to the Judges' table. He did not sit down, but stood looking through his papers, his strong, well-formed fingers playing with his horn-rimmed spectacles. He did not glance at the avid faces, at the privileged hands holding their special admission cards. Nor did he look toward the press. He looked at his documents. The fur-coated spectators saw only his profile.

His beautifully shaped skull revealed the thinker. His wavy dark-brown hair grew in a clear line back from the temples and the high dome of his forehead. It was enough to see that brow to guess how the flashing thoughts behind it would infuriate his enemies. The nose was sharply drawn and rather broad. But the chin was softly molded and betrayed the artist.

Dimitroff turned toward the back bench, where his interpreter sat, with a question. He waited for the reply, and while the frock-coated worthy held forth long-windedly in answer, we got a full view of the accused. At first glance one was conscious of the separate features. Then one saw but one thing: the eyes. The man's personality was entirely concentrated in his eyes. They were large and brown, extraordinarily brilliant and hypnotic. They had the power of forcing weaker men to decisions. Those eyes had brought him his disciples. In them burned the eternal flame of a consuming ideal. Even the interpreter was beginning to yield to them. It would be hard for a Judge to meet these eyes, the eyes of the accused, Dimitroff. The resemblance came to me in a flash. It was the profile of Goethe that I saw before me, as the sculptor Rauch over a hundred years ago had caught it in his bust of the master, the same powerful profile and the same arresting eyes. The accused Dimitroff had the head of the German poet, but cast in a more rugged mold and tempered by Slavic softness. Only the brow and eyes had the Olympian majesty of Goethe; the element of satiety was absent; in its place, the blazing passion of the fighter.

Given the scene and the situation, it was of course the face of a Communist that we were looking at—but, actually, it was an abstraction we beheld. The face of greatness, the face of genius. He might be a master artist, a deliverer of mighty rhyme, an explorer of the poles, a writer of books, a digger of gold or the discoverer of a serum sought for centuries. He happened to be a Communist.

I am convinced that Dimitroff was far from seeking to produce any impression, that like all great statesmen he despised the approval of the crowd, although dependent upon it. Certainly he had not the slightest idea of the theatrical effect he produced, theatrical in the sense of his unconscious measuring the influence of every word on his spellbound listeners with the diabolic delicacy of the manometer. He moved with the cautious grace of a wild animal; his gestures had the iron control and apparent freedom of a great actor. I felt a longing to hear his voice. Judging from the tone of his widely printed speeches, I guessed it to be strong and fierce—the voice of an agitator.

Suddenly everyone in the room, including myself, arose. Every right arm in the room shot up, to salute the officers of the court, every right arm, except the prisoners' and mine. The Judges came in, robed in red and black. They took their places and began to rustle their papers. The journalists sharpened their ears and their pencils. The spectators re-seated themselves. Deep silence. But my neighbor could not help whispering a question in my ear.

"Who is the slender man with the handsome athlete's figure?"

It was Torgler, and he had got his athletic figure in prison!

"He's no Communist," she went on huskily; "he must have been misguided." And she looked with interest at the "misguided" man. He was well-dressed; his hair was brushed smooth; he was obviously the favorite of the assembled ladies. The slight air of artificiality characterizing both the outer and the inner man went unnoticed. Torgler looked white, mute and ravaged; his bearing was impeccable.

In front of us on the reserved benches sat three women: Frau Torgler, as white as her husband, in a dark beret; next to her, Dimitroff's sister, the heroine of Paris, who had shouted her brother's story to the ears of the world; to the left, Dimitroff's little mother, unafraid, a lioness fighting for her son's freedom. Ah, it was from her that he had those eyes. Small and shrunken, wrapped in her peasant's shawl, in frozen self-control she sat there, listening to a language she could not understand. She could do nothing but project hate ahead of her and faith to her left. Her eyes were her messengers.

The big man at the Judges' desk was Senate President Bünger. He conducted proceedings. Round-headed, bald and hearty, with the plump and cordial features of a kindly grandfather, one would rather have encountered him in a nursery playing amiably with the children than in this room, at war with the genius of rebellion. His voice was flat, but precise, and when he was angry it took on a shrillness foreign to it. One would have liked him had he not sat here on the judgment seat, dealing out injustice. This was not the place for him. If only he had taken his old-age pension before this trial instead of three years later! He made a few opening remarks which no one understood. Then a record was read. To the left a hand was raised, a head, a shoulder. A man leaned forward slightly—the accused Dimitroff rising to protest.

I heard his voice at last. It was quite, quite other than I had expected. It was the voice of a gentleman who has wandered into a noisy bar and makes his low-pitched, pointed words audible through the brawl. The voice was not in the least loud, but distinct, melodious, a precise and pleasing instrument for crystal-clear thoughts. Never forced, never shrill, never coarse. Dimitroff spoke German like a Frenchman with careless h's. When he said "Nazi," he gave it the soft "z" of the language of Voltaire. He had almost complete mastery of German, and when he misused a word, it was in such a charming way that one was almost persuaded to adopt it into the language. At one point he remarked that his guilt could be assumed only "by psychopaths, thieves or poets"—thereby placing himself in the last-named group. All his utterances were now seen in a different light. When one read them, their effect was piercing and deadly, but when one heard them from his own lips they sounded like graceful pleasantries, and only after his words had died away did one feel their bitter sharpness. Poor old shrill Grand-papa Bünger!

The accused Dimitroff demanded that General von Schleicher, former Vice-Chancellor von Papen, Minister Hugenberg, former Chancellor Brüning be called as witnesses to testify to the "internal dissension in the parties of the 'Right'" at the time of the Reichstag fire. Bünger's voice rose high as he denied the request. It was time that the prisoner Dimitroff ceased his crazy demands! These witnesses were irrelevant, absolutely irrelevant to the case in hand. Sit down, Dimitroff! One cannot but be reminded of the fluctuations of destiny and the vanity of threats as one thinks now that General von Schleicher—before whom Grandpapa Bünger trembled on that day—has since been shot for treason—whereas, the then-doomed Dimitroff lives in honor in Russia.

The loud-speakers were operating well now; every word came clear. Upon the demand of the prisoner Torgler, the records of the police were read to prove that the alleged preparations on the part of the Communists were non-existent. Here Attorney-General Werner sprang to his feet, a dangerous enemy, young, sharp, savage. In a voice of thunder, he skillfully gave the meaning of the report a damaging twist. Torgler was silent. His "slender athlete's figure" had no resistance. His strength seemed sapped. Attorney-General Werner was buried in Leipzig on October 16, 1936, bequeathing to his widow no more than a message of sympathy from Herr Adolf Hitler, whereas Torgler is still alive, though in doubtful freedom. Surely the knowledge would have been of some comfort on that day. But the gods have their own good time for telling.

Again Dimitroff's hand was raised in protest; all Party secretaries of the districts concerned should be summoned and questioned. No occupation of public buildings had been planned; the charge was slander. In objection, the

[195]

attorney-general roared as he had heard Göring do. Bünger denied.

The witnesses now came in. They were all laborers from the Saxon mines, "political instructors" of the German Communist Party. What might a political instructor be? I had no time to think it out. They had been locked up a long time and had now been brought out—a whole batch of them. Their faces wore the patina of men who have long been deprived of sunlight. They were a shadowy troop of wasted figures. A shudder ran through the room. All eyes turned to the prisoners' bench. The accused gazed dumbly at the witnesses. All except one, Marinus van der Lubbe. His head had sunk to his knees. The unkempt hair rose stiff above that greenish face. Was he still alive? He was the perpetrator of the deed; he had been caught on the scene of the crime with his passport on him. What had happened to him since then? How can a human face grow green? Compared to him the witnesses glowed with vigor and vitality—wretched as they looked. But they at least seemed alive. One by one they stepped forward to be sworn in.

Laborer Kaldenbach spoke in a strikingly finished style. He rolled his r's as they do on the stage; he made dramatic pauses; he formed astonishing phrases. He had doubtless been trained to speak. His testimony was remarkably clear; he had certainly prepared it in prison. I had imagined a Communist workman as quite different. These agents seemed to have been selected with great care. He stood before the microphone, poor and grimy, and delivered his impressive sentences. The revolution was to have begun in the factories, not in the mines.

All at once it became clear that laborer Kaldenbach was a Judas. On the fourth of March, he said, he had listened to Chancellor Hitler's speech. Corruption and exploitation were at an end; the day of improved living conditions for the working man had dawned. The Chancellor had declared the battle won. Kaldenbach now realized that the National

Socialist Revolution had been accomplished without blood-shed, whereas in Russia the workers' blood had flowed in streams. He realized now where he must stand.

A Judas to the cause? Oh, no! He had come to his conclusions in prison, had laborer Kaldenbach. He lifted his worn hands imploringly toward the Judges' table, not with the glance of one who has betrayed his ideal, but with the despairing eyes of a flayed animal begging for mercy. My heart was choked with sorrow and bitterness. Torgler raised his hands and covered his face. The man was allowed to go. Other phantoms murmured other words. It was not necessary to listen.

Another man stepped forward to the Judges' table. He did not look at his enemies. It was in the first row of the prisoners' bench that he sought strength for his trembling words. His gaze remained riveted on the dark, magic eyes of the apostle from Bulgaria from first to last.

"Witness!" cried Bünger, "if you look at prisoner Dimitroff again, you'll be put out!"

"Do not distract him, Herr President," came the mild voice of the accused, Dimitroff. " 'Err President," he said, like a Frenchman. The witness was led away.

I noticed that whenever Torgler was to reply, the Bulgarian had spoken for him, that he had given information on conditions within the Communist Party of Berlin, on subjects entirely beyond his province. It was evident that he was trying to save the man from his own helplessness. What had happened to Torgler? He was so silent, so frightfully silent. Without a sound he heard his men betray him. But when some minor agent remained true to their cause and to him, he appeared to suffer even more. Then he uttered the groaning sigh of a man on the rack.

When Dimitroff asked to have Communist Thälmann called to the stand, the Judge shouted him down: "Thälmann! An unqualified witness! Ridiculous!"

The court adjourned for lunch. The prisoners were led

away. The visitors streamed out into the hall. Most of them went home. They had been served the first course in the sensational banquet; their curiosity was appeased. They could say they had attended the trial; that sufficed.

I too rushed into the hall. I was beside myself with excitement. To the right there was a high fence like that in a zoo. There stood the little old woman with the peasant's kerchief over her head, talking frantically to the interpreter in Bulgarian. But she was not allowed through the gate. She could only press her face against the posts and watch him go by between two policemen. She had given him life; he had inherited her fire, and her fanatic strength of purpose.

I leaned against a pillar and lighted a cigarette—an impossible thing for a lady to do in the Leipzig Hall of Justice—but, I kept seeing the gray-green face of Marinus van der Lubbe. I was to dream of it for years.

I looked about for my companion. She seemed ecstatically happy. Indeed, the patroness was smiling at her; the affair of the cavalry troop seemed to be succeeding. After my third cigarette, she finished her conversation and came back to me in a state of bliss. From her little alligator-skin bag she pulled out two samples for her new sport suit and showed them to me.

"Which do you advise? The herring-bone or the plain? Which are they wearing in Cologne?" My veins were cold with van der Lubbe's poison, with Torgler's pallor. Was she blind to human misery? I turned and ran; I hid behind one of the thick columns. I felt a malicious pleasure in her discomfiture as I watched her go down the stairs uncertainly. Her purpose in coming had been fulfilled. Why stay? Lunch was waiting.

We are back in our places. I can touch the hair of Dimitroff's old mother. I am so close to her.

Torgler rises. The recess seems to have strengthened him.

[198]

He speaks with an actor's clarity, with assurance. He makes a request of some sort. It is refused. He sits down and sinks back into a reverie.

Suddenly van der Lubbe raises his head. It is that of a puppet; it might be named "Hashish" or "the Man from Mars." His face is deader than death, stiffer than glass. A shocked murmur rustles through the room. Others too have noticed it. The dead lips twist convulsively.

"Van der Lubbe is laughing," runs the whisper through the hall.

The body collapses. Only the wild shock of hair is visible, stiff with terror at belonging to that head.

I get up. I have had enough. I press my way through the crowd and stumble to the door. I hurry down the unfamiliar steps, lose my way and finally find myself in the outer hall, groping toward the door. A newspaper man opens it for me. "Take it easy," he remarks in English. He, too, has had that same sick feeling. I stand outside in the cold, clean winter air.

Half an hour later, smiling, I enter the dining room of my happy family. Truffles are served me.

"How was the trial?"

"Not worth talking about! What are you doing this evening?"

"We have tickets for the theater—the Harmony Comedians—you'll enjoy it."

"I am delighted; you are so kind."

In the evening I actually find myself at the theater. The program opens with "Lovely Isabelle of Castille." Above the stage of the Crystal Palace, above the faces of the five singing charmers, I see a green countenance hovering. It is that of a puppet. It might be named "Hashish" or "the Man from Mars."

It took four days before I felt strong enough to return to the court. I felt obliged to go. What these men could stand with death before their eyes I—a mere observer—could endure. It was a chapter in the history of my country. This time I went alone.

The formalities imposed before I could reach my seat were as before. It was the fifty-first day of the proceedings. They were still calling witnesses, this time a workman named Felix. He told of a Party meeting in Freienwalde. They had brought along ordnance maps, lanterns for code signaling and revolvers. They had intended to form units to attack the counter-revolution if it should march upon Berlin.

"The counter-revolution?" pipes Bünger. "What was that?"

"The Nazis," whispers Dimitroff confidentially to his microphone.

"I forbid you to use that word," roars Werner.

"Beg pardon!" says Grigori Dimitroff politely. "The National Socialists." He takes great pains with his sibilants, but they are still French in their softness.

"Hold your snout!" from the Judges' table.

Dimitroff's hand moves in a gesture of pained resignation.

"Proceed, witness!"

The plan was to begin with acts of terror, said the suspiciously complaisant witness—he too had just come out of prison. On the fifteenth of February explosives had been stolen in Freienwalde. They were intended for Berlin. The idea was to exchange them for revolvers, since the local group had no money to acquire weapons otherwise. They had kept changing the hiding place of the dynamite. Finally, it had been concealed in the home of an unsuspecting old man. Thirty pounds of dynamite had been repeatedly moved from one place to another. At last a funeral had given them their chance. The dynamite had been hidden in a child's casket, the few weapons in another coffin. Early in March the theft of the dynamite had been discovered. The witness had fled to Berlin, where he gave himself up to the police toward the end of March.

"Has this any bearing on the Reichstag fire?" asks Dimitroff slyly, and suddenly a fierce debate is on between the prisoners' bench and the Judges' table. Was it a general strike that had been planned or an armed rebellion? A constitutionally permitted self-defense, or a Communist revolution? Well, witness Felix, answer!

The magic glow of Dimitroff's glance is upon him. Like a squirrel under the eye of a snake, workman Felix stiffens to rigidity under the spell.

"Take your eyes from Dimitroff!" shrills Bünger.

"An armed insurrection or a general strike?" the Bulgarian prophet whispers encouragingly.

"Excuse me, I can't go on," groans workman Felix. He is led off, clinging to his two guards.

Foreman Jessel is called to the witness stand. The same limp figure, the same wretched face, the same schooled voice.

The foreman is shrewd. He tries to moderate Felix's testimony. The dynamite was not intended for Berlin to start an insurrection there. It had been taken to the capital merely to avoid endangering the families in Freienwalde, unsuspecting families in whose homes it had been stored.

"Only a protest strike against the fascist dictatorship," Dimitroff explains calmly, "not an armed insurrection. By no means insurrection."

"Well, now, come along, Jessel, what was the plan?" Bünger asks with a show of fatherliness.

"I am not as learned as the prisoner Dimitroff," stammers Jessel in confusion, "I don't know . . ."

He was led away. Perhaps his memory was refreshed outside.

I do not know the facts. I am not a Communist. I do not know who set fire to the Reichstag. But I do know who terrorized his victims, and who suffered in patience, I do know where there was lying and where hopeless struggle. Huddled up on the prisoners' bench I see a deathly sick bundle of humanity, two weak-brained creatures. I see Torgler, tortured to the breaking point, and I see the caged tiger refusing to be tamed. Why all this suffering? They are caught in the trap; they will be made to pay. What is the purpose of this fulsome trial? Dimitroff has perceived his one means of escape; he speaks into the ear of the world, not into that of the presiding Judge. That would be deaf to his loudest tones—but the world hears and understands his low-spoken words. Perhaps the world will save him. It has already heard too much to stand by and watch him die. But what of the others? The Bulgarian shoemaker? The clumsy student? Torgler, the only German among the accused? And what of this sick man, revived from death to delirium, this "arch criminal," van der Lubbe?

I looked at them all once more with wonder in my heart, with a shudder at the fatalities of history. I pitied the Judges. They were merely puppets at the play, pulled about by the invisible strings in the hands of the director. They belonged to the old generation, and, after all, they were bound by the law. It was all so frightful.

Farewell, you judges, who roar so loudly and think so silently. Or do you still dare to think at all? Your minds have been paralyzed since a certain day in January.

Farewell, poor, sick van der Lubbe, may death at least be gentle to you.

Farewell, you two dull-witted Bulgarians, and farewell, Torgler; I doubt whether your well-fed lawyers wished to save you.

And farewell to you, Grigori Dimitroff, in this hall you have been crowned—with immortality.

That night I returned to Cologne.

[202]

XIV

It was high time I came home. The hearing of the "lavatory case" had been set for the eighteenth of December.

The mail containing the summons had also brought a letter from the Imperial University at Tokyo. A friend there had drawn the attention of one of Japan's princes to our fate. How did we feel about Tokyo? Would we care to come? Jules was to send his credentials at once. We began to dream of the Samurai.

We had already hung the Advent Star in the living room.* Christmas was approaching. Ziska and Tapir took their places near the piano, where I sat playing: "Open the door, open wide the door, for the Lord of splendor is coming."

In the afternoon we had a consultation with our lawyer. Then Renate and Anita came to see us; one was to testify against Scheller, the other against Rodens. They had a conference with Jules. I was glad to see the Zombi, though his uniform frightened me.

"You were at the Reichstag trial? What was it like? How was Dimitroff?"

Let's talk of other things, my friends. In Japan there are Samurai, and the little geisha girls are so pretty. We will perhaps be called to the University. Put out the lamps and let us sit in the starlight. Christmas will soon be here; listen to the sweet simple songs, sing them softly with me. We are alive and we are well. Soon a Christmas tree will stand here—like the ones standing in Leipzig on the courthouse square.

* It is the custom among German Protestants to hang an illuminated star in the house four Sundays before Christmas, in anticipation of the celebration of the coming of Christ.

How shabby a mere district court is, a small entrance, a narrow hall—and how shoddy the charge! A university professor is supposed to have declared to someone in a men's lavatory that a former pupil of his was an idiot. What poverty of imagination! Why not say we had set fire to something? Is this a matter for trial? Is this worthy of the new heroism?

Room 134, first floor. We were all there, our witnesses, Anita for Rodens and Renate for Scheller. The Zombi was there, spick and span, aglow with the fire of battle, looking as the ideal Nazi should.

Jules goes forward to meet the lawyer, Herr von Coellen, who comes up the steps in rustling robes. The attorney shows us a legal decision, which officially admits student Scheller is co-plaintiff. This means that in the action brought by the State against Professor Lips the witness Rodens can testify on oath to whatever he pleases. Had we not better turn around at once and take the first train we can catch, regardless of its destination?

There they stand in a corner, glancing furtively at us, Scheller with his cane, Rodens, three strange men and a woman. She, I gather, is witness Schober. Student Fröhlich is there, too. Their lawyer is Dr. Barthels. It was clever to choose him—and dangerous for us. Up to January of 1933 this young man could be found on any night of the week in various bars in the questionable quarters of the city, in a drunken state. After the reforms of the National Socialists set in, he became legal adviser to the Rhenish district of the N.S.D.A.P. Furthermore he belonged to the same student fraternity as Fröhlich, who had doubtless retained him. He is the official Nazi attorney. There is no Judge who will dare to challenge Barthels. Besides, he is in a visibly exhilarated mood. His voice croaks over to us. Our old von Coellen is obviously terrified at the sight of him. We are filled with dismay.

The clerk called: "The State versus Lips."

There were about thirty present, eight of whom were from the press. The *Westdeutscher Beobachter* alone had sent three reporters—aside from those involved in the trial. All this because of an imaginary insult to the student Scheller—in a men's lavatory. It was clear that an important case for the safety of the National Socialist State was at stake.

The Judge began the proceedings by reading the charge in monotonous tones. Then the accused was allowed to speak. Jules briefly denied the allegation.

"Could you have been intoxicated?" asked Barthels. "It was three o'clock in the morning. Possibly you do not remember."

"No one in Cologne has ever seen me drunk—not even in Carnival."

Witness Rodens was called. He had run into Professor Lips in the men's room of *The Lantern*. He quoted the defendant as having used the expression "the idiot Scheller," and furthermore the words, "You scoundrel!"

Incensed, he had repeated Lips' remark to Fröhlich. The latter had gone to Scheller, and Scheller to Burgomaster Ludwig. Now the State had taken up the matter and brought suit against the slanderer Lips. An insult to its least member was an insult to the State itself!

A succession of witnesses testified to Rodens' sobriety, in spite of the fact that he had been unable to make his way back to his table unaided. One after another claimed to have been near enough the men's room to overhear the insult—an insult to a Party member and, therefore, to the National Socialist State.

Von Coellen remained silent. Perhaps it was fear of Nazi reprisals. Professor Lips and his witnesses were denied the right to testify on the ground that whatever they might say would be irrelevant.

In summation, Lawyer Barthels thundered about the destiny of the Third Reich, fingering his swastika ostentatiously the while. Nothing less than a prison sentence to the accused would save the imperiled State.

Von Coellen still said nothing. As quietly as possible Jules attempted to answer the ludicrous and tawdry charges, pointing out how the witnesses contradicted each other, how patently absurd was the whole fabric of their case. The Judge and the jury retired. It was not long before they returned.

"The accused is pronounced guilty. He is sentenced to pay a fine of one thousand marks. In case of failure to pay, the accused shall be sentenced to one hundred days in prison. The costs of the proceedings shall be borne by the defendant."

A thousand marks! We hadn't even a hundred left! A hundred days in prison!

"Heil Hitler!" exclaimed Barthels.

The next day the *Westdeutscher Beobachter* carried heavy headlines:

LIPS LIES!

University Professor and War Veteran in Court Insulted the Director of the Rautenstrauch-Joest Museum—How Lips Tried to Clear Himself
1,000-Mark Fine

". . . Who is Lips? He began as a *Privat-dozent*. In the course of time he succeeded in getting a stand-in with the former unco-ordinated Minister of Culture, which led him to rise to the directorship of the Rautenstrauch-Joest Museum. But this did not suffice. He continued to rise by means of wire-pulling and dinner parties until he became a professor at the University. Now Lips was a made man! He changed from an apparently agreeable person to an arrogant and conceited one. However, pride goes before a fall! And so it was in this case. When young Germany awoke, this opportunist was thrown from his high position as director and professor. The new city council was merciless in driving him out. . . ."

With this as an introduction, the article then turned to the court proceedings. A long paragraph was devoted to Lips' arrogant bearing and obstinacy at the trial. The lavatory testimony was quoted in detail. The rôle of the lawyer, Party-member Barthels was glorified. In a burst of rhetoric the report ended on the note that the purity of Nazi justice had once more been maintained.

Editorially, the same newspaper praised the scientific achievements of Party-member Scheller, ending with the sentence: "The culture of our own people must, of course, stand in the foreground today. Anyone who wishes can, however, occupy himself with the cultures of foreign peoples."

There was an interval now before Jules' appeal could be heard and in the meantime we decided to put all this out of our minds, to devote ourselves to the Christmas season.

Christmas must be celebrated with all one's heart and soul, with all the riches of heaven and earth, says German tradition, and my family had always made the most of the tradition. Everyone must be happy, everyone must have cause for rejoicing.

Ever since Jules had been connected with the Museum, it was the custom for Weiss to appear at our house on the twenty-third of December. He helped me with moving the furniture and the decorations, ending with putting up the tree, which no one was allowed to see until Christmas eve. When we had finished our preparations, we locked the lower story and Weiss and I went through the usual formula.

"What do you think of the tree, dear Weiss?" I would ask every year, and according to ritual he would reply:

"It's the finest we've ever had!" Then Weiss received six silver marks, a box of cigars, a bottle of red wine and our heartiest good wishes for Christmas.

This year things were a little different. I waited until five o'clock, but my old assistant did not turn up. Ziska and I pushed the piano into the dining room and changed the furniture about; we moved the tables against the walls and set up the tree. Then I asked:

"What do you think of the tree, dear Ziska?"

She replied: "It's the finest we've ever had!"

Then I locked the doors; Tapir was the only one allowed to enter. He watched me earnestly as I arranged branches of evergreen over the pictures, on the bronze candelabra and the clock. The old masks peered down at us wonderingly from their dark frames of evergreen festooned with silver tinsel.

When I had finished, I hurried to Jules in high elation. He tried to hide a newspaper from me as I entered. I was frightened.

"Please give it to me! After all, I must see it sooner or later."

Decision in the Reichstag Arson Case! Van der Lubbe sentenced to death! Acquittal of the three Bulgarians!

Van der Lubbe was beheaded with an ax. His Dutch family was forbidden to take the body home. Was there some frightful secret to be concealed? The three Bulgarians, Taneff, Popoff and Dimitroff, were actually set free, although they were kept under observation for some time. The low-pitched, pointed words of the great agitator had cut through the wall of lies. Ernst Torgler, who was also acquitted the same day, was not released from prison until 1935, when he emerged a broken man. The verdict had been pronounced on the day before Christmas.

I put the newspaper out of sight. We heard Ziska singing in the kitchen. Tomorrow would be Christmas.

At the sound of the gong Ziska came in, jaunty in her neat dress and fresh little lace apron. The pretty cap on her head gave her the air of a spoiled young ladies' maid. Tapir had a wreath of evergreen around his neck. Jules stood in the doorway. I sat down at the piano and we all sang the dear old German Christmas song:

> *Stille Nacht, heilige Nacht,*
> *Alles schläft, einsam wacht*
> *Nur das traute hochheilige Paar.*
> *Holder Knabe im lockigen Haar,*
> *Schlaf in himmlischer Ruh!*

After the third verse we drew back the curtain slowly. There stood the tree, reaching all the way to the ceiling. The silver trimming shimmered against the green and the sweet scent of the candle wax mixed with the pungent smell of wood and resin. The odor of marzipan, apples, chocolate and gingerbread blended into a heavenly harmony that warred with the fragrance of a freshly opened bottle of scent.

Ziska cried when she saw her gifts. With tears rolling down her cheeks, she pointed laughingly to a tiny table under the tree. There sat Tapir looking timidly at his little stack of presents, two miniature sausages, two little gingerbread men and a ball. Stiff as a well-disciplined soldier he waited for the magic word of release.

The warmth and light of the candles, the fir twigs on the white tablecloth, the whole transformation of the room filled our hearts with festivity. I had a new fur cape to throw across my shoulders and a silver vanity case to toy with and for an hour it was fun to make believe that I lived in a light-hearted world.

The champagne came on, and we toasted the hour. Champagne is not coffee, and Ziska became sleepy. She took her silver dress clips to bed with her. Tapir trotted to his straw bed. We opened the terrace door to let in the sacred sounds of Cologne, sacred through twenty long centuries, the song of the German bells on the Rhine—which only peal once a year. They sing as though they came from Paradise. These bells were here before Hitler and will outlast him, as Germany will bloom again after him, flowering once more.

XV

We packed Jules' trunks in silence. To stay in Cologne any longer was a menace to freedom and to life. We were certain of three months' salary. I would live alone in our house until Jules could send for me and we could begin our new existence.

The trial had showed how grotesque and savage the situation could be. This was not the end. The persecution would go on incessantly until we either gave up, or were locked up. Since we would not lie, nor bow down before wrong, the time had come to realize clearly that our Fatherland had been taken from us, and that the old German culture which we felt we represented now had been banished beyond the boundaries of a country that burned the books of its thinkers and threatened the lives of its children.

So Jules must set forth on a voyage of discovery. Once in Africa he had found a people who knew nothing of the world outside and yet were wiser than we. Today, Jules must go among nations of cultivated spirit in search of humanity. He had a mind to offer them; he had learning and a name. Where there was freedom, there our home would be. It meant giving up our beloved little house. But what is a little house standing in a desert of hate? We could only keep it at the price of honor. But its very foundation was honor. Love had gone into its making, and industry, too—all German ideals. Two words—freedom and honor—were proclaimed daily over Germany, those two words in whose name injustice was heaped upon injustice and ignominy on ignominy.

We no longer mentioned Buchensee. We behaved as though there were no hillside, no gay little cottage, no stony

hill abloom with edelweiss and plumed pink, no big raspberry bush shaded by the branches of the beech trees. We
did not dare to think what would become of all this. "My
earth." These words would have to be forgotten. And there
were others to be banished from our minds, if we were to
remain strong enough to go on living.

It was Sylvester Eve; we stood on the threshold of New
Year. We looked into a void.

We ate our carp and sipped our wine. There was an ice
for dessert. We went into the living room to hear the midnight broadcast. As the clock struck twelve we heard the
voice of the new director of the West German Radio, Glas-
meier.

"New Year over Germany! New Year over the Rhine!
New Year over Cologne! And New Year over the Teuto-
burger Forest, where Hermann the Cheruscan defeated the
Romans, and Adolf Hitler defeated the Marxists." He got
no farther; Jules clicked the radio off. We raised our glasses
to an uncertain New Year, looked into each other's eyes and
laughed.

On New Year's morning of 1934 we took the train to
Saarbrücken. I had allowed myself three days' holiday and
intended to return home alone. Running the gauntlet of the
police and the customs at the border of the Saarland did not
hold us up long. A New Year's visit to one's old mother is a
thing everyone understands. In Völklingen the flames leaped
skyward from the giant bowels of the blast furnaces. In a
year there would be voting here. There is no part of Germany that is more German than the Saar. But the danger
was that those who wished to show their loyalty to the
Fatherland would confuse Hitler with Germany. They had
as yet no idea of life under the Third Reich.

The house of our brother-in-law, a mining engineer, stood
on a high hill. We entered the garden, greeted our mother
and sister, the chickens and the dogs. As I stood at my win-

dow upstairs, I looked across to the mine. There the great wheel ran night and day, its spokes finely outlined against the sky. The stacks belched smoke and the slag-bank spat fire. The cable cars dipped unceasingly into the valley with their loaded baskets. Beneath all this was the mine itself. In the darkness, while we still slept, the workmen went by on their bicycles, pedaling toward the black pit whose stony core lay etched in blocks of coal, in designs that told of wealth, of hearths where misery dwelt, and of goblins of the inner caves, and of the secret, subterranean world.

What was taking place on the surface of the German earth was infamous and I hated it. But what lay hidden in its bountiful depths? What did it look like under there?

As if in farewell to the land that had mothered me, I felt a longing to see within its walls to peer into the heart of the country in its richest spot.

I gave my brother-in-law no peace. I followed him wherever he went. He opposed me hotly. This was the most dangerous shaft in the Saar; it was no show-place for curious women. Death brooded there. Anyway, women were forbidden to enter the mine. He was a determined man. It took nine hours before he gave in.

In the evening three strange figures entered the drawing room, dressed from head to foot in miners' clothes, heavy caps, long boots, cave lamps in their hands. Our old mother uttered a cry at the sight of us, but we promptly vanished.

Everyone greeted the engineer, never glancing at the two miners with him. We went into a high, light, concrete hall. A man stood at the wheel. Like a steersman at the helm, he kept his hand on the lever that directed the coal corf. His eyes were fixed on one thing, the arrow marking the position of the open corf. A mistake in a centimeter meant death or mangling for those suspended between the vestibule and the abyss below. We lighted our safety lamps. A gust of wind at a bad turn would blow them out. The corf stopped

—a large open platform, unwalled, not closed like an elevator. Dark figures got out and without looking at us murmured: "Glück auf." Everyone here was treated as though each trip might be his last.

We entered the corf. A signal bell shrilled. We plunged downward, deep into the very belly of the earth. My ears closed; a sound of rushing water roared in my head. We stopped. No, we were not yet to get out. In the darkness several miners climbed aboard and we continued downward. It was hot in the home of the goblins; I had imagined them in cool halls of alabaster. Theirs was a black palace, set in murky airlessness.

My brother-in-law went ahead. We found ourselves in a tiny antechamber, its doorway hung with sacks, its walls of black marble. Coal! I ran my hand softly over it. Thousands of aeons ago the gods had commanded it to mass in rigid walls. We glided through the low-roofed passage. No one spoke.

Black, glittering planes of marble. Rather thick, short beams supported the passages, shoring. We climbed; we made sharp descents; sometimes we had to crawl. In the center ran the tracks, and on them the "dogs" dashed past loaded with the treasure of the mine. Coal everywhere. We had been walking a long time. I leaned against the wall for a moment, the air was so hot. I felt something move behind me and started back in fright; I had leaned against the body of a horse. A warm, breathing beast, a dumb slave to an unknown duty. It was blind. It no longer knew the light of day. Jules tugged at my hand in warning, he had not noticed my alarm. The heat grew more intense. We were on our knees again. We had reached "the place." Here they had smashed giant blocks of coal from the earth, bracing the plundered walls with thick, round beams. The dynamiter kneeled before us. Suddenly, he whistled a piercing blast. We scuttled madly into the corridors. The explosion burst upon our ears.

"Glück auf," murmured the men we met, taking us for their brothers in darkness. "Glück auf," and we three were alone again. Our guide held his lantern high toward the glittering roof overhead. The light went out. So it was here they lived, those brooding spirits of evil, whose spasms of fury brought about disaster. They guarded the treasure of the hills, which human eyes might not behold. Should mortal eyes look into the farthest chamber of the last of the hidden mysteries, glimpse the throneroom of King Laurin and his jeweled gardens, he might never return to the light. The guardians of the marvels below would fall upon him and destroy him. "Terrible accident in mine!" said the newspapers. "Disastrous cave-in!"

We ran into the next corridor. A metallic dragon screamed its heavy breath into our faces—a kindly dragon. Its breath was life; it fed a draught of oxygen into our lungs. A ventilation shaft.

We continued onward. Sometimes I stumbled over the tracks; sometimes I stayed behind to run my hand over some conchoidal shape, the spectral profile of a wall. Then Jules' hand would reach out and lead me back to safety. A piece of coal sprang from the pick-ax of a miner right before my eyes; it had the form of a heart. I took it with me.

And suddenly we were back in the little black marble antechamber, and the corf stood waiting.

"So soon?" I whispered regretfully.

"We have been here five hours," said my brother-in-law. "It is midnight. We have covered ten kilometers underground."

Now I knew the meaning of the legend that tells of the man who, after a single night inside the mountain, finds that half a century has passed, that those he loved are dead and his home has crumbled.

Back again in the clear night air, I learned that we had been nine hundred meters deep in German soil. Thereafter I trod its surface with an altered step.

[214]

On the fourth of January our boxes stood at the Saarbrücken station. My little trunk stood apart. The rest were labeled for Paris. As usual, we made our parting cheerful.

Our trains pulled out in opposite directions. For a second we saw each other's faces through the passing window.

Ziska and Tapir were at the station to meet me, Ziska crying for joy, Tapir no less delighted. I told them about the trip down the mine and how it feels to be inside the earth. But my thoughts were elsewhere.

I had a long conference with Anita. There was only one man who could win our appeal, the lawyer who had conducted her divorce. Dr. Bodenheim was a rich man. He did not need to extort large sums from his clients. Formerly an influential leader in the Catholic Centrist Party, he had taken advantage of the coalition at the psychological moment and was now decorated with Nazi insignia and badge of office. He maintained his old connections and had added new ones, and he was more effective in the court room than Barthels, for he could be subtle as well as noisy, whereas Barthels was merely noisy. If I could only interest Bodenheim, the appeal was as good as won. Anita informed me that he selected his clients from two points of view: money or good looks. I had neither money nor beauty. Anita was my only hope; I begged her not to fail me.

Before long we sat in Bodenheim's conservatively elegant office—Anita a faun-like creature with creole eyes, myself a hardened Amazon, in softening make-up. Only two days ago, my face had been powdered with coal dust.

A bell rang, a perfumed secretary made her appearance. We were led down the hall. A sound-proof door closed behind us. I shot a quick glance at the fortress we had come to storm.

A tall, broad-shouldered man—built like a concert grand, Anita had told me . . . Certainly he was as polished. He went in for elegance, to a degree hardly in keeping with his past political career. The play of his voice ranged from the cooing of a dove to the roar of thunder. His gestures were studied, clumsy when he forgot himself. His eyes were false. His nails were manicured, but the hands were coarse. His questions were routine. Just the kind of man we needed. I was encouraged. Wherever I looked, my eye rested on the swastika. It gave to the room the security of an oasis in the desert.

Bodenheim was familiar with *The Lantern* trial; his questions were sly and pointed. I saw that he looked forward to crushing Rodens, whom he characterized as "a would-be gentleman, a stupid, drunken nullity, a typical serving-man who had come up in the world." On the lies invented and sworn to by our enemies we wasted no words. The case was perfectly clear in Bodenheim's mind. He did not require to see Professor Lips; he was familiar with the type of men we were dealing with, their pathology and their jargon.

While I was anxiously wondering whether Bodenheim would consent to take the case, my lips not yet venturing to form the question, he rose abruptly and asked Anita to leave the room. Somewhat nettled, she departed.

When we were alone he leaned across his polished desk and gazed at me in silence for a few awkward seconds. Was he measuring the depth of my purse? Certainly he could find no other interest in me. I smiled—a convulsive, frightened little smile, an attempt at coquetry. A ridiculous little grimace it must have been!

Where was Jules? With his mother, in the Saar.

Why was he there? Why stay here, since he had been dismissed?

I admitted at once that we had for the time being practically no money—only enough for our most urgent needs. Would he take the chance?

He waved the question of money aside. Had I a power of attorney from my husband? I had.

He got up, looked at me half-cynically, half-indulgently, and said: "Now, don't worry! I'll do it. It isn't a case of

[216]

Scheller and Fröhlich here. I am going to try to get back your husband's position for him!"

"But he gave it up himself!"

"His wishes can be carried out. Cologne needs him. And it will be I, Bodenheim, who will patch the whole thing up."

I saw his motive. It was ambition. I was quite content! Let him go on imagining that Jules would one day return to lecture as an apostle of racial theories. The thing was to win the appeal!

"Thank you so very much!"

"Just give me the time to get to the bottom of the affair."

A splendid man! Now he was ferreting, creeping about; later he would come out into the open. And all for our sake. I gave him the power of attorney. The mere name of Bodenheim would be a veritable bomb to Rodens.

I left the office happy and hurried down the Ehrenstrasse to the cathedral. I walked through its echoing aisles, and high among its pillars my glance fell upon a fourteenth-century saint, whose benign smile invited trust. I bade him carry my message of thanks to the kindly Catholic God, for underneath all his Nazi veneer, Bodenheim was still a power in his old party.

I had not realized that my duties in Cologne would be so many-sided. The more devils were loosed—and they seemed to spring out of every crack—the calmer I became. The feeling that Jules was spared all this, that he was already actively working for our future, cheered and strengthened me for the fight. When we were together, I concerned myself only with the arabesques of life. Now I was faced with a variety of tasks. There was the house to be run, our small income to be managed, our campaign to plan and to carry out—alone. It was not too easy. I learned that one's greatest assets are presence of mind and self-control, and that it is often better to appear stupid than to show perception. I learned when to play the helpless woman and when to assume the rôle of a sexless soldier. I learned at whom to glance with anxiety and at whom with scorn. There began for me a course in practical psychology, and when I made a mistake I paid heavily for it.

A curious organization came to the fore: the Honorary Council of the Federation of German museums, a representative group of leading German museum directors. It was not enough that Hitler had robbed Jules of his position; they must also rob their former member of his honor. In this way, they hoped to make an impression "higher up" and to profit by it. We exchanged long letters. These anthropologists hastened—by impugning one of their own members—to draw to themselves the attention of Berlin. Just see what zealous Nazis we are! You dismiss a man and we give him a kick. Long live racial theories!

They opened "proceedings" against Jules. What is the basest charge one can bring against a scholar? That's easy: plagiarism. Jules had once written a popular little book called: *An Introduction to Comparative Ethnology*. They dragged it into the limelight. They held a special session. Its object was obvious and easily attainable. If *The Lantern* affair failed, then the Honorary Council could spring into the breach. The proceedings went on merrily. German scholars now had a productive occupation. Their minds were on fire with the zeal of research. They buzzed with activity.

Naturally, Jules knew nothing about it. Why should I add to his worries? I had provided a number of signed sheets for "his" answer to whatever arose. That was all that was necessary.

Scheller was still intoxicated over the verdict. A man who has been shouted at as Jules had been doesn't rise again. At least not in the Third Reich. They rolled in the puddle of their triumph. Lips was now done for, absolutely done for!

Only Burgomaster Ludwig was not yet satisfied. A fine

was not the way to silence so sarcastic an enemy. He therefore decided to institute a disciplinary inquiry "with the aim of dismissal from service," in the name of the city of Cologne. Why, Jules had been dismissed by the Minister long ago. What was the point of this farce?

Bodenheim enlightened me. There was still three months' salary due, and after that the pension, for Jules' appointment was for life. If the city could put through "disciplinary inquiry ending in dismissal from service," Jules would be out of the civil service and consequently not eligible for pension. Bodenheim informed me that in our city alone three hundred such proceedings had been started. It was simply organized theft. The pension was saved and the opponent quietly annihilated. He was quite literally starved out of existence. Little people were put in concentration camps. The others were dealt with more craftily. Their positions were taken, their money was taken. They were forbidden to leave the city. So they simply died—without a murmur.

I objected; I hammered out letters on the typewriter; I "filed a protest"—all in Jules' name. No one knew that the man at whom all this official destruction was aimed had been freely walking the boulevards of Paris for a long time. Almost daily there were new attacks, intended to break his spirit and destroy his power to work. To have broken the bonds was by no means sufficient. They wanted more. Only complete annihilation would satisfy them. My relief at knowing Jules was safe was so great that nothing else mattered. Ziska was at my side. Jules' letters came by devious ways.

When I consulted Bodenheim about the Honorary Council, the disciplinary inquiry and all the wretched letters from the city of Cologne, he said: "All this will stop immediately, once we win our case. It's only the tricks of the trade. The usual machinery of attack. It's all built up on lies. Worse will come. Those are their tactics. I am beginning to enjoy this game. Ludwig will come creeping to us quite humbly."

[219]

I left his office to the loud sound of "Heil Hitler!" What an admirable lawyer!

"My Panther:

"For the fourth time Paris reveals herself to me in a new aspect. The first time I came she offered me the traditional pleasures and diversions of the light-hearted student. Later, when I was doing research, she provided intellectual companionship. Then came our journey together—those days of complete felicity. And now I look to her for our future. The last time we were here we still believed in dreams and imagined that it was possible to live and work where our hearts were most at home. The time for dreaming is over. Paris is today a watch tower to me. Its free air delights my heart. I am watching carefully.

"My metro station is no longer the Palais Royal. The Hôtel de l'Univers et du Portugal has become too expensive, now that I must be saving my shekels. So I have moved into the Latin Quarter, very near the street where I lived as a student, next to the midwife's. Do you know the Rue Monge? The name of my hotel is *Des Nations*. It is stimulating to a man who does not know what nation will wish to keep him, a fitting address for my letters. The cost is fifteen francs a day; by the month it is only two hundred and fifty. Do not be alarmed at this fantastically low price! I have a bed, a closet, a desk and running water, and am quite content.

"Our friends have been generous with their delightful invitations, but I scarcely have the time for parties. I am kept busy making the necessary contacts, and people are being very kind. Many indications point to Switzerland, either Zurich or Geneva. In one night we could be at Eze. My heart is cheered, and my ear as well; now and again I slip into the Sorbonne. Our great apostle of master Rabelais sends you his compliments. I have written a great many letters; every conference seems to open new possibilities. I am

[220]

meeting all sorts of people, but no Germans. They are either spies, and therefore to be avoided, or are themselves unhappy, and therefore depressing, since one cannot help them.

"I eat in the *Bonne Étoile;* doesn't it sound friendly? Today is Monday and the bargain sales are on—back of the Opéra. I miss you. The latest color for evening just now is a murky raven blue, *bleu corbeau*—I felt it my duty to get the tip for you! I keep thinking you will be with me soon. We shan't be rich enough for a dress at Madame Odette's, but perhaps we can manage a tiny bottle of Caron. There is much to talk about. Keep up your spirits, my old soldier."

The old soldier put down the letter, wondering how to fight down the difficulties. For since the opening of the disciplinary inquiry by the city of Cologne, Jules' salary had been stopped. It was all Ziska and I had to live on. I had grown less sensitive and I had learned the routine, so I took my old friend Trembal out of its box and sent Ziska to the pawnbroker's with it. When I had the receipt I went straight to the Rathaus and called on Inspector Wolke, an old friend from the Centrist Party, who had saved his position by raising his right hand. I showed him the pawnbroker's ticket and said that I would let all Europe know we had been driven to this extremity by the city's breach of contract, if the salary rightfully due to Jules were not immediately released. Wolke asked why Jules did not come himself and I said: "Would you, then, advise him to come to the Rathaus, where people like Ludwig hold the reins, where it is possible for one like Scheller to get his lawsuit into court in the name of the State?"

Wolke murmured sympathetically, "How hard this must be for you!"

"It is, at least," I replied, "a lesson in the ways of the world!"

In good-bye he sent his very warmest greetings to the

Herr Professor and offered to help us at any time. The next day I received word that half of Jules' salary had been released. Trembal could come home.

The mornings were always taken up with such errands. Now that part of the money at least was obtainable, I had to get it as soon as possible, before the authorities at the Rathaus had time to change their minds. The afternoons I devoted to Bodenheim and the gathering of evidence against Rodens.

Meantime "investigations" for the disciplinary inquiry were going on. The man appointed to conduct the inquiry was one Korndörfer whose qualifications were exclusively political. He was to sit in judgment of a member of the university faculty and a member of the bar—although the law expressly provides that in such cases the accused shall be judged by men of equal standing. I was delighted to learn that this Korndörfer had been a classmate of Bodenheim's; he would respond to a Centrist approach. At the end of the proceedings, I was told, they would "listen to Professor Lips." What would happen when it turned out that he had long since left Cologne must be left to the future.

Bodenheim took particular pleasure in dwelling on Jules' "services to the nation." He had prepared a complete list of them, by way of special ammunition: "Editor of the *Koloniale Rundschau*, Berlin," "Knight of the Iron Cross," "decoration for wounds received in service," volunteer of 1914, Aryan and veteran, and similar accolades adorned the list.

The official version of Jules' absence for Bodenheim, and other close acquaintances, was that he had fallen ill while at his mother's and was confined to his bed. Since we only received half his salary, he could not return; it was just enough for myself and the maid to live on. Every time I went to see him the canny lawyer would raise his eyebrows in sympathy and ask:

"And how is our poor friend?"

I would reply tearfully: "Oh, dear! He's not doing at all well."

We understood each other perfectly.

Another letter from Paris:

"Dear Panther:

"There is scarcely an important man here who has not offered his help. Friends come to me constantly—as S. did yesterday—to introduce me to some long-bearded dignitary who they think might be of use. 'The celebrated Dr. X. is extraordinarily interested in your case.' Then they tell me the latest French joke on Hitler. It's all very amusing, but it gets us nowhere. In the Trocadéro they have put a room at my disposal and I am free to visit the locked collection and look at the splendid death mask in rock crystal and the golden feather helmet you are so fond of.

"Yesterday on the Boulevard St. Michel I met our Nazi friend, archaeologist Kühn. He begged me not to betray him. He too is secretly looking for a bearable future, since poor, non-Aryan Rita is dragging them into the mire of persecution. F. was here from Leipzig; he also swore me to secrecy. At Doyen Brunot, a whole group of Germans meet for tea daily; they are all quietly looking for positions. No one knows that they are in Paris. They are all here for a short time and expect to return—temporarily at least—to Germany as vassals to the swastika. I don't see how they can bring themselves to it. The loud 'Yes' and the silent 'No' are beyond my talents. I'm no good at whispering in corners. There's a mob of former celebrities playing around in Paris just now, enjoying the delicacies offered to them as guests, without any serious intention of ever substituting a simpler, but steadier, fare.

"I think I may have to go to Geneva soon, and very likely to London, also. I don't want to raise your hopes with all these vague possibilities. I can't have your imagination hanging on a thread somewhere between Zurich and Shanghai.

[223]

"Darius Milhaud sends his greetings. He is tremendously productive and quite withdrawn from the world. One is ashamed of laying such unharmonious themes as the Third Reich before him. He knows Hitler only through the naughty songs of the little soubrettes, for a 'Bel Adolphe' never fails to bring the house down.

"I spent a delightful evening at Madame de M's recently. They have nine original Gauguins on the wall; they also have some of his teakwood carvings—superb! I heard a good deal about Abyssinia at her last *soirée*. They say it is impossible for a white woman to live there. In Addis Ababa only titles and personal favorites have any influence. Nevertheless it might be a good idea to try to interest the Negus in a museum devoted to the primitive cultures of his subjects' tribes. Anyway, I have written him a long letter suggesting it.

"Georg Bernhard has recommended the only decent cigar in Paris, *Pattes d'éléphant*—by association I am reminded of the good Fräulein Fasbender, now busy banging Scheller's incomparable compositions into the typewriter. How far away Cologne seems! I sometimes eat in a little pub called *Au Rendezvous des Chauffeurs*. The other day they served me some dog's liver. Since then I have stayed away.

"The *Hôtel des Nations* is really a meeting place of all nations and colors, a melting pot of all continents, and should delight an anthropologist's soul. To the right of me lives a Persian, to the left a crippled Chinese who possesses nothing but a celluloid collar and an empty valise. Madame, our landlady, consoles herself all too frequently for the troubles of life with sweet wine. She hopes to marry the house-man. He, however, wants none of her, for she owns 'only the furnishings of the hotel and not the walls,' and looks so dreary that one can well understand the good Albert's reluctance. When she 'gets gray,' one of the servants yells 'go to bed' at her and she obeys meekly.

"So I spend my time between the offices of Ministers and

the rendezvous of chauffeurs. I am quite cheerful and content. Trust me as I trust in the future. I have saved one small item, our savings account, *i.e.*, my head. Isn't that quite a lot?

"And always remember in your sad moments, my dear—you are going to see Eze again, and the Mediterranean."

The cheery tone of Jules' letter raised my spirits and I began to dream of the high rock of Monaco, of the white breakwater of the loveliest harbor in the world, of the sail boats of Algiers and the rocking dories that go out after sea-urchins in the bay of Eze.

XVI

The telephone interrupted my dream. Dr. Bodenheim wished to see me immediately. I was alarmed at the urgency of his tone. Ziska insisted that she and Tapir should accompany me and wait for me in front of the house. We started at once.

"I am worried," said I to Bodenheim. "Has something happened?"

"On the contrary," he replied. "Look here, Professor Lips must return at once."

"What?"

"Yes, I have been talking with Korndörfer. The disciplinary proceedings are going well. But he must speak to your husband. Then the Professor's entire salary will be released at once. I made good use of the 'national services'; those fellows were thunderstruck. Confidentially, the city of Cologne is very displeased with Scheller and cannot find anyone to succeed Professor Lips. Rodens is completely discredited. Your case is practically won. But my client must appear in person."

"You know very well that he's ill!"

"Yes, of course, of course. But, my dear lady, we're by ourselves here."

I was silent for a time, doubtfully eyeing my all-too-suave adviser. Could one, after all, really trust a man who wore a Nazi badge the size of an apple, while all the time he remained a Centrist, a man who divided his time between his duties to the ladies and his duties to a "Führer-unit"? Was he trying to get me to admit that Jules was in Paris? Was he aware of it? Did he intend to sell us out to the Nazis for the sake of a reward to come for the delivery of the recalcitrant professor?

"Have you forgotten the trial?" I asked. "The perjuries that went unchecked and unpunished, the disciplinary inquiry, the Honorary Council? Do you think that life appointments are renounced for a joke? One fine day the city of Cologne will decide to withhold the salary altogether. Then we can starve! Surely you don't advise us to wait for that? Besides, Jules is—ill," I added hesitatingly.

"I will guarantee his safety," said the tempter slowly.

"Are you so powerful with the Nazis?" I inquired coldly. "If you are so powerful as to guarantee his safety, then I cannot trust you!"

"My dear lady . . ." he stretched his hand across the table, and I noticed the smell of perfume, the lacquered fingernails and a conspicuous ring. He withdrew his hand, picked up his pen and began a letter:

"My dear Professor Lips: I consider it my duty as your lawyer to advise your immediate . . ."

Perhaps I would intercept the letter and leave Jules in peace. I did not know what to do. What had we to gain? Possibly win the case and save a pension? Was it worth risking one's freedom, endangering our future in such a cause?

Bodenheim explained that he had also talked with Burgomaster Ludwig, "a man of the highest ideals." I recalled his share in the "toilet-room trial." I had little faith in Bodenheim as a judge of ideals.

I could not decide what to write to Jules. Ziska and Tapir greeted me when I got out into the street. I confided my problem to Ziska.

"We must never let the Herr Professor return to Cologne!" she exclaimed in alarm. Her anxiety threw me into despair. I decided to consult our old friend who had sent us to von Coellen.

"Let him come back. With Bodenheim on his side, he will win the case and get his pension."

But he told me something else. After the trial, von Coellen had retired to the attorneys' room in the court house to

[227]

seek out Barthels and had said to him: "I never knew the Professor made that remark about Scheller. I am disgusted at having undertaken his defense. It was a complete surprise to me; I dropped the case at once. I hope that you will forgive me." Whereupon they betook themselves to the nearest beer hall.

And now our dear friend advised a second appearance in that court of justice!

The next morning Bodenheim sent me a telephone message saying that if his client did not appear in person at his office within two days, he would not continue on the case.

An ultimatum! How could I counsel Jules to return to the Third Reich? "Crazy," was the verdict of one group of friends. "Quite right," exclaimed a second group. I turned from one to the other, completely baffled.

My deliberations were cut short. At ten o'clock that night a telegram was put into my trembling hands. "Arriving tomorrow three-seventeen, Jules."

Tapir did not wear a wreath of welcome. There was no time to put one on him. He squeezed his bulk through the garden gate, barking wildly. He jumped as high as his master's shoulders, blowing his hot breath into Jules' face.

Ziska had assembled the hunting trophies in a row in the living room. Each one bore a sign: "Welcome, master, we are glad that you are back!" "Your household is happy!" The flowers had cards of welcome tucked among them—vases in the dining room, the study, even in the bath. At every hand there was a greeting—Jules' favorite cigars, his favorite cognac, his favorite cakes.

"How soft our chairs are," he said. "Those in Room 12 at the *Hôtel Des Nations* are like rocks. It seems strange to be here! Am I really at home?"

In the evening Jules' talk transported us to the streets and fountains of Paris and to her kindly people. "I am coming back this once, but never again," says the fairy tale, and so said reality to us. Jules went through the house wonderingly,

[228]

as though it had been provided for him by magic and would vanish in the morning like the palace of Aladdin.

When we appeared in Bodenheim's office, none of the things I had pictured in my anxiety took place. The lawyer was delighted to see Jules. With such an "accused" it seemed to him easy to win a case. We talked over the last details and had conferences with Anita, Renate and the Zombi. Ziska and Tapir had a sort of sentry box at the front door; they were determined to defend the master to their dying breath. I scarcely slept at night. If anything happened to Jules I could never be happy again. Every time I heard a footfall in the street I went to the window. I kept a trunk packed for Jules and knew by heart the hour of departure of every train that could take him back to the Rue Monge. We were all in a state of suppressed fever. Friends telephoned frequently to ask whether we were still "all right."

Only one person was calm: the "accused."

On the twenty-sixth of January, 1934, the appeal of the "toilet-room case" was heard. We were present in full force —Anita, Renate, Zombi, Jules and I. The denouncers were also assembled in full array, but this time student Fröhlich had brought a lady with him, and another lawyer had been added to the group, Kunibert by name. Rodens had lived with him for a time under circumstances which were discussed in whispers. Bodenheim greeted us with a hearty "Heil Hitler!" to which the Zombi responded according to habit. The rest of us smiled at our deliverer. When our enemies recognized our lawyer, they clustered together, whispering excitedly.

The door to the court room opened. As before, all the witnesses remained outside. I, too, stayed out, for I might possibly be called. So we only participated indirectly in the affair. One hostile witness after the other was called, but not one of us.—Was sabotage at work again? Discouragement weighed upon our spirits. Only the Zombi spoke up: "This time we'll have our turn, and wait till I turn loose on them!"

But he never got his opportunity. The door opened. The court had withdrawn to pass judgment.

This time a keen-witted Judge had presided. His face showed more than shrewdness—it revealed intellectuality. He controlled the entire proceedings. The "lavatory" had suddenly become important. Three men were alert: the Judge, the lawyer Bodenheim and the accused. This time Herr Barthels did not yell. He was pale and sober. Herr Kunibert never was allowed to speak. Prior to the trial, Bodenheim had showed the Judge the overwhelming evidence against Rodens and also our proof that Scheller had intercepted letters. Bodenheim did not go in for theatrical effects in court. His Centrist training went too deep; he had everything ready before the first word was uttered. Literal-minded Barthels hadn't a chance against him. Unless Barthels could orate, he was lost. This was not the forum for his style.

The former witnesses for Scheller and the State were recalled. They were treated to some bitter remarks concerning the accuracy of their sworn testimony. Bodenheim concentrated on Rodens, subjecting him to merciless torture.

"Answer yes or no, please," he began agreeably.

"Were you educated on Catholic money or were you not? Did you or did you not form a strong pro-Jewish political bloc known as the State Party? Did you apply at the headquarters of the Social Democratic Party for membership therein, or did you not? Is it true that you were denied membership in this Party by its local leader as politically unreliable? Was it proven that you were drunk on the evening of February 7, 1932, after two glasses of sweet wine or was it not? Did you drink champagne at *The Lantern*, and not coffee, as you orginally testified? Did you not join the National Socialist Party *after* Hitler had come into power, when all other political affiliations had become dangerous?"

[230]

All these questions the quaking Rodens answered with a hoarse "yes."

"I shall refer later to the light thrown by your divorce proceedings on your character," said Bodenheim in conclusion. This time it was our lawyer who played with his swastika, and his was the biggest in the room.

Frau Schober, whom Bodenheim greeted as an "old acquaintance" dating from the Rodens divorce case, had the pleasure of hearing that a charge of perjury, based on what she had said about Frau Anna Rodens, had been preferred against her. He permitted himself the hope that the witness might find a physician who would declare her mentally irresponsible, for that would be the best way out for her.

What could Barthels do? Not even protest. It was all true. The lavatory attendant was next called to the stand. Poor fellow! The *Westdeutscher Beobachter* had characterized him as a simple, unspoiled and incorruptible man of the people. He had fallen a credulous victim to private investigations on the part of our Zombi and had admitted to the "nice S.S. man" that he knew neither Rodens nor Professor Lips. On the evening in question he had "spent only an hour" with his bride, and the incidents leading to the trial must have taken place during that time. The gentleman there, the lawyer, pointing to Barthels, had only told him later on all that had occurred, and since his master, the proprietor of *The Lantern*, must not find out that he had been away, he had "remembered" everything the lawyer had told him.

Bodenheim was shrewd enough not to ask the size of the bribe, or to mention the word perjury, for the case, after all, was being tried in the Third Reich.

Student Fröhlich was far less reserved. He took the stand in righteous indignation: "I can no longer recognize Professor Lips as my teacher, now that the Honorary Council of the Federation of German Museums has opened proceedings on a charge of plagiarism against him."

Bodenheim had been waiting for this. With a graceful gesture he unfolded several pages and placed them on the Judge's desk. They contained the protests of the authors allegedly plagiarized, foreign scientists, men of international reputation. Their protest was unanimous—against "the disgraceful, politically biased libel of our highly respected colleague," against "the shameless attack upon the honor of a scientist of standing, whom impartial outsiders feel called upon to defend in the name of the sanctity of pure research and of the honor of science."

The court was taken aback, but Fröhlich carried on unperturbed: "He also collected scientific photographs which are aimed against the National Socialist State. When we were searching his house . . ."

At this point, however, he was interrupted. Herr Bodenheim rose and addressed him as a "miserable maggot in the decay of our time." Could this be legally construed as an insult? Was this an offense against the National Socialist State? In the case of Bodenheim, ardent Nazi, that was out of the question.

"You were the bearer of this denunciation," he continued. "You went to the president of the police and obtained a warrant to search the house of the instructor under whom you had hoped to take your doctor's degree. You declared that his library was crowded with 'Marxist literature' and sent the police into his house. You accused him of being in the possession of forbidden weapons, and denounced him to the secret police. And now, here you are in this room because you hope to make a men's lavatory, where my client met a drunken man, the apex of your activity. You wear the ribbon of a distinguished student corps, and wearing that pledge of chivalry, you appeared in the house of a former Jewish city counselor to help destroy his home and steal a silk rug from it. You are not the clever schemer that you fancy yourself, my good young man—merely an inflated rubber frog. An opportunist! Why all the petty hatred, why all

[232]

these dirty deeds? Because Professor Lips, on arranging for his leave of absence, named Scheller, who is at least a war veteran, to take his place instead of you!"

Bodenheim shot a final bolt at his fellow-Nazi. "Do you really think," he said devastatingly, "that the new State, the State of Adolf Hitler, our State"—he made an impressive pause—"needs creatures like you, who as late as January, 1933, went about disparaging World War veterans? Can our State be served by unprincipled spies, too shifty themselves to be able to feel respect for authority?

"Gentlemen: here sits the accused, a man who at eighteen, on August 2, 1914, flung himself into the trenches as a volunteer. For Germany! There sits a little student, who after five years of awe before this distinguished scholar now plays errand boy for scurrilous denouncers of that same scholar. And there—" he pointed to the sickly figure of the trembling Scheller—"there sits another student. He was suggested by this same scholar to take his place. This student has—as I can readily prove—recently undertaken a cure for morphinism under one of our leading specialists. He owes everything to his teacher—his career, his great opportunity! This student, conspiring with informer Fröhlich, and with political chameleon Rodens—found guilty in a divorce case —attempts to 'destroy' his teacher through a lawsuit based on an incident supposed to have taken place in the men's lavatory of *The Lantern* at three o'clock in the morning! Gentlemen, I appeal to your knowledge of human nature! Look at those three faces; compare them with that of the gentleman whom they are attacking. You will see who lies! Compare one affirmation with the other. Even our admirable official organ of the press, the *Westdeutscher Beobachter*, has allowed itself to be misled by the combine of this trio of informers, men of the type described by our Führer on January the twenty-seventh as 'plague spots on the body of the State!' "

The court withdrew to pass sentence. Jules had not said

[233]

one word except: "I stand entirely on the statement made by me at the first trial."

We were all permitted to hear the verdict: "The case is dismissed. The accused is acquitted. Costs to be carried by the State. Costs of record, amounting to 4 marks and 75 pfennig, to be met by the accused."

At this Barthels jumped up and exclaimed furiously: "The accused comes from the Saar District, where all traitors are to be found today. Who will answer that he will not betake himself there again and cheat the court of the costs of record?"

"I, with my entire fortune," replied Bodenheim scornfully. "Moreover, let me reassure you, my dear colleague. Professor Lips has come from the Saar because he was born there and because his seventy-eight-year-old mother lives there. Have you any objection?"

There was no answer. The case was closed. We left the court room. Only a Nazi can deal with a Nazi.

This time the *Westdeutscher Beobachter* did not publish a report of the trial. It was much pleasanter to leave the words "Lips Lies," boldly headlined, in the memory of their readers. That an appeal had taken place need not be made public. Oddly enough, although we were immediately notified by mail of the outcome of the first trial, the second verdict, the report of the one in our favor, never reached us, in spite of our repeated requests. Incidentally, *The Lantern*, which had become a byword in Cologne, changed its name. After the appeal it was called *The Rocket*.

That we would be obliged to pay for our triumph over the Lemurae we knew. The acquittal had saved Jules a thousand marks, a thousand marks which we could never have raised under any circumstances. There was still the interview with Korndörfer to face, in connection with the city investigation. However, Jules had to return to Paris, where plans for the future were pending. It was important that

Bodenheim should not know of his departure, for he still believed, or rather perhaps was just beginning to believe, in the possibility of Jules' unconditional reinstatement in his two posts. Curious that so subtle a lawyer should have been so naïve in this matter. For the time being we did not contradict him.

That evening we heard Hitler over the radio: "I am proud to count the intellectuals of the country among my deadliest enemies, for that pack of scoundrels are devoting their degenerating brain power to the ruination of our people!" A crushing statement, whose style and content put us promptly in our places.

On January 31, Jules, accompanied by Bodenheim, went to see Korndörfer who was ostensibly carrying on the "investigation with a view to possible dismissal," though actually engaged in an attempt to cancel our pension. They found a young man with ratlike teeth, a brown-shirted boor. He had his hand impressively spread upon his desk. His beady eyes glittered with hate and spitefulness. Jules perceived instantly that he had more on his mind than the withdrawal of the pension—that he had been commissioned to deal the final blow. Bodenheim became noticeably quiet. His "classmate" completely quenched his courage.

The hearing began, though it was hardly a hearing—more like an inquisition. Korndörfer was primed with self-importance, determined to make a showing.

He began with Jules' birth in Saarbrücken. He demanded a history of his parents, a full report of his school and college days.

"You have been in an insane asylum?" he burst out, triumphantly.

"Yes," said Jules, "as a psychologist. It was part of my training for my doctor's degree."

"Where did you get the money for your trip to Sweden in 1913?"

"Certainly not from you!" snapped Jules. His temper had

been rising steadily. "Is this a hearing or a baiting, my lad?"

"You are accused of scientific plagiarism, I believe?" asked Korndörfer, his eyes narrowed with zeal.

"You are not qualified to put such a question," retorted Jules. "I would not think of discussing scientific problems with you. I have the right to demand an investigation by a man of my own standing!"

"You did something special to win the Iron Cross?"

"You were in diapers when I was fighting in the trenches!"

"Were you wounded?"

"I was in a Russian hospital for eight months."

Jules' right hand twitched. Bodenheim held it back, and Jules recovered his calm. It was a trap! The questions did not really come from this long-winded youngster; he was only a mouthpiece for those higher up, who were bent on getting satisfaction for the outcome of the appeal.

"As a student, you got a very quick promotion as assistant in the legal seminar. How did this happen?"

"Ask the Professor who appointed me. He is, by the way, a storm trooper in Valhalla. . . ."

"I attach the greatest importance to your private life. Your wife is—of the Aryan race?"

"I am not familiar with that concept. I am an ethnologist. The term Aryan applies to a linguistic branch, not to race."

"So she is a Jewess?"

Jules turned white with rage. He sprang to his feet. Bodenheim grasped his arm.

"Professor Lips is tired," said he to Korndörfer. "Shall we conclude for today?"

"Certainly. Saturday morning at nine, we will go on."

Korndörfer was right. Saturday morning we went on—in the direction of Paris.

"If ever I run into that fellow again," said Jules, "there'll be murder. He epitomizes the whole thing. Dirt, lies, provocation, everything that is common and vulgar. He started on

[236]

the downhill road by whining for a job under Burgomaster Meerfeld; next, he offered himself to the Socialist Party, who threw him out. Now he sits at a desk in a brown shirt, passing judgment on me. The Third Reich has paid me its compliments once more, in the heroic figure of Korndörfer. It's useless to try to save the pension! I am leaving, and you are coming with me. There will be a lot of writing to do. Perhaps a decision has already been reached."

We went to Bodenheim. Jules told him that he would not meet Korndörfer again. Curiously enough, the lawyer put up no opposition.

"Please see him for me on Saturday, Dr. Bodenheim," said Jules. "It's barely possible that part of the pension can be saved. In two months we shall be penniless."

"And you, Herr Professor?"

"I am returning to the Saar. My wife will go with me and then come back for the last decision. I can't starve. I must look about for another post."

"I hope you are planning to remain in Germany?"

"Naturally. The Saar is my home."

"If you don't want to see Korndörfer again," said Bodenheim, after a few minutes' thought, "let's at least take him down a peg. He's getting altogether too pleased with himself. Write him a letter. Wait, I'll dictate something nice!"

I took a pencil and wrote down his dictation: "Dr. Bodenheim, Attorney-at-Law, Hansaring 32, Cologne. . . ."

"To you?" I interrupted in astonishment.

"Of course, of course. Just wait. You can write to me as your lawyer quite differently than to him. And then, you see, I can show him your letter."

"My dear Dr. Bodenheim: Yesterday I supplied all the information that I could possibly give to Herr Korndörfer in his capacity as recorder for the city. I do not feel well enough to endure any further hearing, as conducted by Herr Korndörfer.

"As you know, I am shortly to be called to a University abroad, so that there is no point in continuing the disciplinary investigation in hand, as far as its financial aspect is concerned. . . ."

"We can't write that," I interrupted again; "it isn't true. We are absolutely without means. Do you think that you can save the pension in this way? Besides, we have no definite appointment in view."

"Leave that to me, my dear lady! I know what produces an effect upon this man. Don't forget, he's an underling. When he hears that a foreign country is interested in you, your wishes will take on a totally different aspect, and you'll get your pension. I know these boys!"

Dropping his usual calm manner, he became very animated in his efforts to convince me. Jules smoked in silence, studying our counselor coolly. Unpersuaded, I continued to write as he dictated:

"As far as I was obliged, for personal and moral reasons, to defend myself, I have done so. Let Herr Korndörfer examine his three chief witnesses, my former students and my stenographer, concerning whom I can only quote the proverb: 'Trust not the informer, lest his tongue turn next on you.' Then let the Board of Inquiry decide.

Yours sincerely,
Julius Lips."

It was in no sense the sort of letter Jules would have written. But, after all, Bodenheim had won the appeal, and saw more clearly into the brown psychology of the day than he. I waited for Jules to say something. He merely rose to say good-bye, adding: "Do as you think best. I really don't care very much."

We thanked Bodenheim for his help and his readiness to act in our behalf, in spite of our absence. Two days later Jules had a letter from him.

"My dear Professor Lips: I have just forwarded to city recorder Korndörfer your communication of February the second, addressed to me.

[238]

"I have explained to Herr Korndörfer that, in view of the contents of your letter, I no longer desire to act as your representative and that I have relinquished the case. Your documents have been delivered to the city of Cologne.

"With German greetings! Heil Hitler!

Bodenheim."

Now we knew why he had dictated the letter which Jules had signed. The Lips affair was getting too dangerous for him. Courage is proclaimed by the Nazis as the virtue of virtues. By their deeds ye shall know them, and by their swastikas.

Perhaps we would not have gone so quickly if we had not received a strange telephone call the evening before Herr Korndörfer proposed to continue his hearing.

I would not care to say who telephoned. At the sound of the name Ziska turned white and handed the receiver to Jules without a word. He, too, was astonished. It was someone very near the top. His signature sufficed to rob a family of its father for a long time, or steal sons from their mothers forever.

"Professor Lips, this is your last uncensored telephone call. From tomorrow on you had better telephone only to your grocer. Furthermore, you have won an appeal. Your lawyer has been told to withdraw from the case. It would be better for you, my dear friend, to take a little holiday. For tomorrow I may be forced to take measures. Yes, to take measures. . . . And do drop me a postcard some time—from somewhere. You know that I am an old admirer of your work. A pleasant journey and good luck to you! I hope you have understood me."

"Very well, a thousand thanks, my dear friend . . ."

"Farewell!" said our rescuer, hanging up. He saved his "Heil Hitlers" for the corridors of government buildings.

At eight-twenty-three the next morning we took the express to Paris from South Cologne, letting Korndörfer wait in vain for his victim. When at ten o'clock four members of the criminal squad arrived in the Siebengebirgsallee with an order for the arrest of Professor Lips, all that Ziska could tell them was that the Frau Professor had just gone into town and that the Herr Professor had left to visit his mother in the Saar.

After searching the house from cellar to attic, the police were forced to content themselves with levying a fine because Tapir's license tag showed last year's date.

The taxi driver peered over the luggage piled high in front and drove us across the Boulevard St. Michel to the *Hôtel des Nations*, Rue Monge. Jules had continued to pay for his room, so that it was ready for him. Number 12.

The door of the house was narrow and the stairs steep and high. To the right one could look into the dining room where Madame was having supper with the house-man, Albert, and her two children. The little man, in a porter's apron and a Basque cap, got up joyfully when he recognized Jules.

"Monsieur Lipse!" he said, beaming. There was no difficulty about my using the room. Whether one, two or more persons occupied the bed had no effect upon the price. We climbed up to the second story.

The door knob was a little reluctant, but Albert finally succeeded in turning it and showed me his prize room, No. 12. Something indigo-orange hit me a violent blow in the eyes—it was the wallpaper, luridly colored and banded with broad gold stripes. However, between the red rep curtains framing the window a small slit of Paris could be seen. To the left was a cupboard just high enough to accommodate a pair of trousers. One had to be careful not to brush against it, for it was perilously balanced on a single right foreleg and half a left hindleg, like some lame old horse. The table under the window, a meter by half a meter square, seemed secure. To the right was a wash basin with running water. It actually functioned. A bookshelf and a night table, graced by a fork, knife and spoon, were next the alarm clock. The most comfortable seat was a huge chest, which one could just squeeze past; it contained the photographs for which student Fröhlich had searched our house in vain, those destined for "How the Black Man Looks at the White Man." Long ago they had been removed from the Nazi roof that had given them shelter in Cologne and had made their roundabout journey to the safety of No. 12, a pledge to future work. There were two chairs in the room, dangerous traps. One was heavily upholstered and had the shape of a Dolomite landscape. The other was hard and solid-looking, but with a tendency to fall apart. If one wished to use it, the best way was to lean against the wall and brace one's foot against the bed, which was covered with a hideous yellow counterpane.

Albert left with the remark that I must make the acquaintance of his pigeons, which were *"parfaitement jolis"* and that "Monsieur Lipse" was the only *"client sérieux"* in the hotel.

"What a wonderful room!" said I, and Albert left, highly satisfied.

"This is where you lived?" I asked Jules. "This is where you wrote those cheerful letters—at that table?"

"Albert is a good old soul, and this is Paris," he replied. "Somewhere in the world there was once a little house with a garden and roses and fruit trees— There was once a dog, and a maid in a neat apron who served us loyally. Once we lived in Germany. You do not yet know what freedom means!"

I hung a few of my clothes under the bookshelf. I washed and got ready, and we went out to supper in a Paris which I did not yet know. We walked down the steps laughing, choking over the whiff of garlic in the hall. Across the street there were dresses for sale, at twenty francs. At the corner an old man was scooping olives out of a keg, very painstakingly running his hand over the wooden spoon after circling the scum to the outer edge. "*L'In-tran—,*" sang the news-boys. We indulged in a last sinful visit to the *Capoulade*, then we finally gave ourselves up to a new and unknown city. It was a Paris without the Rue de la Paix, without taxis, without boulevards, without champagne, without money, where *l'esprit* is the coin of the realm. It was just as splendid a Paris as that which we had long loved.

Des Nations had a room which surpassed anything to be seen in Algiers, Venice, Marseilles or Morocco. It was about the size of a small bathroom, and the door did not shut. One glided past it in embarrassed haste, with one's face turned aside, for otherwise one might catch a glimpse of its temporary occupant. According to unwritten law, he should have held his newspaper in front of his face. Then one knew the cubicle was in use. Otherwise one had to glance through the three missing slats in the door, to make sure. The catch was loose and the door could not be locked. Scattered over the floor lay a litter of dirty newspapers from all over the world, Chinese, Persian, Russian, Sicilian, Yiddish and jour-nals from the Provinces. I presume that this room gave the hotel its name.*

February, 1934, was for me a journey of exploration into an unknown Paris, the great dump heap of wrecked human-ity, of philosophic beggars, living in a state of Oriental hy-giene and genuine light-heartedness. So we learned to love it afresh, this old improbable and incomparable Paris.

Naturally we spent as much time as we possibly could outside the lair in which we slept, as we had no desire to die of suffocation, though we were counting on a resurrec-tion from it to a new life. Nevertheless, we were forced to spend hours of intensive work in this den and I still marvel how we got anything done, with the leaky faucet dripping persistently and the typewriter bobbing up and down on the

* On a later visit to Paris, I found that the *Hôtel des Nations* had changed hands. It is now a very pleasant and well-managed place.—E. L.

table like a ship in a storm. An enormous pile of mail had arrived. The postmarks from Switzerland, Latvia, France, Russia, Rumania, London and Tokyo tempted one to pleasant dreams, but a glance at the contents of these letters showed us that dreams do not easily come true. We worked feverishly. Every new possibility, however slight, meant a session at the whirling loom—we spun our future on Jules' blue typewriter.

There were other more banal occupations which were nevertheless necessary. Among these was my attempt to reconstruct Jules' wardrobe. I had purchased a gaily colored darning egg, and enjoyed seeing the holes in his socks get smaller over it. I sat on the edge of the bed with its forlorn yellow counterpane, and while my needle moved my mind wandered among the beauties of Eze and the Mediterranean.

One day there was a knock. I gave a start of fright, the reflex of my recent experiences in Cologne. Jules was not in, and knocking did not belong to the code of manners prevailing in the Rue Monge. There was a pause, followed by a low but persistent shuffling and scraping. It could not be Tapir. He was in residence in his own house in Cologne on the Rhine.

I opened the door. After all, this was no member of the secret police of Herr Göring. In the dark corridor stood a man, smelling of pleasant spices. He pulled off his hat with a quick gesture.

"Madame Lips?" he murmured. "Heaven be praised, I have found you." His voice was both throaty and resonant, most unlike the Paris voice. I felt around in the dark for the wabbly switch and finally turned the light on. It fell on a black face framed in woolly hair. I had seen such heads before—in the western Sahara. The Tuareg remained where he was. I could not persuade him to come in.

"I am very glad to see you. You are looking for Professor Lips? He will be back soon. Do come in."

But he did not respond to my coaxing. There he stood,

[243]

his head bent low in stubborn humility. By the cut of his hair, I recognized the *imghad*, the bondman and slave who does not dare to step within the shadow of the foot of a white woman. I was so happy to see him! I had spent the most magic hours of my life in his country, among the courageous people of his tribe. Over Germany the swastika had risen—how uninteresting! Over Africa the stars of eternity rose. Under the African sky these proud herdsmen walked today as of old, looking up to the moon and telling stories of clanking spears and steadfast hearts as they had for thousands of years. And here on the threshold of No. 12 in the Hôtel des Nations, in Paris, stood this slave of the tribe of Tuareg, in all the simplicity of the desert plainsman. Only a moment ago I was darning stockings. The sight of him affected me as though I had found an apple blossom in the winter snow.

However, he could not stand there forever. Who knew how long Jules would be? He did not dare to address me, so I asked him what he wanted. Slowly he put his hand into the pocket of his European suit, and, without the slightest change in his animal-like attitude of submission and humility, placed a piece of paper on the threshold. Then he turned away, so as not to be obliged to see me bend down.

It was a sheet of hotel stationery, the handsome paper of the Grand Hôtel du Louvre. A few lines were written on it. It was a pity that Jules was away, I thought, recognizing the written symbols as Targi, a language which I could not read at all.

"Be good enough to tell me what's in it?" I said desperately. But the *imghad* was not used to such sentences. tried again.

"Why comest thou?" I said in the harsh French of the desert. The man murmured:

"*Rendez-vous* . . ." He could manage no more.

"But when? Where? At what time? With whom?"

"Tomorrow. Five."

I counted the hours on my fingers. "Thou art sure? One, two, three, four, five? Yesterday, today, tomorrow?" He nodded earnestly, a conscientious messenger. I laid a franc on the threshold. He glided away. In the next room the Persian began to practice the violin, a frightful sound. From the brushing of his teeth in the morning up to the French lessons which he took in the evening, we were compelled to listen to all the phonetic expressions of his life. But for the letter in my hand I should have thought I had had an hallucination, and would have returned shamefecedly to my stockings. As it was, I waited for Jules more impatiently than I ever had before.

He listened to my excited account, read the letter and said:

"Yes, we will go at five tomorrow."

Grand Hôtel du Louvre, luxurious lifts, carpeted halls. Suite 89. We knocked. The *imghad* who had called on me opened the door without a trace of recognition. He led us into a drawing room furnished in spindly Louis XVI, threw back the portières and vanished. A figure turned from the window. We recognized Boubaka.

The last time we had seen him he was wearing wide trousers, a burnoos, leather sandals and the blue veil with which these free dwellers in the desert cover their faces. He had come after sundown, as we stood gazing across the land of Ahaggar. He had called himself "our brother, who loved us." And he had put an amber chain around my neck, a safeguard against sickness and the evil spirits.

Naturally, he was much too elegantly dressed, and if he had not lifted those hands with their blue-tinted nails, those hands that twirled the lumps of cooked millet in a spinach-green-henna stew so skillfully, would we have recognized Boubaka? He smiled "soft as the moon," as they say in his language. He asked us to sit down; I first, then Jules, himself as host last, as decorum commands. No one would have guessed that the highest ideal of the composed and graceful man of the world before us was—an iron bed. When the French colonial centennial had taken place, Boubaka had been told that he might ask a favor of the Governor of Algiers, and without hesitating he had asked for an iron bed. It had traveled the long distance south by camel back, an iron bed with a mattress and a cover of down. We ourselves had admired it in his tent of hide. The other members of the tribe slept on the desert sands, or on the palm-woven angareb, as we had done. But Boubaka, our distinguished brother, owned a lacquered iron bed, such as white men have—those unbelieving dogs who understand comfort so well.

The imghad brought us bronze bowls of wonderful mocha, ground to the fineness of dust and boiled with sugar. It went to the head like hashish. It would have been indelicate to express our pleasure at seeing each other again aloud, or to ask personal questions, and furthermore, it would have made matters too easy for the listening spirits of evil.

Nevertheless, after an hour and a quarter we found that Boubaka had come to Paris to attend the congress of African chieftains. Why, we had been there ourselves! The director of the Trocadéro had invited us to a session at the Museum and we had been surprised to find ourselves at a magnificent fête, before a lavish array of delicate foods and rare wines, surrounded by a circle of exotic rulers in bristling regalia. A babel of tongues filled our ears, from the guttural dialects of the Sonike and Mande Djula of Guinea to the polished French of Martinique-born students at the Sorbonne. My attention was attracted to a little monarch of twelve, dressed in a violet uniform covered with stars and ostrich feathers, which would have caused General Göring to die of envy. He spoke French like Paul Reynal. Jules fell into conversation with a teacher from Dahomey, a highly intelligent Negro who was at the time attaché at the Ministry of Colonies in Paris. He left with us and we talked about Africa all night.

[246]

If we had stayed a little longer in the Trocadéro we should have met Boubaka, our indispensable co-worker of the desert. He had heard someone mention our name, learned that we were in Paris and found out our address.

"I am happy with a great happiness," said he, speaking French out of courtesy to me, but using the phraseology of his own language, "but sorrow is the reason for thy presence here, Lipis ibn Colon" (son of Cologne—he thought that Cologne was the name of our father—) "for thou art persecuted by Itlère."

He knew everything that had taken place in the German tribe, as it was mirrored in his great soul. Perhaps he wondered a little why one did not simply take a sword and challenge Itlère, but then, the actions of white men have always been strange. He who has grown up on the desert under the stars shows no surprise. Perhaps, too, the demon Itlère was more powerful than the waters of the rivers and the steel of swords.

After the fourth cup of mocha I felt slightly tipsy. I heard Boubaka warmly inviting Jules to return to the land of Ahaggar, to remain there forever.

"Thou shalt be free with great freedom, and rich with great riches," said he. "The imghad shall serve thee, and thou wilt dwell in a great tent. Never will Itlère come there. We shall be brothers and thou and thy woman shall love each other in great love."

Aimer en grande amour! I saw the bunches of garlic hanging in front of the tents, swaying in the wind. He who eats garlic shall live five hundred years, say the Tuareg. In the evening the young men sing songs in praise of their beloved, picking out the melodies on their single-stringed instruments. Formerly this tribe roved from the borders of the Rio de Oro of South Morocco, near the forbidden city, to the massive rocky walls of the Hoggar, to the Senoussi oases in the south of Tripoli, which the Italians had to fight so long to conquer.

Boubaka had also given me the jewel box of gazelle hide, shaped like a huge Easter egg and ornamented with paintings. The braids of the women of his tribe smelled of mutton fat; everything smelled of amber and of mutton fat which has turned rancid in the sun. Were we to seek our peace there? Exchange the savage for the primitive? The hills of Sesame were closing behind us. Germany was no more. We were to become Tuaregs.

Jules wove a garland of graceful negative; the uninitiated would have taken it for an acceptance! Heavens, there was still a world for us: Ziska, Tapir, the house and the book which was to be written, the book of the many photographs which Fröhlich had coveted. Nevertheless, if I had had to decide that evening, I would have straightway gone off with Boubaka and never have returned. Our tent would have stood in the desert.

Boubaka was not offended. He who has grown up on the desert under the stars does not show surprise. He wore a bracelet of black marble on his wrist, like a black snake. He smiled and said some time we would come nevertheless. Our tent was ready for us. We departed in a daze.

Jules' reasons for refusing were, of course, convincing: science, duty, the battle for truth and recognition. However, I cannot free myself from the thought that he did not wish to become a Tuareg because the tribe lives under matriarchal rule, and the women's hair smells of mutton fat.

On the Place Monge there is a big police station. All day mounted police trooped past our hotel into the great boulevards. We heard firing in the distance. We spent my last day writing letters. Tomorrow I must return to Cologne. One was less safe there than among the Tuareg—but what was happening in Paris?

The boulevards were filled with knots of people. As we crossed the Carrousel in the evening on our way to the Madeleine we noticed that the street paving was torn up. Taxis were on strike. There was shouting in the streets. Red flags fluttered against the tricolor. Stormy songs of hatred came from rival groups. From a Metro entrance a wounded man emerged, staggering, blood gushing from his head. Rebellion!

At the hotel I found a very confused letter from Ziska. There was again some trouble with the police; she made some allusion to "our pictures." They at least were here before our eyes, in a large box in Paris in the Hôtel des Nations. Out of precaution Ziska's letter was so framed that I could not tell what was the matter. It concluded: "Tapir and I are well," so I knew that both were still free. Nevertheless, I must go home at once. No more dreaming, no more yearning for the desert. I changed my plans, got a telegram through to Ziska indirectly that I would leave at once and reach home tomorrow morning. Farewell, Paris; farewell, Jules.

The shooting continued. The main avenues of the city were in turmoil. All Europe seethed, and now Paris, too, was in upheaval. It was the sixth of February, my twenty-eighth birthday.

XVII

Ziska broke down when I came home. During the three days of my absence she had been subjected to a hailstorm of alarms, but she had stood firm—our little rock!

On February fourth there had been the attempt to arrest the master of the house. At this she was able to laugh, and told me that she had played the part of the "trembling, frightened maid," wringing her hands in bewilderment, utterly at sea here alone in the house and completely deferential to the power of the State.

On the fifth of February came Korndörfer's renewed summons to the disciplinary inquiry, to be present at the interrogation of witnesses Scheller, Fröhlich and Fräulein Fasbender. This hearing had taken place the day before my return.

On the same fifth of February at ten o'clock in the morning two strange gentlemen rang at the garden gate and asked to speak to Professor Lips. Ziska replied that at the moment no one was at home. When were Professor and Frau Lips returning? asked the strangers. Ziska replied that they might return this evening. She felt more uncomfortable all the time. The police had been and gone with their warrant for arrest. Who could these be?

"We are from the secret State police," said one of them sharply. "We must get into the house! Let us in!"

"I cannot do that when no one is at home," replied Ziska. "Besides, how do I know that you really are what you say you are?"

One of them pulled out a blank brass tag and flashed it at her. The visit, he said, had nothing to do with Frau Lips; he wanted to speak to her, Franziska Zendrich, born in

Cologne-Nippes, June 6, 1915. Terrified, she opened the gate.

"Now, girl, out with the truth," roared the man, when they had reached the hall. "Where is Professor Lips?"

"At his mother's in Saarbrücken."

"And the Frau Professor?"

"She went with him."

"When is she coming back?"

"Perhaps today—perhaps in a week," said Ziska cagily.

"At what foreign university is Professor Lips going to teach?" he went on. "We know everything! Tell us the name at once, or you'll get into trouble yourself."

"I don't know, I don't know," sobbed Ziska. "It isn't true and I don't know, anyway."

"You don't know? What's your job here, eh?"

"A poor servant girl from the orphanage. The Herr Professor hasn't told me his plans for the future."

"If you're lying you'll get it in the neck! The concentration camp is intended for women like you. Come on, now, loosen up. Do you know a storm trooper named Zange? Has he ever been here?"

"Yes."

"How often?"

"A few times."

"I guess he's pretty intimate with your employers?"

"I don't know. I have never listened at the door when he was here. It's not a nice thing to do."

"Where does this storm trooper fellow live?"

"He's not my sweetheart; how should I know?"

"You can tell your master and mistress that we'll be back, my good girl, and then we'll have something to hear, you can depend upon it!"

They left. Ziska watched them from the window of the attic. Behind the two policemen two new figures bobbed up suddenly and joined them, they were student Fröhlich and attendant Fluss.

That evening she had written me the confused letter to Paris, and I admired her shrewdness in deducing a new threat to our photographs from the presence of Fröhlich and Fluss. Fröhlich had come because he knew the pictures, Fluss in order to carry them away.

But poor Ziska's adventurous fifth of February was not yet over. Toward six o'clock the telephone rang. It was the voice of a strange woman; she asked to speak to the Frau Professor at once. Of course Ziska thought that it was some new conspiracy of the police. Suddenly she made out a name she knew. The Zombi—just dragged off to prison!

And our telephone was being watched, she thought.

"We don't know any Zombi," she had the presence of mind to cry into the receiver. "You have the wrong number; don't keep me talking!" She hung up with a bang, dashed out to her bicycle and rode off to the suburb where the Zombi lived. There she found a strange girl in tears.

That morning, at the very hour when the secret State police were in the Siebengebirgsallee, the Zombi and his bride had gone out bicycling together. As they were returning to the city a motor car had suddenly stopped behind them. "Dismount at once, or we shoot!" came the order. They snatched the Zombi's revolver from his hip, pushed him into the car and drove off to his house. There they began to search, turning the place topsy-turvy, tearing through his few books and papers, smashing the flowerpots and ransacking the bed.

"What are you looking for?" the Zombi had yelled, but they told him nothing.

"You know, all right," was all they would say. The frightened girl stood by, crying helplessly. Then they led the Zombi away. She had not seen him since.

Ziska, whose belief in Dr. Bodenheim was unbounded, because he had won our appeal, promised the Zombi's bride help. She rushed to the nearest pay station and succeeded in reaching him at his office, although he generally was not there in the evening.

"This is Professor Lips' maid. Won't you please help me? I am all alone." And this poor girl from the orphanage talked so successfully to the great lawyer that he said he would see her the next day and hear about the Zombi.

"You can frighten all the Nazis, can't you, Dr. Bodenheim?" she asked, and the master mind promised his assistance. All the time his letter of betrayal, renouncing our case on the strength of a letter of his own dictation, was lying unopened at our house. Nevertheless, Bodenheim promised Ziska that he would help her! Such bewildering contradictions were only possible to characters of the Third Reich stamp. Who could work his way through such a maze?

On the afternoon of the same day Ziska was out walking with Tapir in the Siebengebirgsallee when a gentleman smiled most agreeably and raised his hat to her with a great flourish. Who was it but student Fröhlich, come to offer her an excellent position! The Herr Professor, as she knew, was to be arrested any moment, and she might become involved. Such a pretty girl could earn far more money. He had a friend, a rich, pleasant household, no children. . . .

"Denouncer!" cried Ziska, thoroughly familiar with the vocabulary of the day. "Tapir is trained to get his man. I need only give the order." By then Fröhlich was half-way around the corner.

"The idea!" said Ziska. "Imagine their thinking I'd have anything to do with him, of all people! And how he looked at our Tapir," she concluded, "as if he would have liked to shoot him!"

All this had been going on in Cologne while I was drinking Boubaka's mocha and playing with the idea of going to the Tuareg forever. I was ashamed.

When I was finally home again, Ziska's presence of mind and ready answers were over. She fell into my arms and sobbed out all the terror she had concealed from the enemy. If every soldier were like her! Now the responsibility was mine once more and I hoped that I would do half as well as Ziska, the most loyal human being I have ever met on earth.

"Put your hat on," said I; "we have a pressing errand to do. Tapir can come along."

We walked through the Luxemburgerstrasse, over the Barbarossaplatz and into the maze of narrow streets near the cathedral. I opened the door into a shop whose show windows displayed silver candlesticks and gems. A gray velvet tray was put before us, containing rings of all sorts in its slots—gold circlets set with rubies, topaz and small diamonds. I tried the prettiest ones on Ziska's finger, and then we bought the one she liked the best. It was gold set with a large amethyst. But we could not take it home with us, for it had to be engraved. Only two words: "For loyalty." Then we went back to our fortress.

After I had indulged once more in a suitable rage at Bodenheim's letter of betrayal, I decided to make use of him as long as I possibly could. I called him on the telephone and expressed my astonishment at the step he had taken. Had he not assured me in Jules' presence of his readiness to help me? To my surprise he asked me to come to see him the next afternoon. I had, of course, thought he would refuse to see me. He even gave me a hint of what was going on by telling me that he had been called up about some photos. Had I any idea what that might mean? So Ziska's assumption was right; it was again a question of the photographs for Jules' book. I assured Bodenheim that I could tell him all about it.

Meanwhile, there had been changes at the Rathaus. Burgomaster Zülsch, who in spite of being a Nazi was a discriminating Commissioner of Culture, had been thrown out of office. He had objected to the methods which the Third Reich used "to destroy decadent intellectuals" and had to the very last protested against permitting the theft of scientific material from the house of a scholar. As long as Dr. Zülsch was in power, they had been obliged to limit themselves to the triviality of The Lantern case and, making assurance doubly sure, putting the disciplinary inquiry into the hands of Korndörfer.

While I was steeling myself for the coming interview with Bodenheim, I came upon a letter written by the chairman of the Society for the Advancement of the Rautenstrauch-Joest Museum, which clearly stated that the pictures and their copyright were Jules' property. Scheller had throughout taken the stand that the photographs belonged to the Museum—by which, of course, he meant to himself—basing his claim on the fact that the mats on which they were mounted had come from the Museum storeroom. I considered, therefore, that this letter would be significant, in case anyone should take it into his head to "go legal" again.

Thus armed I entered the office of Bodenheim, the super-Nazi. He took immediate command of the interview. Like a tried and trusted counselor, who has only the interests of his client at heart, he gave me a detailed report of how matters stood, informing me of the status of the disciplinary inquiry, just as if he had never moved a finger except in our behalf, as if that letter of betrayal had never been written, and ended by saying that now, as always, he would be happy to serve us.

At last I could get a word in, and I told him outright that he had proved himself a real Nazi, a shifting opportunist who could deliberately deceive a client for his own advantage.

"You are quite right," he replied, "things were getting too hot for me. Korndörfer had begun to threaten me before your departure."

"So you framed that graceful trick, in advance!"

"I will really help you this time."

"But my confidence in you is gone."

"Well, dear lady, in that case let's found a mutual-mistrust corporation."

"As an experiment, let's. We might try out the combination of truth and falsehood."

"How little you know of the Third Reich!"

"You have done a great deal to teach me."

"You needn't pay the bill I sent you, Frau Professor. It was only for the sake of having something to show to Korndörfer."

"What do you really care about? The Third Reich or justice?"

"I care for power."

"Have you read *Laudin and His People?*"

"No, I don't believe I have."

"I'll bring you the book. It might interest you to see what a lawyer with a conscience looks like. But it's by that Jew, Wassermann."

"Oh, do bring it. It would interest me enormously."

"Now, let's stop quarreling. Tell me your scheme."

He began with the case of the Zombi, our poor vanished Zombi, whom I was determined to help. Bodenheim had glibly promised Ziska his staunch support, but I now found out that he knew nothing whatsoever about the matter. I told him the story very discreetly; as reservedly, in fact, as though I were telling it to a storm-troop commander. He shook his head. I did not believe him, nor he me! The mutual-mistrust corporation. I concluded that I would have to take this delicate matter, which gave me no peace, into my own hands.

In regard to our scientific photographs, he said, we were legally in the right. That was hardly news, but it was interesting to have the point made by a representative of the Third Reich. He discussed it pro and con for a time; then suddenly he changed to a bantering tone.

"By the way, just where are these precious photographs at the moment?"

He was really too tricky! I burst into a laugh.

As for the visit of the secret State police, Bodenheim made light of it. It was nothing—just putting the screws on a frightened servant, to see what they could get out of her. He had nothing to suggest.

"And who is to represent us with Korndörfer?" I finally asked.

"You won't find any lawyer to take it on, if even I can't. But for this sort of inquiry one does not need a lawyer. According to law, 'any citizen in good standing, recognized as such by the Board of Inquiry' will do."

That was entirely new to me. "An intermediary, but not a lawyer" had already appeared in Jules' name to treat with the Nazis. Couldn't I try it again?

When I made the suggestion, my hostile partner laughed at me. But I had made up my mind.

"There's something I want to tell you," said Bodenheim. "You and the Herr Professor take far too firm a stand. The Nazis can't bear that. Why the devil don't you keep your mouths shut when those chaps talk nonsense?"

"Would you keep quiet, if some little minor assistant suddenly took your place at your desk and played the chief?"

"Certainly. If he were in power."

"The magnificent thing about you is that when the doors are carefully closed, you now and again whisper the truth! Why are you not a Minister? You are the incarnation of the Third Reich!"

"Great things come slowly."

"Good-bye, Herr Bodenheim. I wonder which of us is going to lie the more in the future, you or I? I'll tell you a secret. The famous pictures are in our house in Cologne-Klettenberg. Now, if you rush right out and notify the secret State police, you can win a star for your collar!"

I continued to make use of him at times, and now and again he gave me some bit of information. I also lent him Jacob Wassermann's book. He read it with great interest, discussed it with me and never returned it. On the other hand, I never paid his bill.

From Bodenheim's office I went home to get a bite to eat. I had to know what had become of our Zombi. By round-about means I found that August Zange was home again. I sent word to him that I must see him and arranged to meet him in the most crowded part of the inner city that same afternoon, in a little café frequented by chauffeurs, which I thought safer than any of the suburban inns.

It was a rendezvous possible only in the Third Reich. I sat in front of a glass of Cologne beer—although I never touch beer—and waited for the Zombi. I hardly recognized him when he entered. No clicking of heels, no "Heil Hitler!" A poor laborer in borrowed shabby civilian clothes, his cap awry over his ear, very far indeed from a smartly uniformed storm trooper on his way to a clandestine meeting with a lady.

I stretched out my hand to him and he joined me in the dark corner. He looked shaken; his gestures were vague and uncertain. He smoked one cigarette after the other. Finally he told me what had happened.

As a storm trooper, he was liable to discipline for any lapse of duty, not by the regular police, but by the special police of the S.S., which was extremely drastic in its punishments, having had orders to keep any and all disturbances within the ranks of the Hitler units from the knowledge of the public.

The Zombi had at once recognized the two men in the car following him and his girl as superior officers, members of the Party police. Denunciations were the order of the day. What the charge was, and who had filed it, would come out in time. As an ex-legionnaire, the Zombi had had the presence of mind to wait quietly for the outcome of the rough-and-tumble house search. This done, the officer in civilian garb ordered the Zombi into the car. Off they drove to troop headquarters in the Mozartstrasse, where they summarily locked him up for the night.

"I never thought I'd get out alive," said he. "Too many of us have disappeared like this. It's always the old soldiers. Well, that would be the end of it. Anyway, I could never get work again. No one wants to employ a storm trooper spy. The staunchest Nazis are the worst, because we have been in the Party longer than they and we don't give in very easily. Anyhow, one way or another, the crash had to come. . . ."

Next morning he was brought before a high Party officer who went straight to the point with his first question.

"Do you know Professor Lips?"

"Yes, sir!"

"Do you know that he is a swine of a Marxist?"

"No, sir!"

"That the Minister kicked him out because he is politically unreliable?"

"I only knew that he had been dismissed, sir."

"And why the hell shouldn't he be dismissed? What in hell did you find to talk about with him? You . . ." The Zombi felt himself obliged to expurgate his superior's mode of address.

"About Africa, sir."

"About Africa? You must think I'm drunk to believe that. A storm trooper in a Marxist den! Treason!"

He had been overwhelmed with threats. "You know, the kind one shakes off the way a dog shakes water off his back. I was to kick the bucket, and all that sort of thing."

"You don't mean—the death sentence?"

"Sure. What do you think goes on in our gang? The next thing I heard was that that swine Lips was in prison in Bonn, and had confessed everything."

"What do you mean—'everything'?"

"That the articles now coming out in the Saar papers on the inside doings of the S.S. had been written by him, and that he had got the dope from me!"

That was devilish—for the Zombi too believed that Jules was in the Saar. No one except Ziska and I knew that he was in Paris.

"He was never in Bonn and never in prison," I told the Zombi, "nor is he in the Saar. What dastardly lies! It's horrible! As though he had time to write articles! And of all things, about the S.S.! What possible interest could he have in that subject?"

"I didn't believe it for a second," said the Zombi. "I know their methods too well. I've had to use them myself in quizzing some of the S.A. chaps. My instructions were: 'Yell your head off at them—it doesn't matter what crazy stuff you tell them. They'll confess, all right. If not what you expect, then something else that will serve.' Sure, I knew it was all a bluff. It wasn't intended for me at all. They wanted to get the Herr Professor; that was clear."

Witnesses to the Zombi's treasonable activities were on hand to testify—lawyer Barthels, Rodens and one of the editors of the *Westdeutscher Beobachter*. Then he realized that it was revenge, because they had seen him with us in court. He was asked whether he had seen French newspapers at our house, or possibly mimeographs. But the ex-legionnaire was sharp—far sharper than the slow-witted upstarts who were examining him. *Rien à faire*—nothing to do but stand up to the crew! He even managed to convince them that he was a particularly meritorious spy. It ended with his signing a pledge never to see Jules or me again, never to speak to us, or to enter our house. He was dismissed with the order, if he ever saw Jules again, "to bash his face in."

And there he sat before me laughing. Nevertheless, I saw how deep his contempt and bitterness cut. The "Movement," which he had once served with all his heart, he now saw for what it was. A structure of lies, denunciations, threats and terrorism, preying upon all that was best in the land. An old soldier had his standards—this kind of thing was nauseating.

"Some day I'll tell them to their faces!" he burst out vehemently. "Some time it will have to come out. I don't give a damn what they do to me." He implored me to take him abroad with us and I solemnly promised we would. How indeed could we desert him? He had risked his life for our sake and for the sake of his convictions.

"Take me with you," he exclaimed, although I had no idea where we ourselves were going. "Wherever there is fighting to be done, I can do it!"

I looked at him sadly. The battlefield on which he had learned to fight was so different from ours. The weapons he could handle were as incomparable as biceps and brain. Zombi, poor Zombi, who had seen so much injustice, who was too deeply infected with the poison of brutality ever to be able to understand the tenacious struggle of the spirit!

Above all I urged him not to run any further risk, under no circumstances to come to our house. I would try at once to get him into a country where an honest soldier can still shoot a gun or draw a sword. He must be patient. And he promised to wait. He had fixed all his hopes on a new life. But I had a horrible feeling that it was too late. He was too embittered, too disillusioned. His ideals were gone, all but one—he still loved truth. And what could he do with that in the Third Reich? He had the brown, healthy face of a bandit; he had the vigor and trained muscles of an athlete; but he had no strength for the human struggle. It was too late. He had lost his faith, his faith in Germany, which he had identified with Hitler. His idol was of straw, and the flames had consumed it and his Fatherland together.

A few weeks after our conversation, he let me know that he had gone to Berlin, where he had been offered a post. In the meantime I had been making arrangements in his behalf. I wrote him that friends in Berlin would be glad to give him a good home. He did not reply, and I was beginning to think that sudden prosperity had turned his head.

I was glad in any case for any good thing that might befall him.

Late in July of 1934, when I had moved to another quarter of the globe, I had news of him in a letter signed "a comrade of your Zombi." Storm trooper August Zange, of Flensburg, had been shot on July the third. He had made libelous statements about storm-troop activities in connection with the National Socialist purge. Zange had asked him, the undersigned, to give Professor and Frau Lips his last greetings. The writer was to tell us that "the Zombi now knew what made a man strong—and it was not firearms." He was sending, under separate cover, a book intended for Frau Lips, who had always been amused by it. Zange had gone to his death cheerfully. His last words were: "No more worry about how to make a living," adding a remark which the undersigned, himself a storm trooper, was not able to repeat lest he jeopardize his own safety.

Before long I held a spotted, dark-green volume in my hand. I knew it well. The Zombi had often pulled it out of his pocket and read bits of it to us and shown us the snapshots pasted in it. The diary closed with the words: ". . . advanced, and there is nothing much more to this. Tomorrow I leave Marakesh. It has all been grand. I shall never again experience anything like it."

There was nothing about the Third Reich in the book. Zombis do not write down their grief.

If there is a special heaven for martyrs, those who have died for truth will sit on a special throne in this special heaven. They will have all their wishes granted, no matter how far-fetched: a platter of ham and dumplings, Moroccans in flight, French wines and Sweet Caporals, henna-palmed dancing girls and—a Fatherland in which one may be honest.

But I am still in Cologne. The next morning's mail brought a new summons for Jules in connection with the disciplinary inquiry. In two days they were to hear the testimony of witness Schoppe, the Rathaus official who had examined Jules the day that we had caught our trout in Buchensee. The time for delay was past. I was to see the famous Korndörfer face to face at last.

He was a man, I a woman. He was my enemy and I wanted him at least to be afraid of me. I put on a lilac satin blouse, straight from Paris, a dove-gray skirt and a little light fur jacket, my prettiest shoes, stockings and gloves. I was armed, without and within.

I took the tram to the Waidmarkt, and walked through the narrow streets near the Rathaus until I came to Number 30 Unter Goldschmied, as the street was still called, from the days of the guilds. Korndörfer lived on the first floor. I walked up the creaking steps. In front of a door marked "Assembly Room" stood several men. To the left I discovered a baize-covered door bearing the card: "City Recorder Korndörfer." I knocked. Someone called "Come in." A man in a brown shirt got up from the desk as I entered and said "Heil Hitler!" I replied "Good morning." The telephone rang.

"Just a moment," he whispered pleasantly, pointing to an armchair close to his own. Then he picked up the receiver and said:

"Korndörfer speaking. Heil Hitler, Herr Doktor!" So it was he. While he telephoned I had time to watch him. He was like a poppy-seed roll—narrow head, flat forehead, pink cheeks and doll-like hair. He had the dainty ears of a sub-altern, the thick hands of a mason. His suit was ready-made, his point of view presumably also ready-made. Both off the rack. His eyes were false, his glance undecided, his voice pitched far too high for virility. As he was evidently talking to a superior, his manner was servile. He looked like a boy from the skating club who is allowed on the men's team for the first time, and is struggling between fear and self-confidence. Was this the "sadist" who had caused Bodenheim to betray us and had raised Jules' temper to white heat? This stupid little boy? I was astonished. He really did not look like much of an enemy.

"Heil Hitler, Herr Doktor, and my most respectful thanks." The telephone conversation was over. I sat at ease in my deep chair.

"Permit me to introduce myself," he twittered, bending from the waist like a boy at a dancing lesson. "Korndörfer is my name."

"It is very pleasant that we are introduced," I said. "I expect we shall be meeting fairly often. I am Frau Lips."

He did what any other boy would have done in such an unpleasant situation—he turned scarlet. Then he seated himself, straightened his back and struck a professional attitude.

"Do I understand you? Not Frau Professor Lips?"

"Quite right. Since, as you probably know, Dr. Bodenheim no longer represents us, I have come to introduce myself as Professor Lips' new legal representative."

"Yes . . . but . . ."

"Here is my power of attorney. Will you please examine it?"

I had filled out as well as I could one of the blank sheets of paper to which Jules had affixed his signature. "I felt that it was nicer to come and introduce myself to you, because I am to attend tomorrow's hearing in place of my husband. He is ill, you know."

"He must come himself!"

"What a pity, you aren't at all pleased to see me! I thought that perhaps you would prefer me. So many hostile men! Isn't it nicer to have a woman to deal with for a change?"

"Professor Lips is reported ill?"

"Yes, reported. You know that he still suffers from his war wounds. He came to see you recently in spite of his illness. But I was afraid he might get excited and have a heart attack right before your eyes, so we obeyed the doctor's orders and he has returned to his care."

"He seemed perfectly calm in my office."

"Dear Herr Korndörfer, an old war veteran maintains his discipline until he drops, as you know. You were in the War, too, I take it."

"No."

"How stupid of me! You are too young. You appear to be a contemporary of mine. A pity we can't have a game of tennis together. I wish I'd got as far as you have. City Recorder! My, my! Whereas I am for the time being merely a defendant. That means your enemy. However, I hope you won't hate me too much." I laughed. He was quite helpless and doubtless wished me to perdition.

"Malicious accusations are constantly being made against my client," said I, growing very dignified over the word "client." "I would really like to know who is back of them."

"What do you mean?" he asked.

"We are said to have some mats in our possession, which the student Scheller is claiming."

"I don't know anything about it," said he quickly. Bodenheim, however, had told me that Korndörfer was involved in the whole business of the pictures.

"Why don't you go to Scheller?" he added.

"I? Go to a man who has denounced my husband, who has just lost a slander suit against him, in spite of the support of the State? A student of his, who has suddenly assumed the rôle of a miniature Hitler?" I was surprised that he listened to me without the slightest rejoinder. I became so pleased with myself that I added: "Of course, never having been at college, you probably don't know enough about the academic world . . ."

"How do you know that we want the pictures?" asked the skating-club junior, giving himself away completely. He was waiting to hear Bodenheim's name.

[265]

"It has reached my ears," I replied, smiling. "I have some connections with the secret State police. In fact, I have some documents in my possession which will be very annoying. I know the inside story, as well as why they waited until Commissioner Zülsch was dismissed before taking action. There's one little thing more that I would like to know. Will we get our pension on the first of March? I must arrange my household accordingly."

"I think that you are not dependent upon that. I understand Professor Lips has accepted a post outside of Germany."

"Oh, dear," I observed in discouragement, "all this lying makes life very hard. Now, I promise you, I'm going. I only wish I could find out who my client's chief enemy is, and who is back of all this persecution. Frankly, at first I thought it was you. But now that I see how nice and young and candid you are—do tell me who it is!"

"Is this a hearing?" he broke out angrily.

"What an idea! Just a friendly get-together of two sympathetic natures! I've enjoyed it so much. Good-bye, Herr Korndörfer. Until tomorrow!"

I was out of the door before he had the time to say "Heil Hitler."

It was one thing to put on a show of nonchalance, not to say recklessness, with lads like Korndörfer and our other irritating opponents; but when I was alone, things looked different. From hour to hour I expected to be locked up, so much so that I wrote a letter to my parents for Ziska to deliver in case this should occur. It hung over me like a nightmare that they might avenge themselves on me in Cologne at the very moment that Jules found a refuge for the future. He would never have been able to return to help me, nor could I ever have escaped from the snare by myself.

The afternoon after my gay visit to Korndörfer, Ziska and I sat talking together, low-spiritedly, discussing what we would do when matters got serious. The telephone rang and we both jumped.

"This is the secret State police. Is Professor Lips at home?"

"I regret not to be able to inform you over the telephone. It seems very odd that the secret State police should communicate with me by telephone."

"Why?"

"Because I have been annoyed frequently of late by false telephone messages."

"You are mistaken."

"I am at your service if you wish to speak to me. I am Frau Lips."

"Will you be at home tomorrow morning?"

"No, but you can come now. I shall expect you."

"Very well, we'll come."

Now what was this? Korndörfer getting even? A bluff of Fröhlich's to break my nerve? For no secret State police could be stupid enough to announce a visit beforehand by telephone!

However, such was the case. They came, two quite common, rough-mannered individuals, a fat man with a bald head and a sullen-looking man with a little moustache. Ziska recognized her friends. She remained in the room. I showed them Tapir's new dog license in case they had come on that account.

"We have come," said the sullen one, "in order to put the pictures in safe keeping."

"Pictures?" said I in surprise.

"Photographs!"

"Ziska, please bring our photographs," said I, pointing to the little cabinet in the corner. "Why do you want to put them in safety, gentlemen? They are pretty, but why should they interest the secret State police? See, that is St. Mark's in Venice; there is my friend Jacquino, of Monte Carlo. Here I am in a bathing suit. This is our dog."

"We mean different pictures." He brought out a slip of paper. "Pictures on mats belonging to the Museum."

"Oh, you mean our scientific data? You should have said so in the beginning. But unfortunately my husband is away at the moment. Ziska, where could he have put those pictures? You don't know, either? He has probably sent them to some publisher. How stupid! Now we can't give them to these gentlemen."

"We must take those pictures with us at once!"

"Isn't that more the line of the ordinary police? What has the secret State police to do with it? I thought the latter was only political."

"The secret State police deals with everything!"

"That is interesting. Thank you!"

"Where are the pictures?"

"I am so sorry. I don't know. I do not rummage around in my husband's things."

"We will give you seven days—until February sixteenth. If you have not delivered the pictures to us by then, you will have to take the consequences!"

Nevertheless, they went upstairs to Jules' study, opened the desk and looked in the drawer in which the finest pictures had been when Fröhlich had first searched the house. They found nothing. Reminding me of the time limit set and repeating their threat of "consequences," they departed. Ziska and I were sunk in gloom. The outlook was bad. "If only we had a few other pictures," sighed Ziska. "Those fellows wouldn't know the difference."

"No," said I, "we'll find another way. The interval must not expire. Tomorrow I'll go to the head of the secret State police."

"For the love of heaven, Frau Professor!"

"The heads are always better than the subordinates. That's an old maxim. And before that I'll go to Korndörfer."

"I hope we'll still be free tomorrow night."

I took Ziska's hand, the one on which she wore an amethyst ring.

"Let us trust our lucky star a little," said I, and with that we recovered our spirits.

XVIII

Nine o'clock was the hour set for the hearing. I came fifteen minutes ahead of time, the first to arrive. Korndörfer, in a light civilian suit, greeted me and offered me a straight chair near the window.

"You are early!" he grumbled, rustling the documents on his desk.

"Yes."

There was a pause. The frantic pumping of my heart frightened me. I was astonished to find myself talking to God, thanking Him that Jules was not here and begging Him to be near me. I was still more surprised to hear myself talking to the city recorder, the Nazi Korndörfer.

"Do you know that the secret State police came to see me yesterday?" I asked him.

"What did they want?"

"To confiscate our collection of photographs."

"I have nothing to do with that."

"I was told it was at your instigation!"

He did not reply. There was a knock; a man came in. He was fat and looked harmless. Korndörfer introduced him.

"The attorney general, Dr. Liebering."

Attorney general? Later I found out that he was simply a town councilor who had assumed this title for the duration of the disciplinary inquiry, probably only in order to intimidate me. One of Korndörfer's little tricks.

The "attorney general" with a show of courtesy offered me a more comfortable chair. The fact was that he wanted to sit near the window in order to observe me better. It was the old device; the light dazzled my eyes and I could not see his face.

There was silence for a time. Then Korndörfer began:
"I really do not know whether we can permit Frau Lips
to attend. She has, it is true, produced a power of attorney
from the defendant. But she is not an attorney-at-law. I do
not think we can permit her presence."

"Of course you can permit me to attend," I retorted. "I
have been so informed at the headquarters of the Inquiry
Division."

"So you have been knocking around that office, too?"
asked the enemy in a fury.

"Like yourself!" I replied.

"I think we will exclude Frau Lips," he persisted. "You
need only say the word, Mr. Attorney General, and she will
be obliged to leave."

"I do not ask her to," replied the fat man. "I have no objections to the presence of Frau Lips."

A friend, I thought with relief, and felt my heart grow
lighter. I could have hugged him, though he did look like a
sea-elephant.

A stenographer came in carrying a typewriter, followed by
a thin man of about forty, the subaltern type; it was witness
Schoppe, the city clerk.

"Let's get started," urged the attorney general, and I remained.

Korndörfer began by dictating the record for the stenographer to type. "Frau Lips, wife of the defendant, appeared
with a power of attorney." Very pointedly, he went on:
"The defendant, according to his legal representative, is at
present in Saarbrücken."

This city, as we know, was regarded at the time as the
meeting place of "Marxist elements," a focal point for anti-
Nazi activities. Barthels had already cited the fact in the
first trial and also against the Zombi, in order to associate
Jules' name with the aura of treason, which Saarbrücken—
ruled at that time by the League of Nations—had for every
Nazi.

So I said at once: "Please include in the record why my client is in Saarbrücken. He was born in Saarbrücken and spends several weeks of every year there. Nor can he remain in Cologne; the illegal withdrawal of half his salary makes it financially impossible for him to live in his own home with his family."

Witness Schoppe spoke up: "That is not the fact. Professor Lips is to receive his full salary until the last day of February!"

I replied: "Beginning with the first of December, Professor Lips' salary was entirely withheld. When it finally was paid, it was one hundred and nine marks instead of the six hundred due! I have had to sell my jewels in order to be able to live at all!"

They were not in the least interested in what we lived on. Herr Schoppe was sworn in and gave his testimony: "After the Hitler régime had come into power, the defendant had conspired with Marxist leaders. Even the Social Democratic Party secretaries had known him well. Consequently, treasonable intentions, if not activities, on the part of the defendant are undeniable."

"Is this a criminal trial or an inquiry bearing on our pension?" I interrupted, and demanded that the Social Democratic Party secretaries referred to be called as witnesses in regard to their "conspiracy" with my client.

Korndörfer replied: "I refuse to summon these witnesses. They are irrelevant." "Irrelevant"—it was the very word that Justice Bünger had shouted at Dimitroff, familiar also from our first trial. And here sat the little poppy-seed roll repeating it once more.

I turned to my "friend" and said: "Mr. Attorney General, please give the order for the testimony of these Party secretaries."

He replied: "If you ask me, I must refuse. You must go at it differently. If you were to make a written request in the name of your client, I could recommend it."

He had helped me again by showing me the technical way. How grateful I was to this man!

"We should require the addresses of Party secretaries Müller and Wieke in order to give them a hearing," said Korndörfer quickly and maliciously. He really thought that I would be stupid enough to give their addresses, thereby offering proof of my own treason. I shrugged my shoulders and said I would endeavor to find out where these gentlemen lived.

"Useless, they have fled from Germany," said Korndörfer with finality. I expressed my regret. This, too, was a lie. Both men had been in concentration camps; one of them had died the week before as the result of his treatment there; the other was living quietly in his own house. I knew these two men well, for they had often come to the Museum to arrange tours of inspection for working-men's clubs and had received the same help and courtesy as the National Women's Clubs, the Catholic Societies and all others who came to us because they cared about the Museum. This was translated into "Marxist activity!"

Schoppe continued: "When Lips came to the Rathaus, he made an embarrassed, timid impression." I compared this with Bodenheim's remark: "You both take far too firm a stand. Why don't you keep your mouths shut when those chaps talk nonsense?"

Schoppe went on, muttering that "his whole impression was the impression of a traitor."

Witness Schoppe himself gave the impression that he was saying what he had been told to say. He seemed to be clinging desperately to a few memorized phrases. When he ended by saying "Lips' claim to a pension must not be granted," Liebering interrupted him.

"That is a decision for us to make, my dear Schoppe," and declared the hearing over. I dropped the sheet of paper on which I had been quietly taking it down in shorthand. Liebering leaned over and picked it up for me.

[273]

"May I ask what the next step in the inquiry is to be?"

"My investigation is at an end," replied Korndörfer. "I shall give my report to the attorney general. He will give it to the Mayor. The Mayor will give it to the president of the government board. The president will then instigate the final proceedings, at which your client must appear. After that a decision will be reached in regard to the pension."

I telephoned Ziska that all was well. I was now going on my second errand, to the president of the secret State police. I intended to take the bull by the horns in the matter of the attempted confiscation of our pictures. If only I succeeded in seeing the bull himself!

In the corridor of police headquarters I asked for the chief. The little policeman looked at me as though I were crazy.

"Why, you can't see him," he said, as though I had asked for God Himself.

"Supposing I knew something about a murder?" I whispered confidentially. Thereupon he betrayed the name and room number of the great unknown: Chief of the Bureau of Criminal Investigation Pütz, third floor, Room 325.

I went up the broad steps and found myself upstairs under the roof. Why, it seemed familiar! Oh, yes, this is where I had come with Jules about getting back our books. It was also where he had been asked: "How long have you been a Communist?" There was the sign: "Knocking forbidden." I knocked and went into the room. A young man in a brown shirt rushed up to me and said I must go into the hall and wait until a gentleman came out of the chief's room. Then I could come in. The window was very high. I wondered whether anybody had ever jumped out of it. In the courtyard below a small police motor-car was getting ready to start. Five minutes, ten minutes.

The door opened, a gentleman came out and I went in to the chief. A very, very fat man sat at the desk, sly but not mean, more the pachyderm than the snake.

I mentioned my name. He got up. I heard no "Heil Hitler" in this office. Those at the very top do not need this expression, only the little people and the insecure ones.

"I have come about a very important matter and it seemed to me proper to address myself to you, Mr. President." ("President" is always right!)

He pointed his red little ears and wrinkled his forehead like a puppy.

"Do you know that yesterday the secret State police came to our house to confiscate my husband's scientific material?"

The pachyderm reacted in an unexpected manner. He burst out laughing like a schoolboy.

"Isn't my business important enough for you?" I asked, offended.

He stretched his heavy paw across the table, patted my hand and said in the gentlest tone imaginable:

"I only take charge of murders, my little woman!"

It was like a detective story. The air breathed crime, pursuit and vengeance. And I, who had come in deadly earnest, stood there like a clown inviting ridicule.

"Where am I to go?" I asked, discouraged. He advised me to go to Crime Commissioner Becker, Room 425. I was to say that he had sent me.

I thanked him and left. Outside it struck me how unprotected he was, in spite of all the signs on his door. How easily someone could have avenged a grievance! He was as naked and harmless in there as Marat in his tub.

Another waiting room. Expectancy, fear, anxiety. At last I was admitted.

Here, too, a fat man sat at a desk. But he hurled a loud "Heil Hitler" at me. However, those who greet you this way after an involuntary "good morning" are not quite the worst.

At last I had tracked down the right man. It was he that had sent the men into our house. He had had "information."

"Another denunciation by Scheller and Fröhlich!" I said. "I wonder where I'll have to go to silence those two!"

It developed that he had not yet seen two letters which I had given the policemen to hand over to their chief. Since these letters contained written proof that the pictures were incontestably our private property, they were my most important trump against the claim advanced by Scheller. They had "forgotten" to deliver them.

The Crime Commissioner struck a bell. The two policemen who came in were taken aback at seeing me. They stood there like a pair of whipped dogs, not in the least like the two bold bullies who had been in my house. Without a word they handed over the letters and vanished. I was alone with the Crime Commissioner.

The ranking official of the secret State police, the dread of countless innocent families in Cologne, suddenly got up, listened attentively at the two doors of his office and closed them carefully. Then he returned to his desk. There stood a little silk swastika mounted in a bronze frame. He picked it up, turned it over playfully in his hand, looked at it a moment and then placed it on the floor near his desk. There it stood, close to the cuspidor. It was of the same height.

I understood—or did I dare to understand? We now sat close to one another. Were we enemies or conspirators? I found nothing to say.

"Where is Professor Lips?" he asked. "Is he well? In good spirits? Don't let him lose courage. He will find friends and work elsewhere! He had many friends in Cologne. Men of his sort are rare. He did not yield. Give him my regards."

I was silent. I was afraid. It would be easy to make a remark that would send me to a concentration camp.

"Has he anything in view? Is he safe? Oh, you need not reply. I am not pumping you! You are afraid—quite naturally. It was I that ordered your books released. I saw your exhibition of masks. I know Professor Lips quite well; he would remember me. He personally conducted my club

[276]

through the Rautenstrauch-Joest Museum. But we are not here to amuse ourselves. Do you know that I have been ordered to arrest you?"

"Me!"

"Professor Lips is not here, the pictures are not here! But you are here!"

"You can't do that! I am all alone! I have a little house and live in it without hurting anyone!"

"I, too, have my superiors, my dear Frau Professor."

"If it is Bureau Chief Pütz, I know him! Let us go to him at once!"

"My instructions came from Berlin!"

"And the denunciations from Cologne! In heaven's name, who is behind these students? They alone could not have all this power!"

"One is behind the other; over one little Führer stands another, then comes a regional Party Führer, over this little man the petty chief of the division, then comes a petty State councilor subservient to a councilor of the State, then the minister—and so it goes on up and up until we come to the very top, where a cloud hangs over everything. That is your authoritarian state!"

Where was I? I did not know whether to be more frightened or astonished. Was this a comedy? Was this the last refinement of intrigue? I decided not to express the slightest opinion, but to deal with facts.

Briefly I gave the history of the whole campaign of persecution, from the attempts to find "corruption" in the Museum to the lost *Lantern* case, from the charge of plagiarism by the Association of German Museums to the disciplinary inquiry. I told him the whole chain of events. I described what the pictures meant to us! An intellectual and material possession, an idea, the tools of scholarship. This to be handed over to those students? Never! First, the pictures were not ours; then they represented an offense against the new theories of race! We needed the pictures! Could he

[277]

not understand this? A carpenter needs his plane, and a tailor his scissors!

The Crime Commissioner listened in profound silence. Was he honest or false? Today I know that he was honest. At that time I distrusted his every breath, his every syllable.

"I am to produce either the pictures, or you," he said slowly. "The students have already tried the attorney general on the pictures, but he declined to take up the case."

"A new lawsuit against my husband! I would rather go to prison at once!"

"No, no! There won't be any lawsuit! That's why the matter has been put into my hands. They are now taking the quieter way."

There must be a solution. I must find some loophole; above all, gain time! An interval, during which some miracle might take place in the Rue Monge.

"You must give me the pictures. I regret it, but I have special orders! Pressure is to be brought to bear on Professor Lips. They want to get you out of the way for another reason."

"Korndörfer! He really is the basest of them all."

"I haven't said anything!"

"No, you haven't said anything. But I'll say something to you. You'll get the pictures. But first we need them for our scientific work. Give me an interval before handing them over. Let us say three months. Up to the first of May."

"Three months! That's too long!"

"Don't you see that we have to go through all the pictures and get them captioned? That will take at least nine weeks. But you shall have your guarantee. I won't run away. I swear to give myself up if I do not keep my word. Won't that do?"

"It might, at a pinch. We might stretch a point. But I must dictate quite definite conditions to you. Write them down:

[278]

"First: Professor Lips' wife swears that she will not leave the precincts of the city of Cologne before and inclusive of the first of May. Any attempt to leave is punishable by imprisonment.

"Second: The pictures which Professor Lips has mounted on mats belonging to the Museum, and which are in opposition to the racial theories of our Führer, shall not be removed from Cologne.

"Third: The above-mentioned pictures shall be delivered in their entirety by nine o'clock of the morning of the first of May to the secret State police.

"Fourth: Frau Lips is responsible with her person for any possible alterations in the pictures. The pictures are regarded as having been confiscated by the State, since they do not coincide with theories of our Party and since, moreover, the director of the Rautenstrauch-Joest Museum claims them as the property of the Museum.

"Typewrite all this, sign it, and don't budge from Cologne! Send me the letter at once. Don't worry too much. I shall make some investigations from time to time. Understand? Be careful to observe all the points of our agreement. The matter has become highly political. No one cares about the pictures, but it is important to take them from Professor Lips."

"I thank you for your candor and your help, Commissioner. You will get the letter tomorrow. You have played fair with me and I want to play fair with you. I am going to tell you that I cannot keep all the points of our agreement."

"Be careful. If I catch you I shall be forced to lock you up. You will be beyond my power once the machine starts grinding."

"I was only confiding in you as a private person. Let me tell you that it is the first unguarded remark I have made since January, 1933. I hope you will not see me a victim of the 'machine.' Thank you, you have indeed helped me. You've been wonderful."

"You, too, and Heil Hitler!"

He took the swastika from the floor and put it back in place next to his inkwell, then escorted me to the door.

I hurried to the nearest pay station: "Ziska, I am still alive! Greetings to the gentlemen who supervise our phone! Everything is settled. I am coming home."

"Thank God! Tapir, your mistress is coming! It's three o'clock. Shall I get lunch, Frau Professor?"

"Three o'clock! I'll be home at once. I am starving!"

My one remaining hope in the matter of the photographs was Eugen von Rautenstrauch. When I called him up the city was full of the noise of Rose Monday.

He was most amiable. The conference in the very comfortable consulting room of his bank opened with small talk.

"Have you had a pleasant carnival, *gnädige* Frau?"

"Delightful!"

I broke the silence with some remark about the Museum. Eugen von Rautenstrauch lamented the decline in public interest in his institution. "No feeling at all for the fascinating science of ethnology—dead and gone. After all those glamorous years!" He sighed. He was genuinely grieved over the collapse of the Museum, but he would not translate his sentiment into action. He dared not.

"It's too idiotic! Dragging those photographs into this racial nonsense is really going too far. As far as I'm concerned, you have my permission to throw them into the Rhine. That would be much more sensible," he said in disgust.

But when I asked him for a brief note, establishing the photographs as Jules' personal property, he drew back.

"I'm sorry. I can put nothing in writing. Tell that fellow at police headquarters that I agree with your point of view entirely. If he wants to telephone me, I'll certify that you are in the right, but only in an informal way."

The fact remained that the photographs were in Paris. How long could I keep their whereabouts undiscovered?

I had become so intimidated that I no longer knew what was right and what was wrong. If anyone had forbidden me to play on my own piano I should have ceased playing, like a guilty school girl. If my clothing had been confiscated, I should have thought I had come by it dishonestly. The supervised telephone would ring. I no longer laughed over the most trivial conversations, since they took place within earshot of an invisible enemy. Our letters arrived opened, and I read them with the feeling that I was doing something incriminating, although they were as harmless as a child's story book. Even Jules' letters seemed not to belong to me. I opened every newspaper anxiously, putting it down with relief when there was "nothing in it." A paper hanger who had once worked in our house was interrogated by the Board of Inquiry in connection with Jules' "dismissal," for he had worked for us after January 30, 1933. He had given Jules "a good character." One was apprehensive about every workman! If he were a Nazi his activity resembled that of the secret service; if he were not a Nazi it was suspect to employ him.

I was nervous with the postman, the milkman, the newsboy. He might be a spy who wrote down my words. In the trains there was a curious silence; no one ventured to talk to a stranger, still less to an employee. Laughing in the street car at the wrong moment might be dangerous. Photography enthusiasts did well to put their cameras aside; any landscape, any group of people which one photographed might be used to prove one's intention of spying, for at that time the open ignoring of the Treaty of Versailles had not yet been "legalized."

A psychosis was creeping through Germany. Who believed whom? From the pedlar to the Mayor everyone distrusted everyone else. No one ventured to express an opinion on anything. This was the "new atmosphere of confidence" which had descended upon Germany, so dear to the heart of the Minister of Propaganda. Every man trembled before his "blood brother" in a grand debauch of mistrust, which was to culminate so horribly on June 30, 1934.

The next policeman whom I had the pleasure of greeting in our house was a *Schupo** who simply asked for our passports. It was probably Crime Commissioner Becker's reply to my admission that I could not keep all the terms of our agreement. He wanted to keep me from doing something silly. I told the *Schupo* that my husband had his passport with him; he needed it in the Saar, where he was visiting his mother. I myself had no passport. My old one had expired long ago. As a matter of fact, it was concealed, perfectly up to date, in Hitler's *Mein Kampf*, the only book that was safe against confiscation. The *Schupo* trudged off disgruntled. That afternoon Becker called me up. He was satisfied to find me still at home.

The whole current of our day was altered. It was impossible to read, to work, to sew, to sit in the garden. Unrest nagged at my heels. Evening brought relative peace. I began taking walks at night with Ziska and Tapir. One saw fewer uniforms and heard less noise. We left the house about eleven o'clock and returned at half past twelve. I carried a walking stick with a silver head, more to keep my hands busy than as a weapon. Tapir galloped ahead like a centaur. Ziska loved these walks, for it was the only opportunity to be a "human being." We had agreed not to talk about the Third Reich. She told me stories of the orphanage and I tried to recall bits of our travels that would interest her, odd housekeeping methods of women of the savage tribes and some of their amusingly masterful ways.

Jules had gone to Switzerland and was then going to London, zealously following up every possibility that offered. He needed duplicates of his books, lists of his publications, photographs of himself and his diplomas. Somewhere someone appeared to be working for us. A good fairy still quite

* *Schupo (Schutzpolizei)*, the regular civilian police of pre-Hitler times, now turned Nazi.—Translator's Note.

unknown or was it a magician—a kindly old man fired with the sacredness of science. I was filled once more with faith and hope.

While the government kept one hand firmly on our purse, it stretched the other out to take from the little that we had. Day after day, storm troopers in uniform appeared at the gate begging for the Party. They tried to intimidate me by showing me lists of names. "Yours is the only house that does not contribute," they said significantly, and then, more plainly, "We shall report you to local headquarters." Once they insisted that we pledge to a weekly contribution of coffee, sugar and flour. Another time it was a question of the well-known "one-course Sunday," when only one dish was to be served and the money thereby saved donated to the National Socialist Party. Next we were told, by men in uniform, how acute the need was for "winter relief" this year. We were hailed at every step by patriotic pedlars of flowers, laces and pasteboard airplanes. There was no errand, no visit, no walk without its hold-up. Anyone who did not wear a badge to show that he had made a contribution was mercilessly importuned.

When I was asked to give money to help the unemployed, it seemed to me the last straw. I went straight to the city headquarters of the National Socialist Party and demanded that our name be crossed for once and all off the lists of those to be solicited, reminding them that my husband's unemployment was the Party's own doing and that it ill became them to cause poverty with one hand and to seek to remedy it with the other. The thrust went home apparently, for after that no more collecting agents in the S.S. uniform rang our bell.

XIX

On the surface the old life still went on. Plays at the theater, concerts, opera, lectures and the cinema, of course. What had we to complain of? All the traditional German diversions were there to be enjoyed by a peaceful population. In fact, they had been "improved," and our enjoyment should have been the greater.

At the theater we were treated to Nazi propaganda, disguised in the blood-and-thunder melodramas resurrected from the repertoire of our grandfathers' day, or, worse yet, in heroic compositions of our own. At the opera Richard Wagner held forth in full blast, with a profusion of swastika emblems to enhance the décor. Concerts featured the Horst Wessel song. At the "scientific lectures" we were regaled with stirring discourses, especially designed for the "enlightenment of the people," and strange indeed was the science underlying them. All government employees and officials were compelled to subscribe, the cost of their seats being deducted from their salaries. It was patriotic to go to the theater. During the days of decadent "asphalt" artists, no such compulsory measures had been needed, but then, that was before the era of national uplift!

It was only in the cinema that one could spend an evening without a vigorous leap to the feet and an energetic raising of the right arm, without being obliged to compose one's features into an expression acceptable to the State. There, at least, it was dark. Before going, it was wise to study the *Westdeutscher Beobachter*, and if one found a film described as "artistically worthless," "lacking in national interest," or "objectionable in theme," one could be sure of a pleasant evening. At that time the output of

National Socialist studios was still relatively small, and the cinema managers were dependent on films imported from abroad. When these were shown, a long waiting line thronged the lobby of the "Capitol," Cologne's finest motion-picture house. One saw well-known faces there, professional men and artists who had lost their jobs mingling with prominent Nazi office-holders and with cosmopolitans from abroad. It was a friendly reunion, a refreshing halt at an oasis in the desert of Nazidom, though the greetings were discreetly limited to cautious little nods and whispers and sank quickly into anonymity in the darkness inside. The film did more than amuse; it brought solace to our strained emotions.

Before enjoying it, however, we had to brace ourselves for the "News of the Week," a feature planned by Dr. Göbbels for all Germany with the purpose of introducing their new leaders to the nation. Within a few weeks we became familiar with the curious rhythmic walk of the Minister of Propaganda, the generous dimensions of the Prussian Minister President and the alcoholic voice of our Rhenish leader Dr. Ley—unkind people said his name had originally been Levy —the sturdy Teutonic build of Baldur von Schirach, leader of the Hitler Youth Organization, the exotic features of Minister Rudolph Hess, the Führer's deputy—Cairo-born. Most frequently of all, of course, the face and form of the Führer himself were presented to his people's adoring eyes, and I took the keenest pleasure in watching him grow handsomer and handsomer. Though at first there seemed to be triple pouches under the eyes, numerous crow's feet at the nose and temples and coarse, ungodlike lines in the face, increasing deification brought increasing beauty. The features became smoother, the glance more brilliant, the complexion clearer. The voice did not respond to treatment, did not acquire a velvet softness; the Bohemian burr stuck.

When he came on, bearing in his hand the Munich "flag of blood" to consecrate some new banner or to salute a "national monument," the focus of a hundred thousand eyes, the idol of choking war veterans and sobbing tender-hearted mothers, glorified by all the heroic paraphernalia of sentimental movie art, I fell victim to a delusion. Before me stood an emperor, known to us all, Hans Christian Andersen's emperor, strutting proudly about in his new regalia. Not one of his million subjects dares admit that his Majesty is parading in his drawers—that none can see the marvelous brocades he is supposed to be wearing. Until a two-year-old child stirs in his mother's arms and pipes: "Why, Mother, he hasn't any clothes on!" This child has not yet been born to the German people.

It was safe to think in the darkness of the cinema. The parade of "our heroes" was followed by an instructive "short," in the tone of a tract, glorifying the joys of self-sacrifice. It invariably closed with a giant close-up of a "Hitler youth," holding a collection box in his hand which was suggestively stretched out toward the helpless spectator. He voiced his appeal in faultless rhythm: "Everyone must give! You too, YOU TOO, YOU TOO!"

The lights flashed on, and a mob of well-drilled brownshirts descended upon the audience, like a swarm of ants on a rotten felt hat, shaking boxes in front of their startled noses. It was easy to tell the regular patrons from the others by the solid blockade massed in the middle of the rows, fenced in from the aisles by their umbrellas. Their stronghold was impregnable. Here and there a group slyly broke into French or English—although a moment before they had been pattering away in the dialect of Cologne. No one was in the least surprised by the abrupt change; even perfect strangers found themselves chatting cordially together—in a foreign tongue—half in fear and half in fun. Solemn, bearded men suddenly took on the ways of schoolboys playing forbidden pranks. In short, it was a picture of "national unity" such as our Minister of Propaganda never tired of celebrating as an achievement of the Third Reich. If in spite of all this one could not escape the jingling box, one refused with a polite "non, merci," or "Thank you sooo much!" and the box vanished. Foreigners were carefully avoided, for unpleasant incidents had occurred, which the foreign press had most uncharitably featured. Hence, the order had gone forth that "racial inferiors," particularly French and Italians, should not be allowed to participate in the honor of sacrifice.

Once the YOU TOO! was over, the danger point was past and one could give oneself up to the enjoyment of the nationally inferior film in peace. It was always preceded by some advertisement, and one of these gave me a very special thrill. The screen flashed a color picture of a European in a sun helmet riding in a ricksha over the globe, passing groups of little-known races of men. The ricksha coolie was slight of build and had painted eyelids, like a dancer of the boulevards. The picture was heavily captioned:

A TRIP AROUND THE WORLD IN THE
RAUTENSTRAUCH-JOEST MUSEUM

It was a poster intended to stimulate interest in the Museum, which I had once drawn for Jules. It was flattering to find that Scheller found some merit in my "decadent Marxist" style.

I was genuinely delighted one day to run across an announcement of a program to be given by the "Harmony Comedians." I had heard them in Leipzig, but that night a green face had hovered before my eyes. The company consisted of a singing quintet and a pianist, who excelled in light songs, intricately harmonized, through which they presented the character of the various nations of Europe that lived their dreary lives unblessed by *Blut und Boden*. Phonograph records had made all Germany familiar with their art. I had supposed that after the "uplift of the nation" these wise cynics had gone the way of the famous Comic

[287]

Cabaret of Berlin, of Max Reinhardt, of Elizabeth Bergner, whose genius now delights London and New York. I thought they had been banished from German life, like everything else that was gay, bold and gifted.

But they had remained, and here they were in Cologne. A month before the concert the house was sold out. No need to build up an audience for them by compulsory measures.

Before the program opened, leaflets were distributed providing "enlightenment." The notice announced that in spite of false rumors to the contrary the Harmony Comedians were all "purely German"; that their chief aim had always been the perpetuation of the German folk song. Unfortunately, it was impossible to change the English names of these artists; their contracts forbade it. The tenor, said an innocent postscript, was the only foreigner among them, but he had served in the World War as a Bulgarian officer, and had therefore fought for a State allied with Germany. He had won the Iron Cross.

The audience read the notices with surprise. Some did not see the connection between the tenor's excellent voice and his military activities in 1914, but all were agreed in loving the songs they hoped to hear him sing. No one had previously supposed that the Harmony Comedians had felt themselves called upon to save the German folk songs from oblivion—but no matter! Just so the amusing devils came!

They came, they sang, they charmed, they conquered—as always. Then came the nuisance. After the first number the collection box made its noxious appearance. A little later a heavy-hipped storm trooper appeared on the stage and bellowed an announcement: "The gentlemen will now sing foɪ the winter relief!" Whereupon the sextet, obviously surprised and annoyed, sang the ballad about the little brown mandolin. There was a pause—more collecting. There had been no applause for the ballad. In the Third Reich silence is the only possible form of protest. During the second part of the program, when the lovers of satiric topical song were treated to a batch of further sentimental rubbish, a murmur ran along the rows: "Interference!" "Censorship!"

At the close of the program the audience refused to leave, calling so vociferously for the songs they had been cheated of that the singers were obliged to begin their concert all over again, eliminating "Blubo" art entirely for the rest of the evening.

All the exits were manned by brown-shirts, shaking their collection boxes zealously: "Don't forget the winter relief. Obey the will of the Führer." But they got almost nothing.

I have described the concert in such detail because it was only one in a chain of similar entertainments all over the country where prominent artists were forced to give up their individuality under pressure from the "Movement" and where an irritated public protested as much as it dared under the circumstances. It was generally understood that both programs and gate receipts of these singers were strictly controlled. Jewish virtuosi were still permitted to perform in those days, because their names attracted the public, but they were compelled to give up three-quarters of their receipts. They provided a source of revenue much more substantial than any derived from entertainments arranged under Nazi auspices, for—except for men in uniform and people who felt it important to be seen—these were unattended. The repression became more and more severe, and the protests kept pace with it, often with shocking results. As late as 1935 Werner Finck opened his program at the Catacombs Cabaret in Berlin one evening in sparkling style:

"Heil Hitler! Good evening to the other ninety per cent!" Tremendous applause. A shout: "Shut your trap, you smart Jew!" To which Finck retorted: "I am not a Jew, I only look as intelligent as one." An audacious bit of repartee, nothing more, and it brought a laugh. However, when on the next day, the pet of the cabaret world was led off to a concentration camp, not one of the many who had loudly applauded him lifted a finger to help him.

The attempt to use Schiller's *Wilhelm Tell* as National Socialistic propaganda had its grotesque side. The directors actually rephrased the Ruetli oath in the words of the pledge of Nazi loyalty, but the tumult that greeted the placing of Gessler's hat on the pole for the freemen of the Swiss cantons to salute led to the withdrawal of *Tell* from the German stage.

To avoid similar difficulties, at the production of *Don Carlos* in Hamburg the plea: "Sire, give us liberty of thought!" was simply omitted. However, the Germans knew their classics better than the producers supposed. When the significant words were due and failed to come, such a burst of applause set in that *Don Carlos* followed in the footsteps of *Wilhelm Tell*. Other tributes to freedom vanished from the boards likewise. Schiller might cause the Nazis uncomfortable moments, yet they did not fail to celebrate his one hundred and seventy-fifth birthday with all the pomp of the Third Reich, forgetting apparently that the very first drama written by the revered poet had carried the motto "Down with tyranny!"

The gutter on Jules' balcony was stopped up; the acacia leaves had got into it, and I was obliged to send for the plumber. The least expenditure worried me, but the walls had become spotted with dampness and the repairs simply could not be put off.

The old plumber had worked for us for a long time. He was an adventurous man; in his youth he had taken part in quelling the Boxer rebellion. Jules enjoyed hearing him talk, and never failed to be around when he came to do a job for us. The old fellow was disappointed at Jules' absence.

As he stood there disentangling his pliers from a roll of wire and tow, I sounded him out cautiously. Every person one met offered three possibilities; complete Nazi, co-ordinated Nazi, or anti-Nazi. I had met no one in the first category except at the Rathaus.

"Well," I said, "I expect business is much better, now that recovery has set in."

He muttered something under his breath, not daring to reply.

"No swastika yet?" I asked, pointing to his jacket.

"Frau Professor," he replied, "I have known you for five years. You can go right off and denounce me if you like, but I will never pin that thing on!" He poked at the gutter; there was a sucking sound. "I guess she wants a new pipe," he said dryly, and at once became absorbed in his work.

In five minutes we were confiding in each other. I told him why Jules was away. Paragraph Four, dismissal. His successor—a student. His salary—stolen. The future—gloomy.

The old fellow snorted with rage. It seems he had been an eager listener at the Sunday lectures in the Museum. He had been particularly delighted with the colored Chinese lantern slides. "What a disgrace to Germany!" he growled, crossly tightening the tow around the pipe. "What a disgrace! Driving away our best men! They'll be sorry when it gets known. Mark my words, they'll be sorry! The whole business is a pack of lies," he went on, shaking his head, "and we know it and can't do a thing about it. Got to keep our mouths shut." Not long ago, he had had thirteen assistants; now he had two. That was "economic prosperity" for you. His own son had become a storm trooper, a March violet, poking around in the shop, which he would inherit some day, and threatening the old man with a "boycott" if he didn't pay up. "That's what they learn nowadays," said the old fellow. "That's your fine Führer principle."

A tile had worked loose and had to be cemented. He fell to reminiscing on China, and I told him he must read *The Good Earth*, and got it for him to take home. It was fascinating to watch the skillful grace of his stiff fingers at their work.

"Why are you against Hitler?" I asked, without warning.

His reply was certainly original. "Oh, the fellow's too ordinary for my taste."

After three and a half hours of hard work, the damage was repaired "for eternity." While he was washing his hands in the kitchen I asked what I owed him. With things as they were, I did not want any debts outstanding. He couldn't say offhand, he mumbled; he would have to do some "calculating." Nor could I get him to talk of payment. He tucked the book on China in with his tow and tools and, after much foot-scraping, he departed.

Late in the evening, after Ziska had gone to bed, I was summoned from my desk by the telephone.

It was my friend, the plumber. Was it the Frau Professor herself speaking? Yes. That was all right then; he had something to tell me. Today in the kitchen—he had not ventured to say it right to my face—he wanted to make us a present of the drain pipe as a little token of his respect. He would not take any money from us under any circumstances. To do so would make him a party to Germany's guilt!

I could have cried. I assured him that I had enough money to pay for honest work, but he interrupted me. The matter was settled. Did I want to rob him of his peace of mind? He hung up abruptly.

How could I let him know how deeply moved I was by his "little token of respect"? In the case among the glass fish from Murano there was a small Chinese god, carved in lapis lazuli. Perhaps the old plumber might see no value in the dull blue stone. But had I an hour ago known the value of his spirit?

The next morning Ziska carried a little package to the post office. It contained the blue Chinese image and a photograph of Jules.

The rough-handed plumber was not the only nobleman of his kind. The garbage collector, the gardener, the postman, all asked Ziska:

"And the Herr Professor? Is he safe? Give him my regards." All these greetings traveled to Paris, *Hôtel des Nations.*

Two officers of the law had come one day to arrest the master of the house, and, balked of their prey, they had levied a fine on a dated dog's license. It was a large fine; I had neglected to get a dog tag for a long time. After I had sworn to Tapir's history, the collector shook his finger at me: "No lying, now, about this license. You traitors are always up to something." My knees went soft. I might manage the affair of the disputed photographs, but a dog license could just as easily land me in a concentration camp! Fortunately, the collector was in a hurry. The National Socialists had announced a celebration that would "make world history." The streets roared with echoing loud speakers. Employers had been ordered to excuse their workers so they could listen. The *Westdeutscher Beobachter* gave a dramatic account of the occasion.

"Today many hundreds of thousands pledged themselves for life to Adolf Hitler, binding themselves indissolubly to the leader of the National Socialist Movement with a sworn oath: '*I swear inviolable loyalty to Adolf Hitler, I swear unqualified obedience to him and to the leaders assigned to me by him.*'

"Hundreds of thousands will lift their hands, as they make their pledge, to the National Socialist flag, which is the symbol of our Movement, and which, coupled with the old traditional flag, is the emblem of our Reich. It is known to all that he who has sworn to the flag—on a red field a white disk charged with a black swastika—no longer possesses anything that belongs to himself alone."

So the old imperial flag, the black-white-red, was still ceremoniously recognized as a national symbol. Adolf Hitler's banner was not yet popular enough for him to be able to eliminate entirely the emblem of the German Empire. At

[293]

the Nuremberg Party rally of 1935 the imperial standard had been flung on the rubbish heap, and the police had issued a proclamation: "Any private person displaying the black-white-red flag shall be considered guilty of an act hostile to the Reich and to the nation." The German people, bred to centuries of loyalty, swore to a new loyalty—temporarily.

I had informed Korndörfer of the addresses of the two secretaries of the Social Democratic Party. Furthermore, on one of the signed blank sheets which Jules had left I had neatly written a request for their summons to the hearing— a formality suggested by Attorney General Liebering. To my great satisfaction, the request had been granted, as I learned from a notice addressed to Jules.

Once again I stood in front of Korndörfer's door at nine o'clock in the morning. He and Liebering were whispering together when I entered, and the stenographer stood by, listening. Decidedly, something was in the air. My knees shook as I remembered my visit at police headquarters and the Crime Commissioner's hint: "They want to get you out of the way for another reason!" They could arrest me on the spot if that was their plan, and I was helpless.

Finally Korndörfer turned to me in feigned astonishment and said: "What, are you here again?"

"But, of course. Is it necessary to present my power of attorney once more?"

"That's inadequate," said he. "There are serious omissions in it. It's not a proper power of attorney."

They would stop at nothing to bar me from the hearing. I struggled to think of a means of countering his objections, but my mind was confused.

"I'll bring you another power of attorney at once! My husband left a second with me, more formally drawn," I said, wondering how on earth I could compose it.

"Just let that be," he said, with a taunting smile. "We

only let you in to be pleasant the other day. That can't be done today. You are not a lawyer. You agree with me, don't you, Mr. Attorney General?"

To my amazement, Liebering nodded. His defection left me utterly at sea. But I made a last attempt.

"It is true that I am not a lawyer, but neither do you constitute a court. You, Mr. Attorney General, are not an attorney general at all—only a town councilor; and you, Herr Korndörfer, have not even passed the bar, and yet you are directing a legal investigation! With all this informality, the 'accused' may be represented by his proxy, even though she is not an attorney-at-law."

"You are mistaken," said the junior member of the skating club. "No matter what you say, we won't admit you again."

"May I remind you that the witness scheduled to testify today has been summoned at our request?"

There was an icy silence. They waited for me to leave. In an effort to gain time I offered to engage a lawyer, if they would pay enough of the pension to cover his fee, or failing that, to invoke the Poor Law to appoint one instead. Korndörfer would not listen. It was all "irrelevant."

Suddenly he changed his tactics. He turned to me with an indulgent smile. He looked more like a poppy-seed roll than ever.

"Now, do be reasonable, Frau Lips. You can't do any good by staying. You only want to hear me question the witness."

"Certainly!" I exclaimed, "and to see the documents! We do not even know what the inquiry is about."

"Show you the documents! Never in the world—never—do you understand me? Only Professor Lips or an authorized lawyer can see the documents!"

"Who is your superior?" I asked furiously. "Or are you the court of last resort? To whom are you responsible?"

He, too, lost his temper.

"I am responsible only to the President of the Government Board," he bellowed.

At this I forgot completely that just a little while ago I had been afraid of being arrested. I broke out into a tirade against the whole structure of the Third Reich, with all its major and minor crimes. The pent-up emotion of those months of strain and suffering found words that should have meant my end. But three Nazi witnesses to my treason stood there dumb, thinking I know not what. At last the attorney general—perhaps he had a daughter of my age—said:

"Why do you always come yourself, Frau Professor? Haven't you any friends who could help you?"

"Friends? The friends who are faithful to us are as persecuted as we are. Some are in prison, some were able to escape. The others wear the same uniform as you, Herr Korndörfer."

I saw a dangerous change come over the faces of the two men; they had been human for a moment, but were returning to the heroic again.

"So your husband has no one?" Liebering's tone was half hostile.

Suddenly I was ashamed of having shown my emotion. It was futile. All that was left for me was to make as graceful an exit as possible.

"You win," said I, smiling at Korndörfer, "I am going! Good-bye."

"Heil Hitler," he replied.

"Heil Hitler," said Liebering.

"Heil Hitler," said the stenographer.

I turned and said again distinctly, "Good-bye."

Outside the door I ran into the witness. There was only one—the other had died after his term in the concentration camp. It was Müller. He had been screwing up his courage, and now he ventured in. I saw his right arm go up and heard a hoarse "Heil—" either he had stopped at the "Hitler" or else uttered it very softly. He had just been released from a concentration camp, after pledging himself in writing to a course of "model behavior." Perhaps I had been mad to suggest him as a witness. Would he tell the truth? Indeed, could he?

So Korndörfer's chief was the President of the Government Board. I lost no time in addressing a formal memorandum to him, stating the facts in the case and asking him either for support under the Poor Law or official permission to represent Jules. I hardly hoped for a reply, but felt I must leave no stone unturned.

Ziska, Tapir and I took our evening walk in a new direction into a desolate neighborhood south of Klettenberg, over mountains of debris, building foundations and piles of brick. At last we came to the house of party secretary Müller. Tapir lay like a sphinx in front of the door and Ziska stayed with him. I went up alone and rang the bell. An eye looked out at me, through a peep hole. The former leader of men finally opened the door. He was trembling. He had been subjected to examination for three hours, he said. Korndörfer had so intimidated him that he no longer knew what he was saying. "I said that my nerves had suffered in the concentration camp," he murmured. "Do you think they can make a trap for me out of that? Will they take me back? Anything but that! How he did storm at me! But I was meek. I stood at attention. Every time he spoke to me, I answered, 'Very well, sir!' I believe I succeeded in persuading him of my submissiveness."

Horrified, I said good-bye to him. He slipped behind the door of his house like a frightened ghost. As these words are being written, Müller is once more in prison. His crime consisted in collecting funds for the relief of penniless wives and children of political prisoners.

I had been so accustomed to protests, petitions, appeals and official documents of all sorts—even in Jules' letters I looked first for legal details—that I had forgotten what a personal letter was like. A hand-addressed envelope had become a luxury, and when one morning Ziska brought me one, I turned it over with a feeling of strangeness. The Capri postmark was like a warm ray of the sun, and the signature testified that not all the world was on the watch for war, and that there were still human beings whom one could love, who were kind and gentle and charming.

"My friends," the letter ran, "I have a curious communication for you. I have been here only three days and aside from you I am telling no one where I am. Schiller was of the opinion that death was not too high a price for a single moment in paradise; conversely, I shall need a month of this paradise to save me from death. Meanwhile, it is bliss to be here, whatever comes.

"Yesterday I went straight to San Michele and wandered about, guided by the blind man whom Axel Munthe has appointed custodian of his treasure garden. Later I climbed to Torre di Materita for a glimpse of that face so marked with peace and wisdom. Dr. Munthe unfortunately was not well enough to receive me, but sent a message asking me to return tomorrow morning at eleven.

"Tomorrow, that is to say, today. You know when one climbs that steep path one wonders whether the feeling of oppression is due to the cliffs, the mountain orchids, or the man one expects to meet at the top. I was very prompt and pulled the bell, a little doubtful whether Axel Munthe would really receive me. It seemed a miracle in a barren world.

"I waited on the terrace below for admission into the realm of unreality, playing with a little green grasshopper I had caught. As I looked up, I saw the master of the house coming down to meet me, his steps unheard on the living carpet of green. One treads this garden on the soundless feet of the gods. Munthe had a stick in his right hand and his left held the collar of his dog, Gaorm. They came toward me like dream figures from the pages of a book. Munthe has a most winning way; at the same time he is impressively noble. All my troubles fell away from me when I clasped his hand with its three-thousand-year-old Egyptian snake ring and heard the voice that had dictated the book of San Michele through the hush of sleepless nights.

"Oh, I need not describe it to you. We walked through the park and into the house, every pillar of which is precious. The sage stood at my side, showing me Greek masks through his darkened eyes as though they were living faces. The cases of unmounted gems suddenly lost all their material value and received another and higher value—that of beauty. Munthe led the talk to Phidias, to Wilhelm the Second, to Canova and to the besieging horde of journalists from whom he had fled to Torre. We talked in English—I began to feel myself a figure in a dream, also.

"He asked about you. I told him your story. He shook his head over the changes going on in Germany. 'I no longer understand,' said he, 'the country of Schubert, the country of music.'

"Just before I left, I found the courage to ask a favor, one I have long craved in waking as in dreaming hours. I wanted to see the sphinx once more, the treasure of treasures, of which he rarely speaks, though it is the great achievement of his life. He had taken it so miraculously from the sea, to its lofty home, revealing the mystery of its ancient past to no one. I begged to be allowed to look at it again.

"Munthe led the way to a parapet of the white house and there it was, just as you and I and the man of magic himself once saw it. That half-decayed face of red granite is still turned toward the sea. Munthe placed my hand on the hollows of the eyes carved into uncanny shadows by the erosion of the sea, saying that there were people who believed this sphinx had the power to fulfill wishes and that since I had so often thought of the figure when I was far away, I must frame some wish in my mind.

"I felt the sun-warmed stone under my hand, and

[299]

strangely enough, I remembered nothing of the woes and sorrows of my life; it all seemed blotted out. I was standing beside a man in a garden. The last time I had been here, I had stood with you. My companion and his dog seemed to vanish, even the figure of the sphinx grew dim. I saw my two dear friends before me, and I thought: 'May they find refuge from the savage ruin of their native land, find home and shelter, may they live and work in peace!'

"I came back to my hotel in a state of exhaustion, but I could not sleep. I cannot rest until I have sent you a word of greeting—a message from the magic garden to which you first led me, a message from an ancient sun-warmed stone, resurrected from the sea.

"You may laugh at me, but these things are real. The sirocco is lifting over the bay, outside the Faraglioni shine in the moonlight, the sphinx gazes out upon the sea from which she rose. I have placed my hands upon her eyes and I believe her. Axel Munthe sends you his greetings. He tells you to hope. It is not possible that the spirit of evil shall remain master of our century.

"I am writing you from the South, on a night of moonlight after a day of wonders. Life seems made of simple things, elemental and terrible, like the sphinx, which is said to have powers of fulfillment."

Miracles were possible, after all. The letter from Capri had been opened by the censor, yet found its way to me in the Third Reich.

Hidden under it on my desk lay another, an official letter in a blue envelope.

"Frau Lips is hereby admitted to appear as her husband's representative in the pending disciplinary inquiry.
By order of
The President of the Governing Board
signed and testified: Liebering"

I dashed to the telephone and asked for Korndörfer.

"I have been authorized to defend my husband," I said to him. "When may I come and examine the documents?"

"I no longer have the documents," he replied. "Attorney General Liebering has them at the Rathaus."

My triumph was short-lived. He was a clever lad, after all. I telephoned Liebering, who of course knew all about the authorization, having signed it himself.

"Come late tomorrow morning," said he, "or better still at two o'clock. I shall be in my office. If you come at two, we shall be undisturbed."

Storm troopers outside the Rathaus, storm troopers within the building and at every door. Though I was used to them, by now, I was glad for once that I was blonde. Liebering had a nice office. He got up from his desk and introduced a young man, who wrote down every word I said.

I seated myself opposite Liebering at the desk and he ceremoniously pushed the documents toward me. They filled three thick folios. I had brought along a pad and made notes; as authorized "counsel for the defendant" I might do so.

My excitement and curiosity changed to disgust as I ran over the papers. I choked as I read, like the Caliph in the story of the East, who unknowingly inhales the poison secreted in the leaves of his book by the wily physician, Duban, dropping dead at the final sheet.

Page after page elaborated the trumped-up charges against Jules. Whatever remained that could possibly be interpreted as favorable was crossed out or marked "irrelevant."

Suddenly I read the sentence: "Lips told me again and again that Adolf Hitler ought to be driven out of Germany with a dog whip." Sworn and testified to and set down in the record. Ten days after he had lost his case Scheller had gone to Korndörfer with this sentence. On that morning we had boarded the train for Paris, and Bodenheim had given up our defense. It was the morning that the police had appeared at our house to arrest Jules. So Scheller finally was making a complete thing of it! This sentence alone would have sufficed to put Jules in prison for life and perhaps do more than that.

I was horrified; I could not go on. It was utterly futile to attempt to contest a lying monologue with any mere legal measures or evidence. It was senseless to take these documents seriously except as a warning of danger.

I made no further notes. I gave Liebering my hand and said: "You were nice to me and I want to thank you. But I am surprised that you can bring yourself to touch anything like that"—pointing to the neat official-looking documents which contained so much filth and poison—"good-bye."

I must add that this was my last appearance in the disciplinary inquiry. I was not able to be present at the main hearing. As "Professor Lips' legal adviser" I received official notices of the meetings, but I was beyond the German frontier by then. The final decision reached us on American shores. "In the name of the German people" reads the document which the Consul General of the German Reich forwarded to us. At the bottom there is a neat line with an official seal: a stylized eagle with a sword and a swastika. Ten closely printed pages justify the government's usurpation of a pension due under its own law.

XX

On March 21, Adolf Hitler opened his famous 1934 campaign against unemployment. The Munich radio broadcast his speech over all Germany. Everyone was obliged to hear it. The milkman and the mayor, the postman and the president, the workman and the passer-by, every last man in the country had to listen in. Not to have heard it was tantamount to "sabotage." Every government employee had his ear to the loud-speaker. Not a stroke of work was done— even the telephone watchers left their snooping and the members of the secret State police left their spying.

"Work and freedom!" promised the Führer. Exactly what we were looking for, just exactly!

While his voice was thundering over the German radio our telephone rang, not once but six times.

A friendly Catholic priest called up, Renate called up, another friend called up, and an S.A. and two S.S. men called up. Each one of these heretics who dared to call during the historic speech of the Führer began his conversation with the same words:

"The telephone supervisors must be listening to Hitler. For once we can chat undisturbed. Tell me how you really are?"

The spring sun was warm on the grass. I sat in the garden with my dog. The almond tree was in bloom. The peach blossoms were a deep pink against the blue sky. I told Tapir about the frogs that sing at night in the cisterns of Eze, and the cars that thunder along the Corniche. Tapir hated to have the bristles on his chin tickled, but this time he tolerated it because I was so seldom at home nowadays that he did not wish to offend me. We fell to wrestling and slid against the cherry tree. Tapir showed his savage white teeth in a laugh, then wrinkled up his nose, and I just managed to escape his tremendous sneeze. Ziska appeared on the terrace in a black dress and a little cap, and I thought how pretty she looked against the clear spring sky. She seemed to be excited, but that was nothing new in these days.

As she came toward me, I recognized what it was that she was handing me on the little tray—the telegram.

It might have been a message from my parents, or my mother-in-law or friends, but as Ziska and I looked at each other we both knew that it was "the" telegram, the one for which we had been waiting in hope and fear, the star pointing to a new world. Jules had found the land of our future and the three little lives depending upon his were to be altered by this still unopened piece of paper.

"Expect the Panther Saturday," was all it said. No signature. The map of the world opened before me. Abyssinia? Versailles? Zurich? London? Or Tokyo?

I got up. Tapir thought I was going to throw a stone for him, and, when none appeared, slunk away to his kennel disappointed. I broke a little twig from the cherry tree and looked at the blossoms, thinking that the fruit of this tree which Jules had planted would never ripen for us. I put my hand in Ziska's and we walked back to the house.

Money for the journey! I sent for the picture dealer. He bought the handsome painting of the gray, overcast Norwegian fjord.

We talked of a beginning, not of an end. We talked of the things Ziska was to pack into my trunk. I must certainly take the evening dresses. "The Frau Professor might meet a Minister. One never knows in Paris," said the girl who had never been outside of Cologne.

I was about to violate the second point of my contract with the secret State police, the first being that the photographs remain in Cologne on the Rhine, the second, that I make no attempt to leave the city, under penalty of arrest. I had signed my name to this. There was no difficulty in leaving; the trick was to return.

Ziska undertook the heavy responsibility of concealing my absence. She had presence of mind and imagination. If it was at all possible, she would manage it. I relied on her, if the necessity arose, even to impersonate me. Strange officials came to the house frequently these days. It was hardly to be expected that Becker himself would come. And if he did? Had he not put the swastika on the floor? If Ziska received him at my desk as the lady of the house, was he obliged to remember my features? He saw so many people.

The next morning friends took me to Aachen in their motor car. From there I took the train to Paris. No one had seen me.

At the Gare du Nord I collapsed into Jules' arms. I was ashamed when he said that I looked pale. A taxi strike was on and we took the Metro to the Rue Monge.

We sat side by side on the chest containing the photographs, and Jules read me a letter from Addis Ababa.

"We thank you for your splendid suggestion regarding the assembling of the cultures of all the primitive tribes of Abyssinia into a single unit for display and study. His Majesty has considered the matter with much interest and pleasure, recognizing the great cultural advantage which the execution of your plan would mean to our country. It is therefore all the more to be regretted that we are obliged to inform you that your plans are at least forty years in advance of possibilities here in Abyssinia. . . ."

There were other envelopes with foreign stamps, containing bizarre offers and refusals. I looked anxiously at Jules.

Then he pulled out a slip of paper. It was not a letter; it was a cable and contained an invitation from Columbia University in New York.

I was deeply moved. Over a thousand German university professors were scattered in exile. They sat on chairs resem-

[305]

bling those in the Rue Monge. They slept on beds as hard as prison cots. Their crime was that they wanted to be free, that they felt that they had in themselves some of the old culture of Germany and were determined to preserve it. Their crime was that they loved freedom and scorned the man who presumed to erect barriers between Germans, barriers of race, barriers of narrowness, barriers of intolerance. More than a thousand such men, who had once contributed to the fame of our country throughout the world, in operating rooms, or on lecture platforms, by their books and on their travels, were now homeless.

With grateful hearts we went directly to the cable office and sent our eager acceptance.

As soon as we had sent the cable, we wrote to Leipzig, a discreet but happy letter. I asked my parents to help me dispose of the house in the Siebengebirgsallee and to look after a few other details, taking care to give them an honest account of all that had happened.

I was obliged to go back to Cologne. For one thing, we should have to sell some of our furniture in order to defray the cost of my passage. However, I was bent on keeping our favorite pieces. Somehow or other I must manage to get them out of Cologne before our persecutors had any idea that we were thinking of leaving the city. The books, the piano, the furniture and the rugs must be saved, though I had no idea how it could be done. For the last time I would have to give notice to our faithful Ziska. And Tapir?

He could not go with us to New York. He had grown up in a garden; he loved hedgehogs and moles and his bed of straw. Have him shot? No, I could never face that. Tapir must be left in the Rhineland, in safe and kindly hands.

All this we discussed over our breakfast in the café. From the bar we went through a jangling glass door to the room in the back, where we always sat at the same table. We never ordered. The garçon would bring the meal—one coffee, one tea, two crescents, a bottle of Vichy and two cherry brandies, and then he would stand and talk with us. He had shrewd black eyes and a tuft of hair on his nose. We liked him and we delighted in his philosophy.

"*Si je pouvais, je ferais mon petit Stavisky pour moi-même. De l'argent sans travail; quelle merveille!*"

When I was in Cologne and Jules drank his coffee alone the garçon knew that things were not going well, but when I turned up on one of my short visits he felt that everything was in order.

"Have you found your country?" he would ask whenever we came, as if we were looking for a lost glove. This morning we could tell him of "our country."

"America!" he exclaimed with enthusiasm. "Listen, patron, they are going to America! They will make dollars, millions of dollars!"

These millions were for the moment very far away. When the first great excitement was over we felt that there was a great deal to do before we could see the Statue of Liberty. Jules' duties at Columbia were to begin on the first of May, that same first of May on which I was either to hand over the photographs to the secret State police or go to prison. I could not sail with Jules. It was hard to think of cheating Becker; he had behaved so generously toward me. In any event, I must return to Cologne to arrange for breaking up our house.

Once again the best way of working together was to work separately; Jules must find a publisher for his book and I must look after the little things.

On my third day in Paris I received an answer from my parents. I must leave at once for Italy with them to recuperate; my plans sounded "hysterical"; Jules must return to Germany at any cost. Our panic was madness; no one was persecuting us. My mother wrote: "Even if they were to send Jules to a concentration camp, they would have to release him immediately. He has not committed a crime.

Come back at once. We will take you to the coast, and perhaps later on to Sicily."

Easter fell on the first of April. Ziska's reports came regularly and caused us no anxiety. Nothing more was likely to occur before the holidays; and during the holidays—well, the Rhineland is always easygoing at such times. We could count on a short truce.

So I stayed in Room 12. Sometimes we ate in the *Bonne Étoile*, but frequently we brought a little something from the Mouffetard, the market in the narrow steep street where swaggering students purchased their rations and took them home in newspaper packages, every article of food looking like a freshly dug tuber, with the good earth still clinging to it. Pastries, olives, lobsters, gruyère, roast chicken, lettuce, pears, bread, hot fried potatoes, white beans and pots of chocolate with cream—everything can be bought in this street, warm, cold or tepid. Above these stands shines the golden horse's head of the sinister butcher's sign: *Au panthéon hippique*. Interspersed among the edibles are soap, slippers, photographs, artificial teeth, petticoats and wreaths made of glass pearls to hang on a loved one's grave. The pleasure of buying there is far greater than one's appetite for the dust-covered delicacies. Still, it is the dust of Paris! Anyone who does not know the Mouffetard does not know Paris. It is as much a part of the city as the Folies Bergères, the bird market or the Madeleine; and it is certainly less "rigged up" for tourists than the apache dens of Montmartre.

Jules had written a few ethnological articles for periodicals, and the money thus earned paid for the entire luxury of our stay at the Hôtel des Nations. He counted up our fortune. It was too little for the voyage to America and too much for our few remaining days of the Latin Quarter life.

On Maundy Thursday Jules gave me a surprise: "How would you like to spend Easter in Eze with me?"

[308]

Eze-sur-mer, the French maritime Alps, the sanctuary of our happiest days! It was not merely a place of recreation for us, it was an asylum of the spirit to which we were bound by magic ties of friendship and affection.

We were ready in no time. A letter to Ziska telling her not to expect any news of me for ten days, she was not to worry; in case of need our friend Dr. M. would help her. A telegram to Monsieur Beaume, Hôtel Terminus, Eze-sur-mer to reserve Room 2! Off to the Maison de France to get our tickets. We were happy enough to inspire an old rag-picker to call out after us through her gaping teeth: "Voilà les jeuns amants!"

The seats on the train were marked PLM—Paris-Lyons-Mediterranean. Once again we rode past the cocoa-colored rocks of Théoules, the flowers of Provence and the silk-producing mulberry trees beyond Lyons. At Toulon the Maritime Alps begin their slow crescendo, rising from Cannes onward to giant screens that shut out the wind and rain and cold, admitting only Africa's fragrant breezes to caress the Côte d'Azur.

Our companion in the railroad carriage was a Corsican soldier, on his way to a farewell visit to his family before starting on a fifty-day trip to Shanghai, where his regiment had been ordered. A tremendously fat woman squeezed in between us—une femme comme un tank, said the soldier —and kept us from sleeping all night. But what did that matter?

We had been away from Eze sixteen months. The name of the station is spelled out in flowers. We were sorry that the Club Sportif was closed, for we were fond of a game of boule. A few of our friends had come from their nearby villas to meet us. The fig trees were just beginning to show their frog-green buds—in order to eat figs one must come in October. We walked across the Corniche into the park. The Cinzano sign had been freshly varnished; a new fountain played over the goldfish pool. High in the sky lay Eze-enhaut, where the sea pirates of earlier days had carved their hide-out caves in the rocks. Nietzsche wrote a few chapters of his Zarathustra at Eze. "I am a wanderer and a mountain climber. I have no love for the plains; it seems I cannot sit still very long."

Number 2, our old abode, is the pleasantest room in the hotel. The mosquito netting had been let down. Madame Charles proudly drew my attention to the new closet.

"We had begun to fear that you were prisoners of the new régime," said Monsieur Beaume in greeting. The idea that we might have become Nazis had never entered his head; we took it as a great compliment.

Dorino presented me with a bunch of white camellias. "The lobster is served, M'sieu et 'dame." Félice played us an air on his guitar while we ate. The vanilla bloomed purple against the house.

We ran down to the shore for a plunge into the Mediterranean; fished for sea-urchins; bronze lizards jumped over our feet. At two o'clock the *train bleu* passed and we waved our glistening hands at it from the water.

In the afternoon we took the Littoral to Monte Carlo and saw Jacquino again. I slipped up behind his black-coated back: "*Impair!*" I said, "*les trois derniers!*" He was so startled that the rake fell from his skillful hands. He blushed with shame at the unwonted clumsiness.

In the Café de Paris they were playing snatches from l'Arlésienne. The old musician was still there, still plying the plush-covered coffee spoon to make weird sounds on his strange instrument. In the evening we had a drink with Jacquino in a little bar near Beausoleil, far from the haunts of the tourist. He wanted to hear all our experiences, but we wanted news of the horse, Pierrot, and the cat, Titine. Jacquino, however, was a realist. "You must find a new country," he insisted.

On the day of the automobile races, we sat in the grandstand in front of the shop "Aux Dames de France." It was the sixth Grand Prix. We recognized Earl Howe by his usual blue silk suit; Nuvolari, by his yellow polo shirt. They were all there: Straight and Etancelin, Dreyfus and Moll, and of course Chiron, Louis Chiron, the *fils du pays* and our favorite. For ninety-nine rounds he dashed through the streets of Monte Carlo at a fiendish pace; at the hundredth, and last, round he came to grief. His over-confidence made him careless, and he drove his car into the wall of sandbags at the railroad station, losing the lead. The youngster, Moll, of Algiers, shot past him to a victory in which he took little pride. Chiron consoled the victor and himself at the same time: *"C'est la vie, petit coureur du midi, c'est la vie!"* To-day Moll is dead, killed in an accident in Tripoli.

The German racer, Caracciola, did not participate actively. He appeared in a magnificent brown car bearing the number I.A. 4444. He also wore a brown suit and a swastika.

The fan-shaped branches of the palm trees shone silver in the night before the Casino. The frogs sang in the cisterns of Eze. By day the sea lay glistening in the sun. Our holiday was perfect—but it came to an end, after the manner of all perfection.

Our baggage was at the railroad station. We were taking the night train. In the darkness, the agaves thrust their ghost-like columns toward the sky. Cars thundered along the Corniche from Nice to Menton. In the little bar, a game of *belotte* was on. The cat Titine had gone prowling in search of amorous adventures. Everything was as it should be and as we loved it. We lingered, postponing our return to reality.

The twang of strings made us turn. A festive little troop approached, surrounded the surprised passers-by and bore us along. We scarcely noticed that we were moving toward the station and that this little celebration was intended to make our departure easier. At the head of the parade marched Félice the waiter, striking the strings of his guitar in vigorous chords. He was followed by Casimir, the magician—he worked as a trainman, but that was by the way—who played the mandolin. Dorino followed with a harmonica, the cook, Giuseppe, with a lute, and the Arab, Rhamani Khadur, with his little wooden flute. The station master was cutting metallic capers on his banjo. A few strangers joined the group —the South cannot resist a bit of song and a bit of sentiment. Our serenaders were merry, if not musical. They brought me flowers and would not let us thank them, but rather thanked us for having come. They assured us of their affection and wished us happiness in the new world.

"À bas les Nazis," they called. "Vive L'Allemagne, vive l'Amérique!" Then voices faded away. Our train pulled out.

We parted two days later at the Gare du Nord, Jules bound for London and I bound for home—that is, for Cologne. Home lay across the Atlantic now.

PART THREE

FINALE—A BEGINNING

"Until you have crossed the river don't insult the alligator's mouth."

Proverb of the Ewe Negroes.

I SLIPPED OUT OF THE TRAIN LIKE A CRIMINAL dodging his pursuers, and walked straight into Ziska.

"Was Eze lovely, Frau Professor?"

When she had received my letter announcing my ten days of silence she had at once "become suspicious." My brown face told the rest of the story. Ziska had more wits than all the Third Reich put together.

Becker had telephoned four times to assure himself that I was there. Each time "I" had relieved him by answering the telephone.

Heretofore our days had been filled with waiting and watching, with the apprehension of fresh catastrophes, but now there began a phase of clear-cut action. When Ziska heard that our new country was to be America, her first remark was: "I must begin to learn the language, Frau Professor," although she had never actually understood that there was any other idiom than the dialect of Cologne. I explained to her that it would be impossible for us to take her with us, that we would be immigrants, the tolerated guests of a generous country. Under the circumstances we could not have a maid, or a dog, or any other reminders of home.

"Then I shall come along later," said Ziska, and we said no more about it.

We could not have a dog in New York. My dear old Tapir! He was six weeks old when I chose him from a litter of four pups, the offspring of prize-winning parents. I had shown him his straw bed and his garden. I had taught him little tricks and watched him grow up. Once he had half swallowed a needle, which had to be cut out of his tongue. Once I had fallen down the steps and he had brought Ziska to my assistance. In Buchensee he was our guard, in Cologne our clown. He was a silent and dependable companion. He had helped Ziska guard the house when we were in Africa; he was the non-Aryan who frightened off the Nazis. He had a gift for humor and bore our whims with dignity. He was now six years old. I could not have him shot. No one of our friends could consider taking him. They were either breaking up their own homes or uncertain about the future. But I would provide for Tapir. I intended his little life to continue unsuspecting and cheerful. We owed it to him.

April was coming to an end and with it the date set for delivering our photographs. They had gone to London with Jules. At night I would lie awake wondering how to ward off the impending catastrophe. All of a sudden I had an inspiration. Jules had had duplicates made for the Museum of almost all the pictures; they were in the Museum at that very moment. That might solve the whole problem. The students could not be expected to admit to the secret State police that it was not the pictures they cared about, but the scientific data concerning them which Jules had written on the reverse of the much-discussed mats. In any event I could not let the interval expire and then appear empty-handed. I decided to go at once to Becker.

He received me pleasantly. I told him that fairness had prompted me to come before the interval was over and that I was not going to give him the pictures. I was prepared to pay the Museum for the precious cardboard on which they were mounted. There was no need for Jules to deliver his photographs to the Museum, since it already possessed them in the form of duplicates. The students who were directing the Museum had apparently not yet had time to become familiar with the archives of their institution; otherwise they would have found these duplicates long ago. (That they could not use these for scientific work, since they did not possess the originals, did not really concern the Crime Commissioner.) I also told him how the Peill Collection had been "acquired by Scheller" and that Scheller had stated in the disciplinary inquiry that Jules had said that Hitler should be driven out of Germany with a dog whip.

"Is he in safety?" asked Becker at once. "If everything else failed, that would be serious indeed!"

Yes, Jules was in safety. This time Becker did not need to place the swastika silently on the floor. He showed his sympathy quite openly.

"Your idea about the duplicates won't do," said he; "there has been too much dust raised about these pictures . . ."

I was about to interrupt him.

"You can bring the pictures to me," he continued patiently. "Here at the headquarters of the secret State police, and I can have them burned with other material prejudicial to the nation. Then, from the technical racial point of view they can do no more damage."

"My dear friend, my dear friend . . ." I repeated. My relief was so great that I was unable to speak.

"I wish the pictures delivered this afternoon!" he ordered sternly.

That afternoon Ziska appeared at the office of the Crime Commissioner. She carried a large sealed cardboard package, labeled: "Professor Lips' pictures—'How the Black Man Looks at the White Man'."

To insure the security of the German nation, the contents of the package were burned in the stove in the office of the secret State police in Cologne.

"And what are you planning to do?" asked Becker. "Are you staying here?"

I said that I intended to move to another city. What was to become of Jules' scientific library, a whole wall of books which belonged to him personally and were in the Rautenstrauch-Joest Museum?

"Don't do anything," advised the Commissioner. "You must remain absolutely quiet, even if you lose the books."

"Lose them? But . . ."

"Either you take my advice or you don't. But you should not attract any attention in the Museum just now."

I followed his advice. He was so much wiser than I. Thus it happens that these volumes are still in the Rautenstrauch-Joest Museum.

"I shall delay all pending actions," said my excellent friend of the secret State police. "But I must give you one last piece of advice: act quickly and disappear quickly, and if possible go far!"

I might have satisfied him on the last point, but I did not do so. My experience with Bodenheim had rooted distrust too deeply in me.

"One thing I can tell you," said Becker as I was leaving, "there's a clean-up due in the Party; that I know positively. Then elements like Scheller will disappear from their positions. It's to be a thorough clean-up, too."

They did clean up. They shot the Zombi and they put Crime Commissioner Becker on the street without any pension. They were thorough, for they dismissed the last decent people who had inadvertently been allowed to remain and made beggars of them. "Elements like Scheller," however, retained their positions and climbed up to further honors. Herr Andreas Scheller is still director of the Rautenstrauch-Joest Museum in Cologne.

His is not a single instance. Scheller got rid of student Fröhlich, whose ambitions had gone to his head. The director of the renowned Wallraf-Richartz Museum of Fine Arts is a young man who was unable to obtain a professorship in Cologne on account of his criminal tendencies and his low professional standing—until the Third Reich raised him to glory, together with other men of the same sort. He immediately moved into a villa in the most expensive neighborhood of the city, where under the national slogan "common good before individual good" he serves the German people as a simple fellow-countryman. The director of the Museum of Industrial Arts, a blond "Aryan" with a Jewish wife, lost his position on account of his marriage, and was also replaced by one of his subordinates. The new Mayor of Cologne, once an executive in a Jewish banking firm, was not ashamed of having formerly accepted a considerable salary from the "traducers of the German race." The chief of the German Labor Front, who can be seen any evening in a well-known bar in front of a collection of empty wine bottles, built himself a villa on the Rhine costing several hundred thousand marks, thus preaching the simple life by example! The Dean of the University, Dr. Kuske, a former Social Democrat, suddenly appeared in the streets of Cologne decorated with a swastika. The conductor Abendroth delivered his colleague, Professor Braunfels, to the slaughter without a protest; he himself was blond, the other was dark. The President of the Government Board, Dr. Beyer, was replaced by one of his minor subordinates, who owed his rise in the world to skillful denunciations made in the year 1933.

These men form a scum on the great ocean of Germany. But we must not forget that down in the depths there still survives, though silenced, all that has made Germany a country of poets and thinkers, of music and legend. Force has merely stunned, not destroyed, it. All else, however wide it spreads, lies only on the surface.

Only those who have left the country can perceive it and can state it. In 1848 Carl Schurz left because he loved Germany. And Hoffmann von Fallersleben became an emigrant. It was he who wrote *Deutschland über Alles,* which they are not ashamed to sing in the Third Reich. Hordes of untutored brown-shirts traveling along the Rhine, break sentimentally into the *Lorelei* all unaware that this most German of songs was written by an inferior Jew—named Heine.

Crime Commissioner Becker helped me, but he paid for this with his existence. Our Zombi is dead. Lawyer Bodenheim, on the other hand, continues to enjoy a large and growing practice.

From London there were daily air-mail letters. My replies were all opened; the postal authorities assumed that I was trying to smuggle money out of the country. So I began one of my letters: "Dear censor: Do not take the trouble to read these lines. A poor devil is writing to his comrade! Neither of us has any money. Do you object to my writing to London so often?" Jules received this letter with the penciled word "No" added by the Nazi censor.

Dealers were now coming and going in our house. They carried away our carved dining-room furniture, chairs, kitchen cabinets, the guest-room furnishings, silver platters and clothes. My advertisement had been answered by a blond "Aryan" who had made a deal with me. Later in the evening his chief, an old Jew, appeared to settle up. He flitted away like a bat, trembling lest he be detected.

As soon as I had some money I sent for the shipping agent to discuss how to save the things I had kept. He had been recommended to me by a reliable person. As I talked with him, I discovered to my horror that an entirely new industry had sprung up in Germany. Beneath the ranks of those who flourished by denunciation there was a group who lived on the fear of the persecuted. The man I was interviewing was one of them. He demanded a thousand marks for getting my furniture across the border, although Belgium was only two hours away by train. He told me of shipments from Berlin to Palestine which went by way of Cologne so that the traces might be lost. He was an expert swindler, and spice was added to the situation by the large swastika in his buttonhole. I thought of the mass oath taken to Adolf Hitler, an oath which all officials had sworn. I gave him no information. I would engage him only in a case of extreme necessity.

A source of happiness was a recent letter from Jules. The great news was that he had found a publisher for his book! Now the storm-tossed pictures had a final haven, these spirits resurrected from the fire in the offices of the secret State police. The English title of the book was *The Savage Hits Back.*

Jules' reception in London had been cordial and productive, and, to one interested in the codes of human conduct, particularly illuminating. The "English gentleman" was a reality. Lovat Dickson signed a generous contract with Jules, giving him sufficient advance royalties to assure the trip to New York. He is a member of that choice group of publishers who are bound to their authors by ties of personality —with whom misunderstandings are simply out of the question. The meeting between him and Jules not only launched the book smoothly, but its author as well, since it resulted in the prompt securing of an American visa and a cabin on the *Majestic*, westward bound.

I was less fortunate. On applying to the consul in Cologne for a visa, I was dismayed to find that I had to go to Stuttgart, the nearest general consulate. That meant fresh expense, greater risk and loss of time. I wrote to Stuttgart and while waiting for a summons, I devoted myself to settling matters in Cologne.

The disciplinary inquiry portfolio had reached the hands of chief of the County Supreme Court, Dr. Leer. The wheels of justice had turned again, and the documents were removed from the jurisdiction of the Rathaus. With the sworn testimony on the "dog-whip" statement among them, we might expect serious trouble. I went to the legal department of the administrative building and succeeded in getting hold of the papers that were most important to us. They handed them to me, stupidly enough, and this was due to the fact that the man I saw was too incompetent to know what he was about.

I sent Jules a gay letter before he left London. Ziska enclosed a signed photograph; there was a pressed flower from the garden and Tapir's black paw mark in ink.

Wednesday, the twenty-fifth of April, the *Majestic* left. Southampton. Jules was well and safely aboard as a non-quota emigrant to the United States. The pictures had re-mained in London to be captioned.

Accidentally I heard that a Belgian nobleman was giving up his castle on the Rhine. Because of his Roman profile he had been beaten up as a Jew in one of the small towns. Offi-cial apologies over the unfortunate mistake came too late to appease the outrage. He intended to leave forever. The newspapers said that the possessions of the Comte de B.—over twenty van loads—were to be moved across the border.

More than twenty wagons to cross the border? I must speak to their owner.

I had in the meantime decided to store our things in Paris. The cost of transfer would not be too high, and, be-sides, Paris was the most accessible city in all Europe.

A courteous reply came from Comte de B. He would be in Cologne the following week at the Dom Hotel and would be glad to receive me.

He not only received me, but was delighted with my idea. He was quite ready to have my two vans of furniture—the packers estimated that two vans would suffice—attached to his wagon train at Krefeld, the point of transfer for his things. In view of the "regrettable incident" that had oc-curred there was to be no customs inspection of the Count's possessions. I could with perfect safety take anything and everything I wanted. What a pity I had no valuables! It would have been fun to defy the Nazi embargo on private funds, for instance. The best I could do, however, was to withdraw our balance in the Schaafhausen Bank, amounting to four marks in all, and when I called to collect it, I saw a huge-bellied S.A. man confiscating the account of former Minister Stegewald "for the Party."

I arranged with Comte de B. to have my furniture in Kre-feld on June second. My two vans were to be detached from his in Brussels; it would be easy to get them to Paris from there.

[322]

On May Day thousands of young birch trees were uprooted. Every house in Germany was to be decorated. Garlands of evergreen, banners and flowers adorned plaster busts of Adolf Hitler in the country's shop windows. Originally adopted for demonstrations by Communists and Socialists, the celebration was proclaimed as "National Labor Day" on tremendous posters showing the hammer and sickle joined with the swastika. Was this intended to symbolize the conquest of Marxism—was it a modest form of plagiarism, or sabotage? Herr Göbbels was at his loudest over the radio, taxing the Führer, who followed him, to superhuman vocal efforts.

The general consular office in Stuttgart asked me to come on the sixteenth. Everything worked out admirably; such papers of Jules' as were necessary for my visa had been sent from London. I brought everything that they required, birth certificate, baptismal certificate and marriage certificate, and the police certificate of conduct in duplicate. I got the papers from the police station in Klettenberg under the pretext that I needed them as the wife of a native of the Saar District in order to enter the Nazi Party in the Saar. For the sake of propaganda they charged me nothing!

A thorough medical examination yielded an "all right!" Written and sworn replies to delicate questions: "Are you a professional beggar? A bigamist? A prostitute? The purpose of the trip?" "To join my husband." How delightful that sounded! The mention of Columbia University helped enormously. I swore to all my statements before the Stuttgart consul, raising my right arm for the first time in Nazi Germany there under the American flag. Clutching the blue document tightly, I quickly climbed the tower for a last view of Stuttgart and the Neckar River.

In Cologne all the steamship offices stand in a cluster opposite the cathedral. At the North German Lloyd I inquired the price of a passage to New York. Instead of answering, the young man at the desk asked my name and address, what kind of a visa I had—whether quota or non-quota—the purpose of my trip and how long I proposed to stay in America. I almost fell into the trap and might never have seen the new world. Under the pretext of helping me, he tried to find out everything about me—orders from the secret State police. He could not be persuaded to tell me the price of the ticket before his thirst for information had been quenched. As I left the office, I noticed that one of the women clerks was following me and hid for half an hour in the shop of "4711," where I bought some eau de Cologne and soap for my Paris friends. I left the store, cut through the Stollwerck Passage to the other side of the square and into good old Thomas Cook's, where I received all the information I wanted without an inquisition and the promise of a good cabin into the bargain. I wanted to travel on an American ship and chose the *President Roosevelt*, of the United States Line.

Every last task was done—except the hardest one of all! I set my teeth and inserted an advertisement in a Cologne newspaper. "Wanted: a good master or mistress, if possible with a house and garden, for my German Boxer. Male, excellent lineage, housebroken and trained, whom I am obliged to give away. Only those partial to Boxers and desiring a faithful companion need apply. Full details requested. Box W. E. 489."

Of the ninety-six answers, twenty-seven showed serious interest. Six closed with "Heil Hitler!"

"As I am very unhappily married," began one letter, "I beg of you to give me the dog. We live in a single room, but . . ." A grandmother sent the picture of her grandson: "From the expression of his face you can see what a lover of animals he is."

Ziska and I took two days to decide. Finally we wrote to one candidate, letting Tapir put his paw on the letter by way of signature. The steward of a large estate on the Rhine, where there was a big park in which Tapir could run, was looking for an honest friend. Ziska, Tapir and I went out to see for ourselves. We found a fine country seat and an elderly man at whom Tapir—who was generally slow in making friends—jumped affectionately. It was a huge place. A flock of sheep were just coming in from pasture. Tapir stood rooted to the spot; he had never seen anything of the kind. He was a son of the city. Suddenly he ran up to a dark brown moorland sheep and gently nibbled at its slender leg. The sheep stood still and the two animals licked each other's noses. That settled the matter. I promised to bring Tapir to his new master the day before I left. I could not possibly have found a nicer refuge for my four-footed exile. The pleasure of the steward dispelled my sadness a little. I was convinced that Tapir would be well off there.

The white wind-driven acacia blossoms now lay in great piles around the house. They smelled as fresh and sweet as cream. Indoors it was horrible. We had sold many of our things and we missed them. The rugs were rolled up, the piano glowered at us sulkily. The street resounded with the racket of a rifle club celebration, one of the hearty rallies sponsored by a nation in arms. Brown uniforms goosestepped by our house. A group gathered round a coach illuminated with red, green and blue electric bulbs in the form of a swastika. Inside were two fat figures, the king of the rifle club, and his wife. It was Herr Ebel, Commissioner of Culture to the city of Cologne, making a tour through the town to the fanfare of the Horst Wessel song. Ziska had the idea of pelting him with potatoes in the dark, and I had difficulty in holding her back. I did not want my American visa or my steamer ticket brought to light at that moment.

I went to the piano and played a soft farewell. The kindly dusk drew on, veiling the emptiness of the rooms, the heaped boxes on the floor, the blurred walls bereft of their paintings.

II

At last the Honorary Council of the Federation of German Museums came to a decision, weightily considered and weightily worded. The verdict came in a document citing the opinion of ten of Jules' former colleagues, all duly coordinated:

"While Lips' *Introduction to Comparative Ethnology* cannot be regarded as plagiarism, it is our conclusion that both the content and the style of the work in question are unworthy of a scientist. It must therefore, from the standpoint of professional honor, be unqualifiedly condemned as failing to meet our standards of scholarship.
Heil Hitler!
(Signed) Professor Jacob-Friesen,
Director, Landesmuseum, Hanover."

Eventually, Jules replied to this group of co-ordinated anthropologists:

"In view of the fact that I, an 'Aryan,' a World War volunteer and wounded veteran, have been relieved of my offices by the present German Government after my voluntary request for leave of absence, I admit to a totally different conception of professional honor than that apparently held by the Council. It is not consistent with my conception of professional honor that undergraduates be made directors of ethnological museums by virtue of their political party affiliations; that party politics hold ascendancy over science without a single voice of protest from our branch of science, above all others, on the very grounds of professional honor.

"It was my conception of professional honor that compelled me to follow the dictates of my scientific conscience, regardless of consequences, to serve science but never political expediency.

[326]

"You consider yourself obliged, dear sir, to close your letter with the greeting 'Heil Hitler.' I prefer to follow scholarly usage and sign myself

Yours very respectfully,

Julius Lips."

My last days in Germany I wished to devote to my parents though we had grown very far apart. My only brother had donned the black uniform and was marching in the ranks of the "co-ordinated." Two years later when my father died, while I was making my home on another continent, my brother enriched himself and the coffers of the Party with my inheritance. We had been a happy family, united in love and loyalty—but here too the Third Reich had its effect upon "human ties." My father never became a Nazi. He kept silent. My mother knew nothing of politics. I was willing to forget that they had preferred a concentration camp for Jules to life in a free country. They invited me to take a motor trip with them through the South of Germany and I promised to meet them in Frankfort after I said good-bye to Cologne forever.

The days were busy with last-minute chores. Our books were disappearing into packing boxes, that is, our personal ones; all others were lost, as were the many treasures we had gathered on our expeditions, gifts to Jules from missionaries and scholars abroad, and which he had temporarily left in the Museum.

While strangers were walking up and down the steps in the Siebengebirgsallee, Ziska and I took Tapir out to the estate on the Rhine. We had luggage with us; a food bowl and a drinking dish, a tennis ball, a collar and lead. We took a little local train. Tapir sat on the platform looking about. We avoided his unsuspecting eyes.

A sow with her rosy litter was basking in a pen in the sun. Gobbling turkey cocks strutted about. In the park the grass grew two feet high. Tapir galloped through it with grotesque

[327]

leaps; it tickled his belly. His tongue hung out. When I unwrapped the tennis ball he wagged his tail. Ziska sat looking as though she were about to die. Quickly—let us get this over, without tears.

A bowl of buttermilk was brought in. Tapir sniffed doubtfully at the unfamiliar drink. The man assured me that he would care for Tapir lovingly and faithfully and he thanked me for the gift—as though Tapir were a thing that one could give away.

The door was open. I got up and beckoned to Ziska; Tapir started after us. I told him to sit still, and while he dipped his pink tongue into the basin of buttermilk I betrayed him. We went out hastily and closed the door. Ziska cried bitterly.

Large letters across the furniture vans spelled out their destination, Krefeld. At last the curiosity of our neighbors could be satisfied. My desk stood in the street. Under it a little boy sat playing with a swastika flag. An S.A. busybody put his hand on every piece of furniture. The piano was carried out, the books and beds, the bronze harem lamp, the *Contes barbares* of Gauguin. The loaded vans departed.

I unscrewed the door plate and walked up the stairs through the house, depositing in every room the Tuareg curse against evil-doers. It delivers their souls to the jackals. It brings confusion to all calumniators and sickness to thieves; it peoples their houses with vengeful spirits. Today our house is occupied by the minister of our former parish, who flourishes there in all the sanctimony of the convert to National Socialism. He smells the roses in our garden. May he sleep well and not too often dream of the desert devils of the Tuareg tribe.

The eighty-two exotics which had gladdened the window of my room I destroyed, cutting to shreds the little aguardiente from Eze, my favorite from the station at Monte Carlo, the rosette palm from Madeira, the echinocactus

[328]

from Algiers, the epiphyllum which produced its salmon-red buds at Christmas time and the old men's beards with the yellow buds, brought by a missionary all the way from Peru. With my plants I had the courage that had failed me with Tapir. I took a single cactus with me for the founding of a new family. I hope the customs authorities of New York will forgive me, for I know that the importation of plants is forbidden.

I took a last walk in the garden with Ziska. The first roses were out, the salmon-colored Ophelia which I loved best; Madame Drouchky and the white rose, and the simple dark-red one, on which poets live. The crimson ramblers on the back wall still showed traces of the ladder. They had all been planted by Jules. Before our coming, there had not been a blade of grass. Now the branches of jasmine and golden-chain met overhead, and the place was sweet with forsythia, spirea, lilacs and snowballs. The violets were still out, and the poppy was about to unfold its luminous silky leaves. I picked up a handful of earth and took it with me. In the courtyard Tapir's straw bed was empty. Near by lay a dry bleached bone.

We closed the windows and the doors and picked up my two bags. The trunks had gone to Paris in the vans. We left the house, brushing against the thick hedge in the garden.

My last night in Cologne I spent in the *Belgischer Hof,* quite close to the cathedral and the station. I was kept awake by an amorous pair in the next room. In the street below a man was being arrested. A scrawny little "Hitler youth" was yelling: "He said that the Führer . . ." was all I caught.

It was sultry and hot. I wondered how Tapir was faring and what new teasing enemy was taking his place with the squirrel Karasek out at Buchensee. As to the story of the end of Buchensee, that must wait for quieter days.

I arose heavy-eyed after a sleepless night, but such nights are common in the Fatherland nowadays. Ziska came to take me to the train. She brought me a bunch of roses from our garden and confused greetings for the Herr Professor, which she begged me to deliver exactly as she sent them. It seemed unreal to be carrying messages to America. Her good face was bathed in tears. Brown uniforms hid her waving hand.

As I write this, a ship is steaming westward across the Atlantic. Ziska is on board. She has decided to familiarize herself with skyscrapers and become a good American citizen. There is something we shall miss when we are together in our New York apartment: the starting at the ring of the door bell, the constant anticipation of disaster, the frequent visits from the police.

I met my parents in Frankfort and drove with them to Heidelberg. "To the Living Spirit" says the dedication carved above the door of the university building, a gift of former Ambassador Schurman. At that time the statue of Pallas Athene still kept watch over the entrance gate. In January of 1936, however, the daughter of Zeus was removed, and a Nazi eagle enthroned in her place as guardian angel of the house of learning. "To the German Spirit" says the new dedication. With the Nazi spirit thus in charge, Old Heidelberg made ready to receive the scholars of the world at its jubilee.

It was summer. We looked from the Schloss Hotel down upon the Neckar. How beautiful my country was! We motored on to Baden-Baden, past bitter-sweet firs of the Black Forest. A hedgehog lay curled in comfort at the edge of our road. We looked at the marble chapel which Count Stourdza had erected to the memory of his son. We sauntered along the famous promenade. Once again I was received into the charmed circle of the co-ordinated, though I had less right to it than the shabby street sweeper, who stood respectfully aside to let me pass. Co-ordination kept the broom safe in his grasp.

I never mentioned politics to my parents. They were sorrowful, and I was sad. But we were miles apart. The tragedy was common to thousands of German families. Below the thin crust of filial courtesy, an abyss yawned. Over it the faint stars of childhood shone, eternal in a shattered world.

In the gambling hall I found croupiers from Monaco at one of the tables. We were delighted at the meeting. They were surprised at finding me alone.

"Monsieur is at the other table?" asked the chief.

"A little farther than that. He is in New York."

"*Madonna!* And you, Madame?"

I told them why I was leaving this country forever. They told me why they wished to do so. They had been brought here under false pretenses, lured from Monte Carlo to act as models for the Nazi croupiers. They had been promised permanent jobs and they had been cheated. They had trained a few boor-like peasants for their own suave calling —with what results one could see at the next table—and now they could go. "*C'est ce gouvernement là!*"

In all Baden-Baden I heard no "Heil Hitler" and saw no swastikas, although there were many flags on the buildings. When I asked the managers of the resort about it, the reply was: "Why, we are expecting international visitors!" How could I have forgotten that business came first and co-ordinated convictions later? Now that the swastika has become the accepted symbol of the Reich, things will probably change.

My parents took me as far as Graben-Neudorf, a railroad junction on the way to Saarbrücken. The place was famous for its asparagus and there were advertisements on every hand praising the white vegetable. Beneath these were signs showing an old Polish Jew in caricature, labeled: "The Jew is our misfortune. To the devil with him!"

At Saarbrücken—still free in those days—I saw our relatives, then took the night express to Paris. Where had I taken leave of Germany? Not in Graben-Neudorf, and not on the frontier. I almost think it was in Cologne on January 30, 1933.

This time I did not stop in the Rue Monge; it seemed a little risky. My first errand sent me in search of our furniture. It had come through safely and was at the warehouse of the Porte de la Chapelle station. The heat hung heavy over Paris. At the Sûreté I was obliged to pay duty on my silver.

Finally everything was arranged in what was for Paris an astonishingly modern store-house, the rugs in the salle des tapis, the silver in the vault. The piano was put in a room set aside for musical instruments. There were perhaps two hundred others, all with their legs removed, prone on their sides. They rested on velvet-covered boards, their monstrous bodies shrouded in white cloths. There they lay stiff, silent and white, like tribal priests prostrated in prayer.

"*Les mites!*" I groaned. "Look at these moths!" They were flying about in dozens. How would our things look in the three, four or five years which must elapse before we could get them?

The agency of the United States Line is in the Rue Auber, near the Opéra. There I exchanged my Cologne receipt for a real ticket. My interview with the young American clerk awoke me to the fact that I must now busy myself with the English language. English and mathematics had been my worst subjects at school.

The last day I had kept for myself. Once again I went through the homes of the homeless. I ate in the *Bonne Étoile*—four courses with white wine, five francs. I went to the *Mouffetard* and the *Café Monge* ("*Ici on consulte le Botin!*"), to say good-bye to the garçon with the hair on his nose. I showed him a photo of Jules taken on top of the Empire State Building. The tremendous skyscrapers in the background called forth a series of shrieks of excitement. Had he not prophesied that we would make dollars, millions of dollars? *Hein?* I passed by the Hôtel des Nations—there where the round sign stood out from the wall was Number 12. The Place Monge smelled of horses. Vendors in the market were closing their stands and offered me some snails cheap, but they did not seem just the thing to take on an ocean voyage. Then I circled the bizarre corner store with its display of wax angels, glass roses and grim wire wreaths, reminders of the passing of all earthly things; and so to the post office, where I sent a cable to Jules, fixing the date of my arrival in New York.

Le Havre is a melancholy city, full of the tears of many separations and departures, but I drove through it with a light heart. When we reached the harbor we could not see the ship. The passengers were directed to a large hall, where we showed our papers and changed francs into dollars, fifteen for one. I received an alarmingly small number.

"Doesn't anyone on board speak French?" I managed to ask in my first independent attempt at English. But by the time I got off the boat I had quite a nice vocabulary. "Mushroom" I thought at first was some special place on the ship —a room, yes, but what kind of a room? I was able to edify the first New Yorkers I met with expressions like "racketeer," "sugar daddy," and "bucks." Kind friends on board had taught them to me as essential.

I found two telegrams in my cabin, one from Jules, another from my parents. Friends in Cologne had written to say good-bye and there was a note from Ziska.

The last letter I opened bore the Rhenish postmark of the town nearest Tapir's new home. I read:

"My dear Frau Lips: I am so unhappy that I scarcely know how to write to you. Fräulein Ziska, to whom I sent the news at once, advised me to write to you at the ship. I am doing so, hoping that you will forgive me for sending such bad news.

"Our Tapir is dead. I say 'ours' for I had already come to love him as though he were my own. When I went to his kennel yesterday afternoon, I did not see him at first. Then I saw something lying in the grass. It was he, stretched out with a tennis ball between his paws. Blue froth was coming from his mouth. The veterinary, whom I called at once, recognized it as vitriol

[333]

poisoning. Tapir was still warm. The poison must have been in a piece of meal cake. You know how fond he was of that. A lump of it lay next to his bowl. Someone must have known very well what he liked. I could not understand it at all, for I have no enemies here. Then I saw a piece of paper lying in the grass weighted down with a stone. I am enclosing it in my letter as evidence.

"May the curse of murder rest on the whole lot of them. Tapir would have been happy here, believe me, Frau Lips! He had already made friends with the sheep, he would strike his paw against their thick coats and then they would lick one another. Poor Tapir was a victim—such an innocent victim. I have had a cross made for him, if that is any consolation.

"Tapir
Murdered, June 20, 1934."

"I planted the little rose bush from the entrance gate over his grave—the one you liked so much. Forgive me that such a thing could happen, Frau Lips. I do not know how they found out that he came from you. . . ."

I unfolded the scrap of paper which had lain by Tapir's corpse. It was dirty and still showed the impression of the stone. It carried a swastika drawn in red; beneath it was scribbled:

"To Professor Lips: He who will not yield to Hitler
Deserves to die like a dog."

A cluster of clouds, a streak of smoke along the horizon— we passed the coast of France.

That evening we were in Southampton. Bobbies in helmets and chin straps flanked the pier. Towering cranes seized whatever was on the docks—crates, motor cars, wardrobe trunks—landing them with mathematical precision on the freight deck of our ship. Along the gangplanks men hurried with baskets of lobsters, crates of apples, artichokes, chickens, oysters, and melons.

[334]

At Cobh passengers were brought aboard in a steam tug. Country pedlars came on deck offering blackthorn sticks for sale, souvenirs of a country we had not seen. An hour later the gulls left us, last messengers of harbors at hand. Europe sank into the waves of the Atlantic.

Not being a completely reliable sailor I had looked forward to the crossing with uncertainty, but I lay in a deck chair enjoying the sun and the wind as though I were on the Mediterranean. I watched such clouds as are seen only over the ocean; I felt the morning breeze grow warm under the rising sun. I watched twilight turn into night and night put on a crown of stars.

Every night we turned the clock back an hour in order to keep time with the universe. I began to walk about the ship and to meet my fellow-travelers—old people and children and lovers. There was a dog called Whisky and the photographer had a Siamese cat. Birds sang in their cages in the sun. Life went on normally.

Once I stood leaning against the railing, wondering what would happen to the roses at Buchensee when the winter came. I thought of Jules' enemy, the field mouse, which eats roots. One of my neighbors at our round table in the dining room joined me, a courtly gentleman of the old school, who pretended not to notice my lamentable English by talking French to me.

"May I ask what you are thinking of, Madame?"

"Of a squirrel called Karasek."

At last a night came when a shaft of warm air from the Hudson thrust against the cool ocean breeze, when the fiery wheels of Coney Island whirled against the sky and the shining towers of the metropolis rose from the water.

The landing next morning was exciting—medical inspection, mail delivery, passports, stewards and sailors and officials flitting about in spotless white. The promenade deck was full of trunks covered with adventurous looking labels.

[335]

The band played. The gangplank was dropped. Our good captain with the steady blue eyes shook hands all round.

I stood at the railing and looked down at the crowded pier. Then I hurried down the gangplank. I ran—I ran until I had reached my goal.

Jules was waiting—patiently. He put my head against his breast underneath his coat—as he used to do in the old days in Cologne when I needed comfort.

"You were prompt—just as we planned in the Gare du Nord."

The sun stood over the magical city. It was summer.

We set forth to enter a country at whose gates stands a statue to liberty.

DATE DUE	